A-Level

Mathematics

for Edexcel Mechanics 1

The Complete Course for Edexcel M1

Contents

Chapter 5

Dynamics

Chapter 6

Moments

Reference

About this book

In this book you'll find...

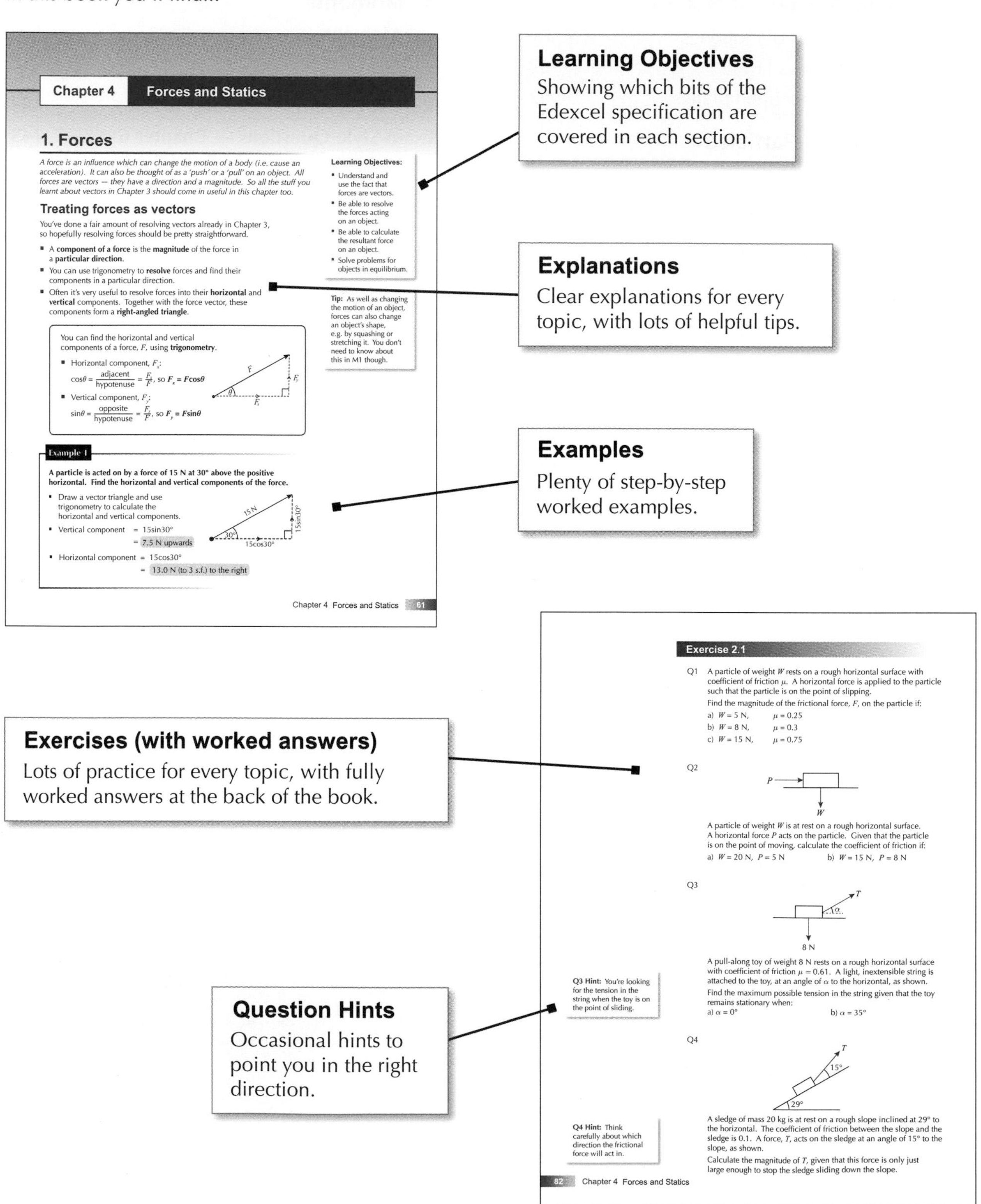

Review Exercise — Chapter 4

Q1 Find the magnitude and direction of the resultant force in each of the following:

a) b) c)

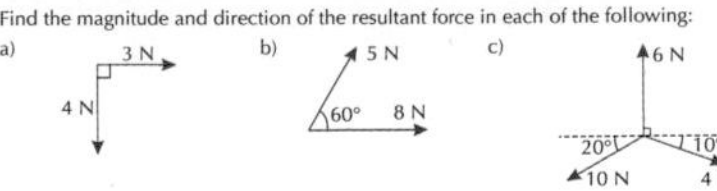

Q2 A force $(x\mathbf{i} + y\mathbf{j})$ N, acting in a direction which is parallel to the vector $(2\mathbf{i} + 7\mathbf{j})$ N, acts on a particle, *P*. Find the angle between the vector $\mathbf{j}$ and the force.

Q3

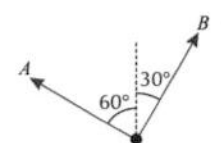

A particle of mass *M* kg is suspended in equilibrium by two light wires *A* and *B*, with angles 60° and 30° to the vertical, as shown. The tension in wire *A* is 20 N. Find:

a) the magnitude of the tension in wire *B*,

b) the value of *M*.

Q4

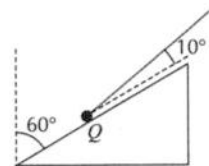

A particle, *Q*, of mass *m* kg, rests on a smooth plane which makes an angle of 60° to the vertical. It is held in equilibrium by a light, inextensible string angled at 10° to the plane, as shown. The magnitude of the tension in the string is 70 N.

Find the mass of *Q* and the normal reaction of the plane on *Q*.

Q5 The diagrams below show a particle on the point of slipping on a rough surface. Calculate the coefficient of friction, μ, between each particle and the surface shown.

a) b)

84 Chapter 4 Forces and Statics

Review Exercises

Mixed questions covering the whole chapter, with fully worked answers.

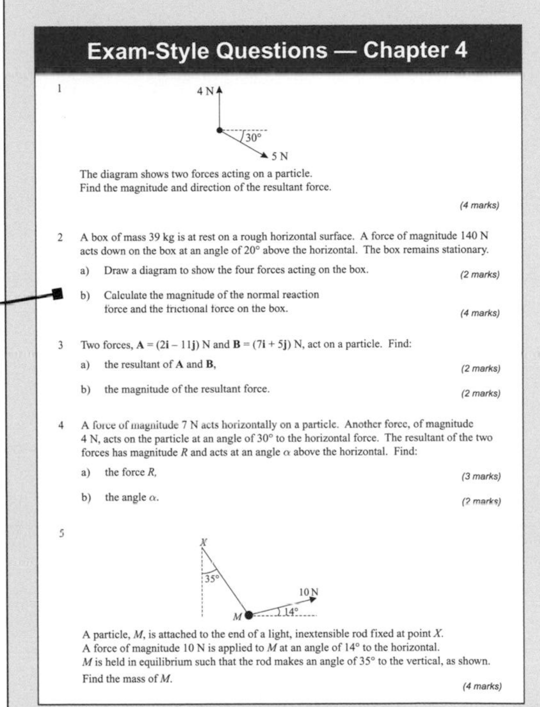

Exam-Style Questions — Chapter 4

1

The diagram shows two forces acting on a particle.
Find the magnitude and direction of the resultant force.

(4 marks)

2 A box of mass 39 kg is at rest on a rough horizontal surface. A force of magnitude 140 N acts down on the box at an angle of 20° above the horizontal. The box remains stationary.

a) Draw a diagram to show the four forces acting on the box. *(2 marks)*

b) Calculate the magnitude of the normal reaction force and the frictional force on the box. *(4 marks)*

3 Two forces, $\mathbf{A} = (2\mathbf{i} - 11\mathbf{j})$ N and $\mathbf{B} = (7\mathbf{i} + 5\mathbf{j})$ N, act on a particle. Find:

a) the resultant of **A** and **B**, *(2 marks)*

b) the magnitude of the resultant force. *(2 marks)*

4 A force of magnitude 7 N acts horizontally on a particle. Another force, of magnitude 4 N, acts on the particle at an angle of 30° to the horizontal force. The resultant of the two forces has magnitude *R* and acts at an angle α above the horizontal. Find:

a) the force *R*, *(3 marks)*

b) the angle α. *(2 marks)*

5

A particle, *M*, is attached to the end of a light, inextensible rod fixed at point *X*.
A force of magnitude 10 N is applied to *M* at an angle of 14° to the horizontal.
M is held in equilibrium such that the rod makes an angle of 35° to the vertical, as shown.
Find the mass of *M*. *(4 marks)*

Chapter 4 Forces and Statics 85

Exam-Style Questions

Questions in the same style as the ones you'll get in the exam, with worked solutions and mark schemes.

Glossary

All the definitions you need to know for the exam, plus other useful words.

Practice Exam Papers (on CD-ROM)

Two printable exam papers, with fully worked answers and mark schemes.

Published by CGP

Editors:
David Ryan, Lyn Setchell, Sarah Williams, Jonathan Wray.

Contributors:
Andy Ballard, Jean Blencowe, Michael Coe, Mark Moody,
Susan Nelson, Rosemary Rogers, Janet West, Chris Worth.

ISBN: 978 1 84762 809 1

With thanks to Helen Greaves and Glenn Rogers for the proofreading.
With thanks to Alastair Duncombe for the reviewing.

Groovy website: www.cgpbooks.co.uk

Printed by Elanders Ltd, Newcastle upon Tyne.
Jolly bits of clipart from CorelDRAW®

1. Modelling

A mathematical model is a mathematical description of a real-life situation. Modelling involves simplifying the situation so that you can understand its behaviour and predict what is going to happen.

Situations are modelled by treating real objects as mathematical objects, as well as by making assumptions.

Learning Objectives:

- Understand the terms used to simplify a mathematical model.
- Make assumptions to mathematically model a real-life situation.

Definitions

Mathematical models use lots of words that you already know, but which are used to mean something very precise.

The definitions below refer to a '**body**' — this is just another way of saying 'an object'.

Tip: You won't be tested on these terms, but you need to be familiar with what they mean as they come up all the time.

- **Light** — the body has no mass.
- **Static** — the body is not moving.
- **Rough** — a body in contact with the surface will experience a frictional force which will act to oppose motion.
- **Smooth** — a body in contact with the surface will not experience a frictional force.
- **Uniform** — the mass is evenly spread throughout the body.
- **Non-uniform** — the mass is unevenly spread out.
- **Rigid** — the body does not bend.
- **Thin** — the body has no thickness.
- **Inextensible** — the body can't be stretched.
- **Equilibrium** — there is no resultant force acting on the body.

- **Particle** — a body whose mass acts at a point, so its dimensions don't matter.
- **Plane** — a flat surface.
- **Lamina** — a flat body whose thickness can be ignored.
- **Beam** or **Rod** — a long, thin, straight, rigid body.
- **Wire** — a thin, rigid, light body.
- **String** — a thin body, usually modelled as being light and inextensible.
- **Bead** — a particle which has a hole in it which a wire can pass through.
- **Peg** — a fixed support which a body can hang from or rest on.
- **Pulley** — a string passing over a fixed peg.

Modelling

The modelling cycle

Modelling is a **cycle** — having created a model you can improve it by making more (or fewer) assumptions.

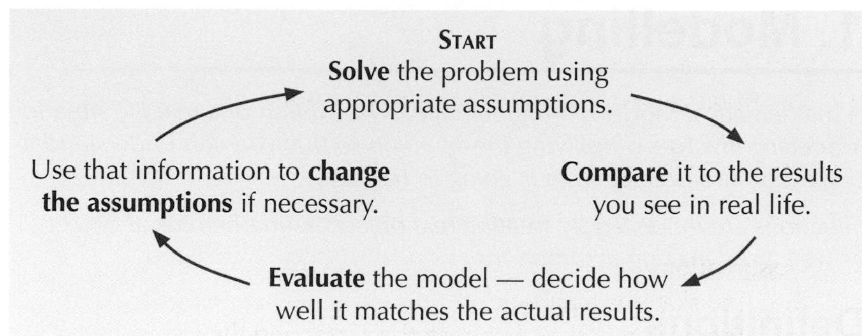

Keep going until you're satisfied with the model.

Labelling forces

You have to know what **forces** are acting on a body when you're creating a mathematical model, so you need to understand what each **type** of force is.

Tip: Throughout the whole of M1, the effect of gravity can be assumed to be constant: $g = 9.8 \text{ ms}^{-2}$ (unless you're told otherwise).

- **Weight** (W)

  Due to the particle's mass, m, and the effect of gravity, g:
  $W = mg$ — weight always acts **downwards**.

  $W = mg$

- The **Normal Reaction** (R or N)

  The reaction from a surface.
  Reaction is always at **90° to the surface**.

  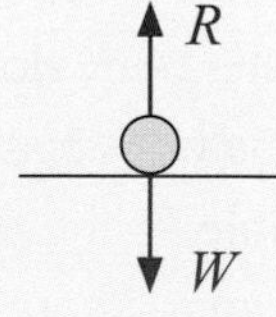

Tip: Taut means that the string is tight and straight.

- **Tension** (T)

  Force in a **taut** rope, wire or string.

  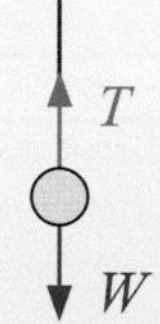

- **Friction** (F)

  Due to **roughness** between a body and surface.
  Always acts **against motion**, or likely motion.

  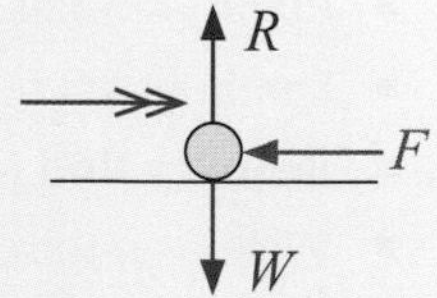

- **Thrust**

  Force in a rod (e.g. the pole of an open umbrella).

Examples

Draw a diagram to model each of the following situations. In each case, state the assumptions you have made.

a) A brick is resting flat on a horizontal table.

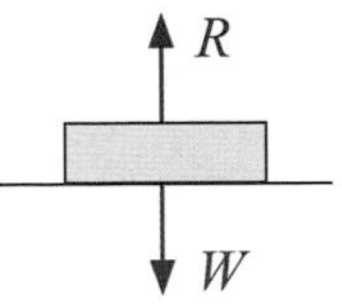

Assumptions:

- The brick is a particle.
- There's no wind or other external forces involved.

Tip: 'Resting' or 'at rest' means that the object isn't moving.

b) An ice hockey player is accelerating across an ice rink.

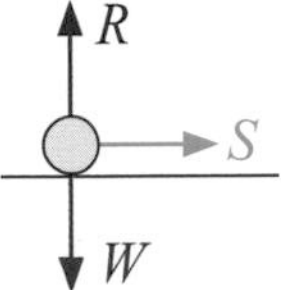

Assumptions:

- The skater is a particle.
- There is no friction between the skates and the ice.
- There is no air resistance.
- The skater generates a constant forward force, S.

Tip: It's quicker and easier to use just a letter for each force in your diagram, e.g. S for the forward force.

c) A uniform square lamina, *ABCD*, is held by two vertical strings, *P* and *Q*, at points *A* and *B* respectively.

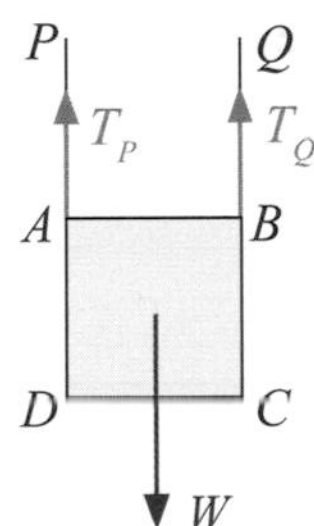

Assumptions:

- The lamina is rigid, so it doesn't bend.
- The strings P and Q are light.
- P and Q are inextensible.
- There are no other external forces acting.

Tip: The weight of a rigid object can be assumed to act at a single point — the centre of mass of the object.

d) A golf ball is dropped from a tall building.

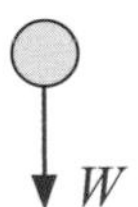

Assumptions:

- The ball is a particle.
- Air resistance can be ignored.
- There's no wind or other external forces involved.
- The effect of gravity (g) is constant.

e) A book is put flat on a table. One end of the table is slowly lifted and the angle to the horizontal is measured when the book starts to slide.

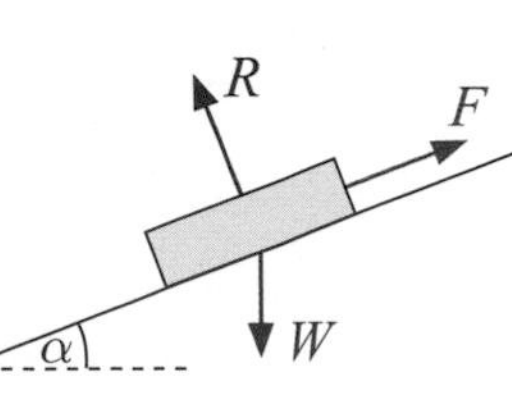

Assumptions:

- The book is a particle.
- The book is rigid, so it doesn't bend or open.
- The surface of the table is rough, so there will be a frictional force acting between it and the book.
- There are no other external forces acting.

f) A pencil is placed on a table and a ruler is put across the pencil so that the ruler balances. A 1p coin and a 2p coin are placed on the ruler either side of the pencil, so that the ruler still balances.

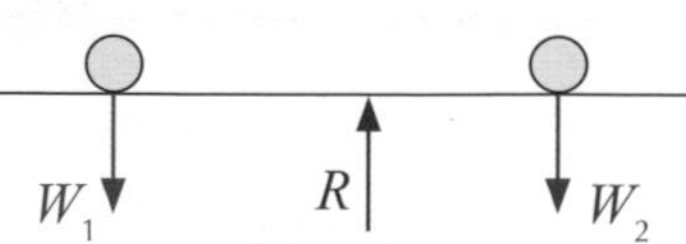

Assumptions:
- The coins are particles.
- The ruler is light and rigid.
- The support acts at a single point.

g) A sledge is steadily pulled along horizontal ground by a small child with a rope.

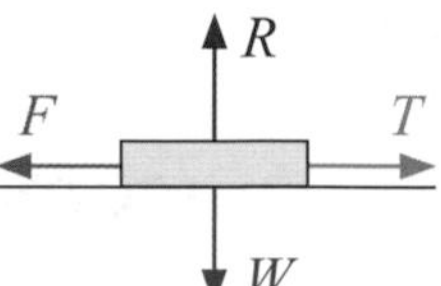

Assumptions:
- The sledge is a particle.
- Friction is too big to be ignored (i.e. it's not ice).
- The rope is a light, inextensible string.
- The rope is horizontal (it's a small child).

h) A ball is held by two strings, A and B, at angles α and β to the vertical.

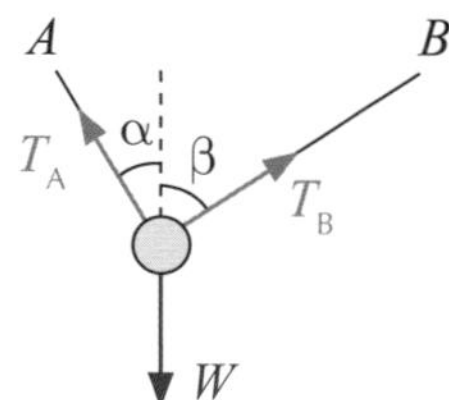

Assumptions:
- The ball is a particle.
- The strings are light.
- The strings are inextensible.

Exercise 1.1

For each of the following questions, draw a diagram to model the situation and state any assumptions you have made.

Q1 An apple falls from a tree.

Q2 A shoe lace is threaded through a conker. The conker hangs vertically in equilibrium from the shoe lace.

Q3 A sledge is steadily pulled up an icy hill by a rope.

Q4 a) A wooden box is pushed across a polished marble floor.
b) A crate is pulled across a carpeted floor by a horizontal rope.

Q5 A person pushes a small package along the road with a stick. The stick makes an angle of 20° with the horizontal.

Q6 Hint: The car's engine will generate a driving force, D.

Q6 a) A car is driven up a hill. b) A car is driven down a hill.

Q7 A plank of wood, AB, is 6 m long. AB rests on two supports, C and D, where the length AC = 1 m and the length AD = 4 m. Two masses, P and Q, are attached to the plank such that AP = 0.5 m and AQ = 5 m.

Chapter 2 Kinematics

1. Motion Graphs

Kinematics is the study of the motion of objects. In M1, that means describing an object's displacement, velocity and acceleration.

Displacement-time, velocity-time, speed-time and acceleration-time graphs are used to represent an object's motion graphically.

Learning Objectives:

- Be able to interpret displacement-time graphs to find a body's displacement and velocity.
- Be able to interpret speed-time graphs to find a body's distance travelled, speed and magnitude of acceleration.
- Be able to interpret velocity-time graphs to find a body's displacement, velocity and acceleration.
- Be able to interpret acceleration-time graphs to find a body's velocity and acceleration.
- Be able to draw displacement-time, speed-time, velocity-time and acceleration-time graphs.

Displacement, velocity and acceleration

- **Displacement** is an object's **distance from a particular point** (often its starting point), measured in a straight line. It's not necessarily the same as the total distance travelled.
- **Velocity** is the **rate of change of displacement** with respect to **time**. It can be thought of as a measure of how **fast** an object is moving. It's different from **speed** because it takes into account the direction of movement. If distance is measured in metres (m) and time is measured in seconds (s), then velocity is measured in metres per second (ms^{-1}).
- **Acceleration** is the **rate of change** of an object's **velocity** with respect to **time** — i.e. how much an object is **speeding up** or **slowing down**. If velocity is measured in ms^{-1} and time is measured in s, then acceleration is measured in ms^{-2}.

Displacement-time graphs

A **displacement-time (x/t) graph** shows how an object's **displacement** from a particular point changes over time. Displacement is plotted on the vertical axis, and time is plotted on the horizontal axis.

- The **height** of the graph gives the object's **displacement** at that time.
- The **gradient** of the graph at a particular point gives the object's **velocity** at that time — the **steeper** the line, the **greater** the velocity.
- A **negative gradient** shows that the object is moving in the **opposite direction** to when the gradient is positive.
- A horizontal line has a **zero gradient**, which means the object is **stationary**.

Tip: A displacement-time graph is not the same as a distance-time graph. The height of a distance-time graph gives the **total distance** that a body has travelled up to that point. The gradient of a distance-time graph gives an object's **speed**, rather than its velocity (i.e. it says nothing about the direction in which the object is moving).

Tip: The 'straight path' bit tells you that all motion is in a straight line — so, given the distance travelled, you can work out the girl's displacement after each stage of the journey, measuring them from her starting point, $x = 0$.

Tip: You should choose which direction you are going to take as being positive. Then any displacement in the opposite direction will be negative.

Tip: The graph goes below the horizontal axis because the girl's final displacement is –0.5 km, i.e. she goes back through her starting point and finishes 0.5 km away in the opposite direction to her initial motion.

Example 1

A girl goes for a run along a straight path. Her journey is as follows:

- **She runs 1.5 km in 5 minutes, then rests for 2 minutes.**
- **She then jogs 0.5 km in 4 minutes, in the same direction as before.**
- **Finally, she runs 2.5 km back in the direction she came, passing her starting point along the way.**
- **She finishes 20 minutes after she first set off.**

Show her journey on a displacement-time graph.

Taking her initial direction as being positive, draw the journey one stage at a time:

1. The graph should start at ($t = 0$ minutes, $x = 0$ km), then increase to a height of 1.5 km over 5 minutes.
2. In the next stage, the girl rests for 2 minutes, so this part of the graph will be a horizontal line.
3. The girl then jogs 0.5 km, from a displacement of 1.5 km to 2 km, over 4 minutes. She is travelling in the same direction as before, so the graph still has a positive gradient, but she is not travelling as fast, so the line is not as steep.
4. In the final stage, she travels in the opposite direction for 2.5 km, finishing at ($t = 20$ minutes, $x = –0.5$ km). In this stage, the graph has a negative gradient, as she is moving in the opposite direction to before.

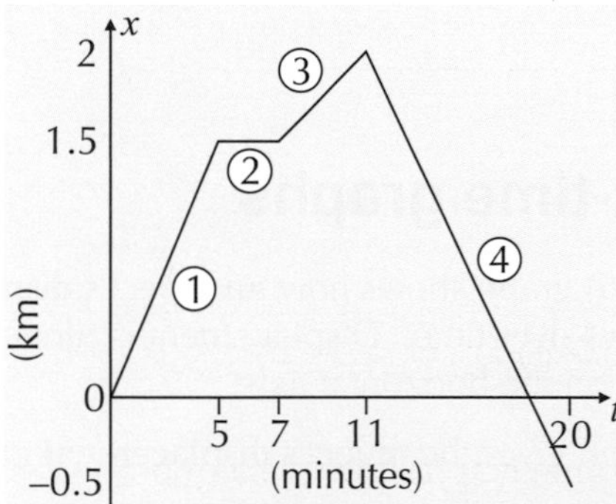

Example 2

A cyclist's journey is shown on this displacement-time graph. Given that the cyclist starts from rest and cycles in a straight line, describe the motion.

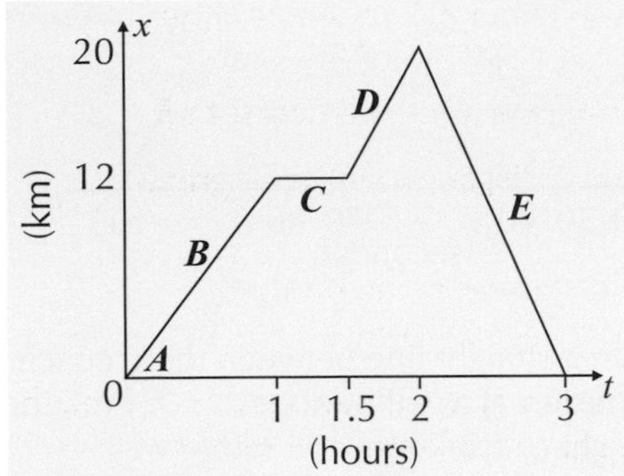

A: Starts from rest (when $t = 0$, $x = 0$).

B: Cycles 12 km in 1 hour.

Velocity = $\frac{12 \text{ km}}{1 \text{ hour}}$ = 12 kmh^{-1}

C: Rests for half an hour ($v = 0$).

D: Cycles 8 km (from 12 km to 20 km) in half an hour.

Velocity = $\frac{8 \text{ km}}{\frac{1}{2} \text{ hour}}$ = 16 kmh^{-1}

E: Returns to starting position, cycling 20 km in 1 hour.

Velocity = $-\frac{20 \text{ km}}{1 \text{ hour}}$ = –20 kmh^{-1}

Tip *B*: Calculate the gradient of the graph to find the velocity.
Remember: $m = \frac{y_2 - y_1}{x_2 - x_1}$

Tip *C*: The line is horizontal, so there is no movement.

Tip *E*: The gradient is negative because the cyclist is travelling in the opposite direction to stages *B* and *D*.

Exercise 1.1

Q1 The displacement-time graph shows a car journey. Calculate the velocity of each stage of the journey.

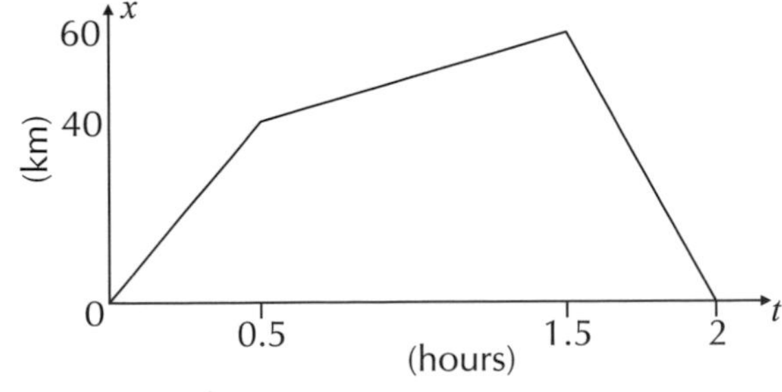

Q1 Hint: Make sure you get your signs right — remember that a negative gradient means a negative velocity.

Q2 The displacement-time graph below shows the movement of a particle travelling in a straight line. Describe the particle's motion, given that the particle starts from rest.

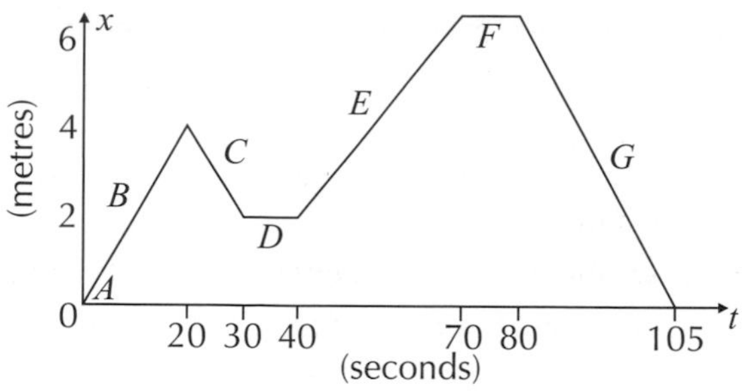

Q3 A coach travels in a straight line between three coach stops, A, B and C. Its journey is as follows:

- Leaves A at midday.
- Travels 30 km at a constant speed to B in one hour.
- Stops for 30 minutes.
- Leaves B and travels 60 km at a constant speed to point C in the same direction as before, moving at a constant speed of 40 kmh^{-1}.
- Stops for 30 minutes.
- Leaves C and returns to A at a constant speed, arriving at 6:00 pm.

a) Draw a displacement-time graph to show the coach's journey. Plot the time of day on the horizontal axis, and the coach's displacement from A on the vertical axis.

b) Find the velocity of the coach during the final stage of the journey.

c) Find the average speed of the coach over the whole journey.

Q3 Hint: The average speed of an object is given by:

$$\text{speed} = \frac{\text{total distance travelled}}{\text{total time taken}}$$

Q4 A man leaves his house at 1:00 pm. He walks at a speed of 5 mph for one hour, then at a speed of 3 mph in the same direction for the next hour. He then rests for an hour. The man's wife leaves their house at 2:30 pm and travels at a constant speed to meet him at 3:30 pm.

Draw a displacement-time graph to show the two journeys.

Q5 A man walks with velocity u ms^{-1} for 500 m, then with velocity $-2u$ ms^{-1} for 700 m. He then walks 600 m with velocity $1.5u$ ms^{-1}.

a) Find the man's final displacement.

b) Show his journey on a displacement-time graph.

c) Find his total journey time. Give your answer in terms of u.

d) Find his average speed in terms of u.

Q6 A car travels in a straight line with speed u ms^{-1} for t seconds, stops for 100 seconds, then returns back the way it came with speed $2u$ ms^{-1}.

a) Draw a displacement-time graph to show the movement of the car.

b) Find an expression in terms of u and t for the total distance travelled by the car.

c) Find the average speed of the car (including its rest time). Give your answer in terms of u and t.

Speed-time and velocity-time graphs

Speed-time graphs

A **speed-time (v/t) graph** shows how an object's **speed** changes over time.

- The **height** of the graph gives the object's **speed** at that time.
- The **gradient** of the graph at a particular point gives the magnitude of the object's **acceleration** at that time — the **steeper** the line, the **greater** the magnitude of the acceleration.
- A **negative gradient** shows that the object is **decelerating** (slowing down).
- A **horizontal** line means the object is moving at a **constant speed**.
- The **area** under the graph gives the **total distance travelled**.

Tip: Just like with displacement-time graphs, motion needs to be in a straight line.

Example 1

A train travels along a straight track.
Its journey is shown on the speed-time graph below.

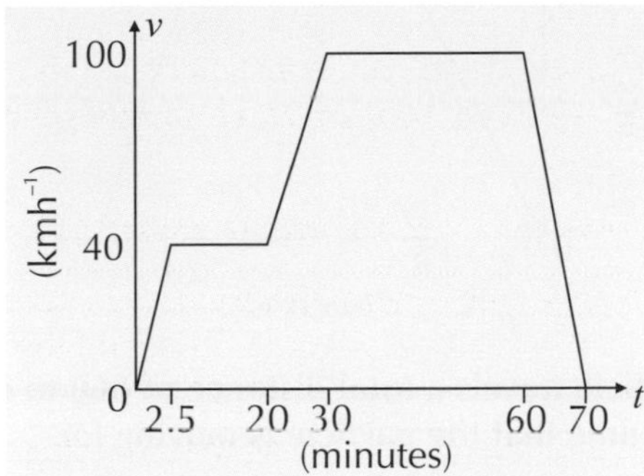

a) Find the total distance travelled by the train during the journey.

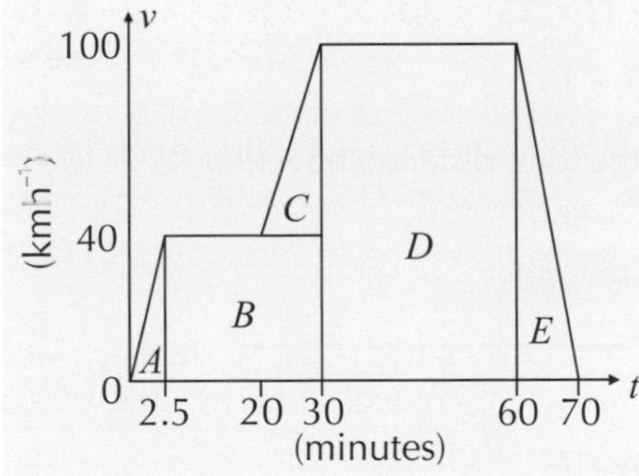

Tip: Split the graph up and find the area of each part individually, then add them together to find the total area — you can split it up any way you like.

The total distance is given by the area under the graph.

Area of A: $(2.5 \div 60 \times 40) \div 2 = 0.833...$

Area of B: $27.5 \div 60 \times 40 = 18.33...$

Area of C: $(10 \div 60 \times 60) \div 2 = 5$

Area of D: $30 \div 60 \times 100 = 50$

Area of E: $(10 \div 60 \times 100) \div 2 = 8.33...$

Total area = 0.833... + 18.33... + 5 + 50 + 8.33... = 82.5

So total distance travelled is 82.5 km.

Tip: Make sure you use the correct units in your working — in this example, the speed is given in kmh^{-1}, so you need to change the time from minutes to hours by dividing by 60 in your calculations.

b) Find the rate of deceleration as the train comes to a stop.

The rate of deceleration is given by the gradient of the graph in the last stage of the journey.

$$\text{gradient} = -\frac{100 \text{ kmh}^{-1}}{(10 \div 60) \text{ hours}} = -600 \text{ kmh}^{-2}$$

So the train decelerates at a rate of 600 kmh^{-2}.

Example 2

A particle accelerates uniformly from rest to a speed of 30 ms^{-1} in 8 seconds. It then travels with constant speed for 15 seconds. The particle then decelerates uniformly to rest. The movement of the particle is shown in the speed-time graph below.

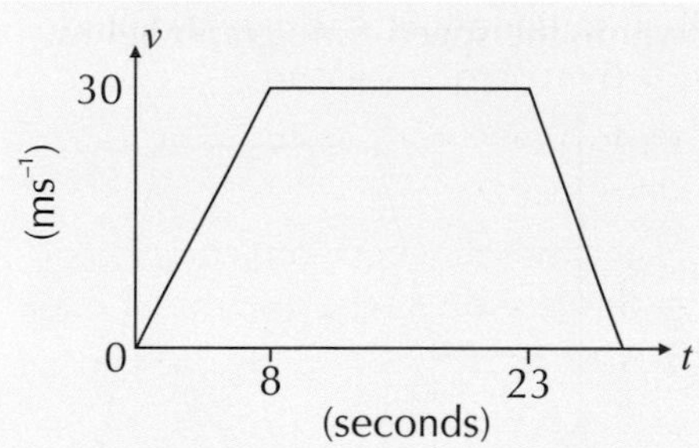

Given that the particle travels a total distance of 660 m in a straight line, find the total time that the particle is moving for.

- Find the area under the graph — call the total time that the particle is moving T seconds:

$$\text{Area} = \frac{1}{2} \times (T + 15) \times 30$$
$$= 225 + 15T$$

- This is equal to the total distance travelled:

$$225 + 15T = 660$$
$$\Rightarrow T = 29 \text{ seconds}$$

Tip: Saying that something 'accelerates uniformly' means that the acceleration is constant.

Tip: This example uses the formula for the area of a trapezium — $A = \frac{1}{2}(a + b)h$. You could split it up into two triangles and a rectangle if you prefer.

Velocity-time graphs

A **velocity-time (v/t) graph** shows how an object's **velocity** changes over time.

- The **height** of a velocity-time graph gives the object's **velocity** at that time, and its **gradient** gives its **acceleration.**
- A **negative gradient** can mean that the object is **decelerating** in the **positive direction**, or that it is **accelerating** in the **negative direction**.
- A **horizontal** line means the object is moving at a **constant velocity**.
- The **area** under the graph gives the object's **displacement**.

Tip: Remember that velocity is different from speed in that the **direction** of motion is important. So for velocity-time graph questions, you need to decide which direction is positive.

Example 1

A car starts from rest and reverses in a straight line with constant acceleration to a velocity of –5 ms^{-1} in 12 seconds. It then decelerates to rest in 3 seconds and remains stationary for another 3 seconds.
The car then moves forward along the same straight line as before but in the opposite direction, accelerating uniformly to a velocity of 8 ms^{-1} in 6 seconds. It maintains this speed for 6 seconds.

a) Show the car's movement on a velocity-time graph.

Draw the journey one stage at a time:

1. The graph should start at (t = 0 s, v = 0 ms^{-1}), then decrease to –5 ms^{-1} over 12 seconds.
2. In the next stage, the graph should return to (v = 0 ms^{-1}) in 3 seconds.
3. The car is then stationary, so the graph should remain at (v = 0 ms^{-1}) for 3 seconds.
4. In the next stage, the graph should increase to (v = 8 ms^{-1}) in 6 seconds.
5. Finally, the car travels at a constant velocity for 6 seconds — this is shown by a horizontal line.

Tip: If an object is moving with negative velocity, then the graph will go below the t axis.

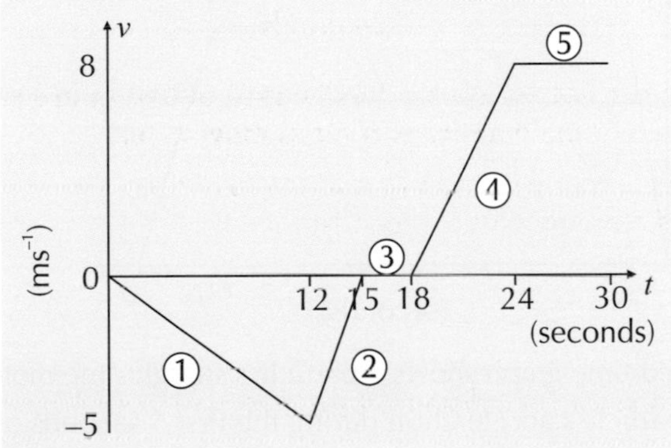

b) Use your graph to find the car's final displacement from its starting point.

- First find the area below the horizontal axis:

$$\text{Area} = \frac{1}{2} \times 15 \times -5$$
$$= -37.5 \text{ m}$$

- Then find the area above the horizontal axis:

$$\text{Area} = \left(\frac{1}{2} \times 6 \times 8\right) + (6 \times 8)$$
$$= 72 \text{ m}$$

- Now add these together to find the final displacement:

$$\text{Displacement} = -37.5 + 72$$
$$= 34.5 \text{ m}$$

Tip: To find the **total distance** travelled, you would add the magnitudes of the areas together:
37.5 + 72 = 109.5 m

Exercise 1.2

Q1

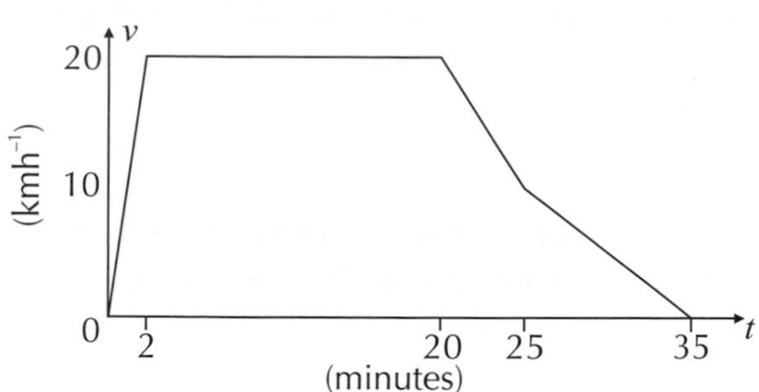

The speed-time graph above shows a bus journey.
Describe the motion of the bus, given that it travels in a straight line.

Q2 A car sets off on a journey along a long, straight road.
It accelerates steadily for 5 minutes, reaching a speed of 40 kmh^{-1}.
It travels steadily at this speed for 25 minutes, then decelerates uniformly, coming to rest 4 minutes later.
Draw a speed-time graph to show the journey.

Q3

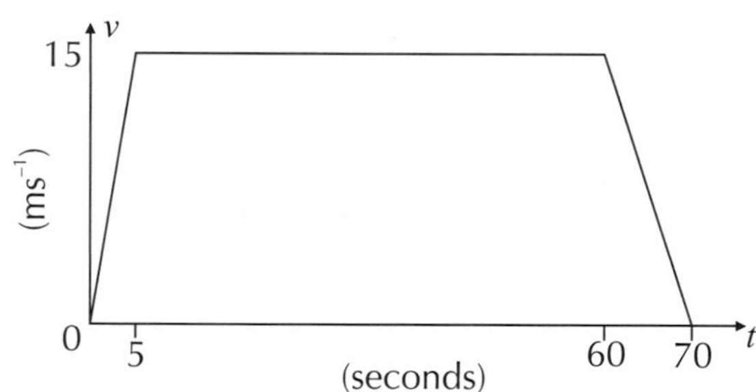

The speed-time graph shows a particle's straight-line motion. Find:

a) the particle's acceleration during the first 5 seconds of motion,

b) the particle's deceleration during the final 10 seconds of motion.

Q4

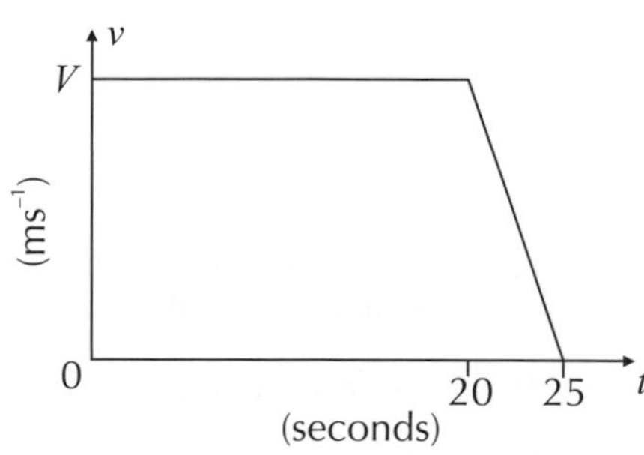

Q4 Hint: The car is already moving at the start of the measured time frame, so the graph doesn't start at (0, 0).

A car is travelling at V ms^{-1} along a straight track. After 20 s, the driver brakes and the car decelerates uniformly, coming to rest in 5 s. In total, the car has travelled 900 m.

a) Calculate the value of V.

b) Find the distance that the car travels while braking.

Q5 A runner accelerates uniformly for T seconds to a velocity of 6 ms^{-1}. She travels at this speed for 2 minutes, then decelerates uniformly to rest in $2T$ seconds. She travels a total distance of 765 m in a straight line.

a) Draw a speed-time graph to show the runner's motion.

b) Calculate the value of T.

c) Find the runner's acceleration during the first T seconds of motion.

Q6 A particle accelerates from rest at a constant rate of A ms^{-2} for 30 seconds. It reaches a velocity of V ms^{-1} and travels at this speed for a further 180 seconds. Given that the particle travels in a straight line:

a) show the particle's motion on a speed-time graph,

b) find an expression for V in terms of A,

c) find the value of A, given that the particle travels 2000 m in total.

Q7 A particle is travelling in a straight line. It passes point A with speed 10 ms^{-1}. Immediately after passing A, it accelerates at 4 ms^{-2} for x metres up to a speed of 50 ms^{-1}, then decelerates at 10 ms^{-2} for y metres to point B. It passes B with speed 10 ms^{-1}.
The particle takes T seconds to travel between A and B.

a) Show the particle's motion on a speed-time graph.

b) Find the area under the graph in terms of T.

c) Calculate the values of x, y and T.

Q8 A train is travelling at a steady speed of 30 ms^{-1} along a straight track. As it passes a signal box, it begins to decelerate steadily, coming to rest at a station in 20 seconds. The train remains stationary for 20 seconds, then sets off back in the direction it came with an acceleration of 0.375 ms^{-2}. It reaches a speed of 15 ms^{-1} as it passes the signal box.

a) Draw a velocity-time graph to show the motion of the train.
How long after leaving the station does the train reach the signal box?

b) Find the train's deceleration as it comes into the station.

c) Find the distance between the signal box and the station.

Q8 Hint: This is a velocity-time graph question, so make sure you decide which direction is positive — any velocities in the opposite direction will be negative. At these times, the graph will go below the horizontal axis.

Q9 A stone is thrown vertically upwards with a speed of 9.8 ms^{-1} from the edge of a cliff. It decelerates until it becomes stationary at its highest point, 1 second after being thrown, then begins to fall back down.
It lands in the sea below the cliff edge with speed 29.4 ms^{-1}, 4 seconds after it was thrown.

a) Draw a velocity-time graph to show the motion of the stone.

b) Use your graph to find:

(i) the distance the stone travels before it reaches its highest point,

(ii) the distance the stone travels from its highest point to the sea,

(iii) the height of the cliff above the sea.

Q9 Hint: Remember — displacement is not the same thing as distance travelled.

Acceleration-time graphs

An **acceleration-time (a/t) graph** shows how an object's **acceleration** changes over time.

- The **height** of the graph gives the object's **acceleration** at that time.
- The **area** under the graph gives the object's **velocity**.
- If $a = 0$, then the object is moving with **constant velocity**.

Tip: You'll only deal with constant acceleration in M1, so all the graphs will be made up of horizontal lines.

Example 1

The acceleration of a parachutist who steps out of a plane and falls vertically downwards is modelled by the acceleration-time graph shown.

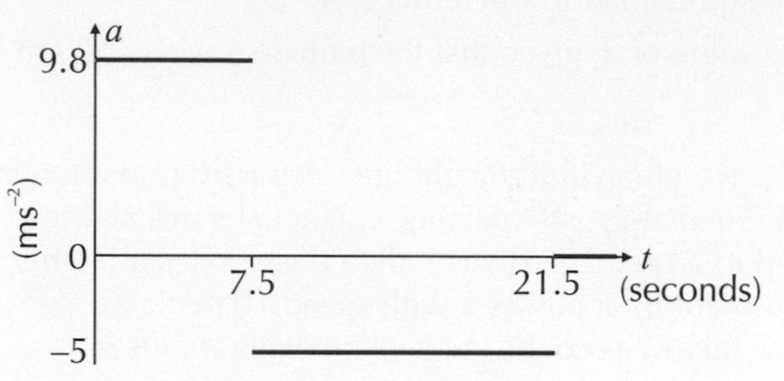

Tip: A negative acceleration can mean that the object is decelerating (i.e. speed decreasing). However, it can also mean that the object is accelerating (i.e. speed increasing), but moving in the negative direction. In this example, you can assume that the parachutist is moving in the same direction (downwards) during the time shown — so the negative acceleration is a deceleration.

a) Describe the motion of the parachutist.

- She falls freely with acceleration 9.8 ms^{-2} for 7.5 seconds.
- The parachute opens and the air resistance of the parachute causes her to decelerate at a rate of 5 ms^{-2} for 14 seconds.
- After 21.5 seconds, the acceleration is zero and so she falls with constant velocity.

b) Find the parachutist's constant velocity.

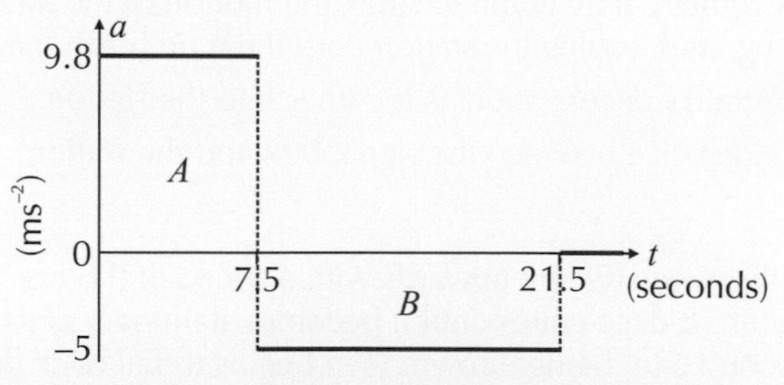

- You need to find the area under the graph:

  Area of A: $9.8 \times 7.5 = 73.5$ ms^{-1}

  Area of B: $-5 \times 14 = -70$ ms^{-1}

- The area of A gives the velocity that the parachutist reaches in free fall (i.e. her velocity just before she opens the parachute).
- The area of B gives the change in her velocity during the time that she is decelerating due to the air resistance of the parachute.
- Add the areas to find her constant velocity:
  Velocity = $73.5 + -70 =$ **3.5 ms^{-1}**

Tip: The area of B is negative because the parachutist's speed is decreasing.

c) Draw a speed-time graph to show the parachutist's motion.

1. Take the time that the parachutist steps out of the plane to be $t = 0$ s. At this time, her speed is 0 ms^{-1}.
2. From part **b)**, the parachutist accelerates to a speed of 73.5 ms^{-1} in 7.5 s.
3. When the parachute opens, the parachutist begins to decelerate. She slows to a speed of 3.5 ms^{-1} at time $t = 21.5$ s. (This is also from part **b)**.)
4. After $t = 21.5$ s, she travels at a constant speed of 3.5 ms^{-1}.

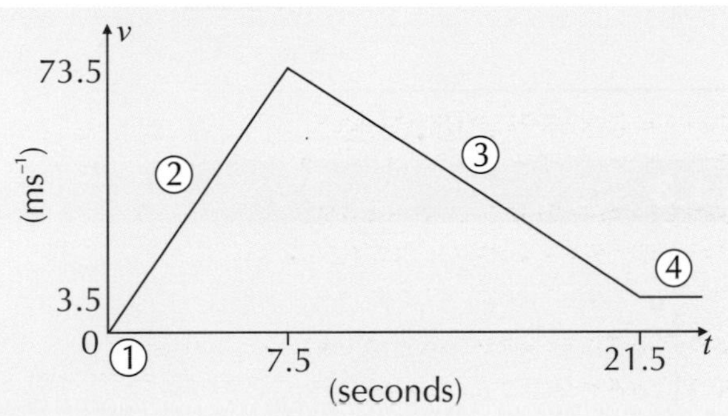

Example 2

The speed-time graph below shows the movement of a particle. Draw an acceleration-time graph for the particle's motion.

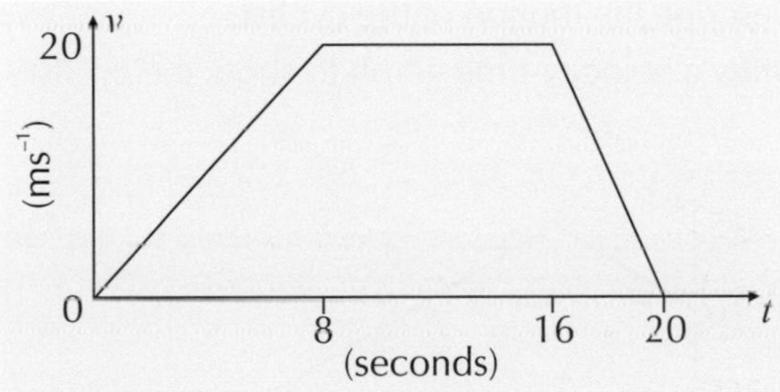

1. The particle starts from rest and accelerates to 20 ms^{-1} in 8 seconds. The acceleration is given by the gradient of the line:

$$\text{acceleration} = \frac{20\ \text{ms}^{-1}}{8\ \text{s}} = 2.5\ \text{ms}^{-2}$$

So this part of the graph will be a horizontal line through $a = 2.5$ ms^{-2}.

2. It then travels with constant speed for 8 seconds, so this part of the acceleration-time graph will be a horizontal line through $a = 0$ ms^{-2}.

3. Finally, the particle decelerates to rest in 4 seconds.

$$\text{acceleration} = -\frac{20\ \text{ms}^{-1}}{4\ \text{s}} = -5\ \text{ms}^{-2}$$

So this part of the graph will be a horizontal line through $a = -5$ ms^{-2}.

Tip: Remember that a negative gradient on a speed-time graph means the particle is decelerating.

So the graph will look like:

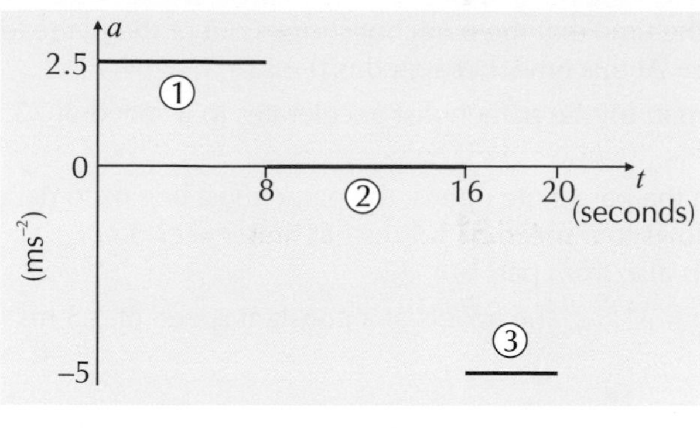

Exercise 1.3

Q1 Hint: The 'one direction' bit tells you that if the acceleration is negative, then it's a deceleration, and not an acceleration in the negative direction.

Q1

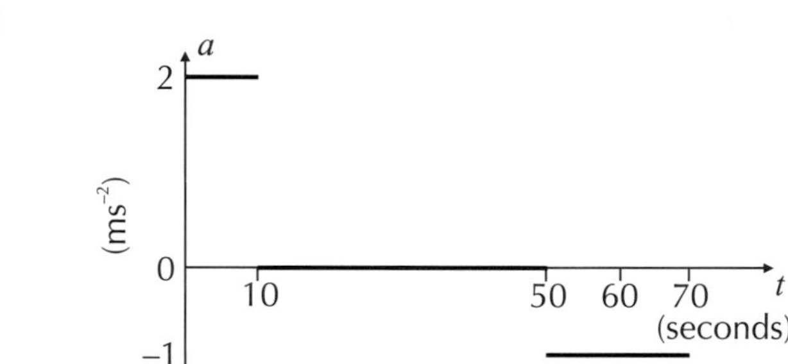

The acceleration-time graph above shows the motion of a cyclist. The cyclist starts from rest and travels in one direction.

a) Describe the motion of the cyclist.

b) Draw a velocity-time graph to show the cyclist's movement.

Q2

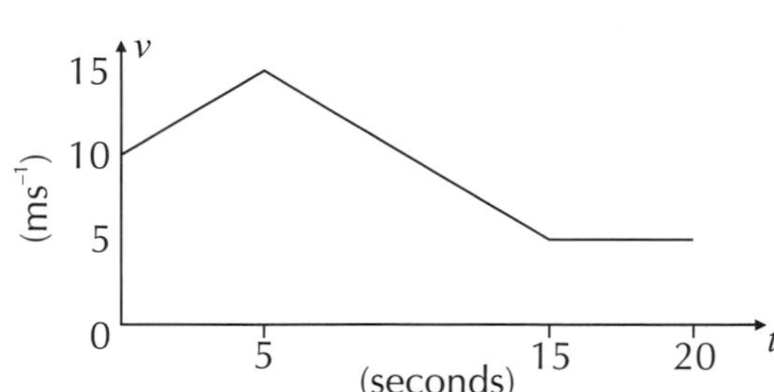

The velocity-time graph above shows the motion of a particle. Draw an acceleration-time graph to show the particle's movement.

Q3 A pebble falls through the air from rest with acceleration 9.8 ms^{-2} for 1.5 s. It hits the surface of a lake, then falls through the water, decelerating at a rate of 5 ms^{-2}. It reaches the bottom 2.5 s after entering the lake.

a) Draw an acceleration-time graph for the pebble's motion.

b) Find the pebble's velocity when it hits the surface of the lake.

c) Find the pebble's velocity when it reaches the bottom of the lake.

d) Draw a velocity-time graph for the pebble's motion.

e) Use your velocity-time graph to find the depth of the lake.

2. Constant Acceleration Equations

There are five constant acceleration equations — these are used to find out information about objects which are accelerating (or decelerating) uniformly. None of them are in the formula book, so you'll have to learn them.

Constant acceleration equations

- The constant acceleration equations are:

$$v = u + at$$
$$s = ut + \frac{1}{2}at^2$$
$$s = \left(\frac{u+v}{2}\right)t$$
$$v^2 = u^2 + 2as$$
$$s = vt - \frac{1}{2}at^2$$

u = initial speed (or velocity) in ms^{-1}
v = final speed (or velocity) in ms^{-1}
a = acceleration in ms^{-2}
s = displacement in m
t = time that passes in s (seconds)

Remember — these equations only work if the acceleration is **constant**.

- You'll usually be given three variables — your job is to **choose the equation** that will help you find the missing fourth variable.
- In M1, all the motion you'll deal with will be in a **straight line**. You should choose which direction is **positive**, then any velocity, acceleration or displacement in the **opposite direction** will be **negative**.
- You can derive the *uvast* equations using motion graphs and a bit of algebra:

Consider a particle moving with constant acceleration *a*.
The particle will accelerate from an initial velocity *u* to a final velocity *v*.
As it accelerates, it will cover a distance *s* over time *t*.

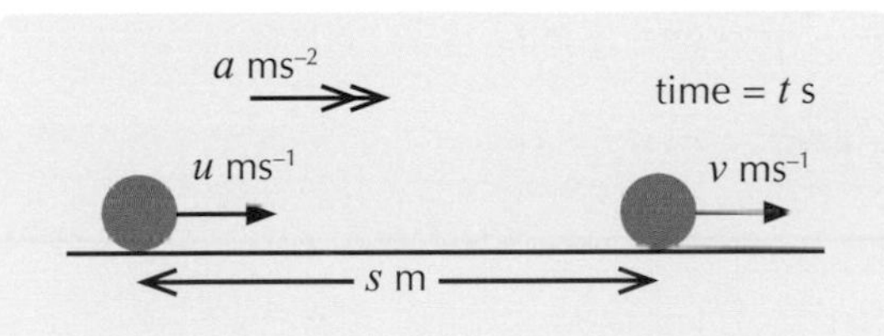

The velocity-time graph below shows the movement of the particle.

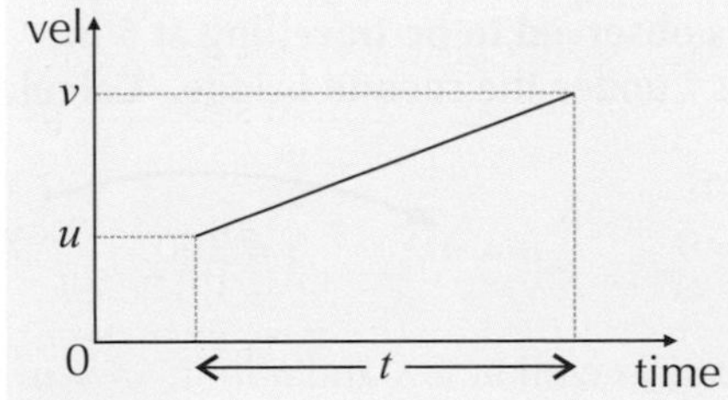

- The **acceleration** of the particle is given by the **gradient** of the graph: $a = \frac{v-u}{t}$, or $\boldsymbol{v = u + at}$

Learning Objectives:

- Know and recall the constant acceleration equations.
- Be able to use the equations to solve problems involving motion with constant acceleration.

Tip: The constant acceleration equations are often called '***uvast***' equations because of the five variables involved.

Tip: Look back at pages 10-11 for more on velocity-time graphs.

- The **distance travelled** is given by the **area** under the graph:

  Area of A = ut

  Area of B = $\frac{1}{2}(v - u)t$

  So $s = ut + \frac{1}{2}(v - u)t$

  $= ut + \frac{1}{2}vt - \frac{1}{2}ut$

  $= \frac{1}{2}ut + \frac{1}{2}vt$

  $\boldsymbol{s = \left(\frac{u + v}{2}\right)t}$

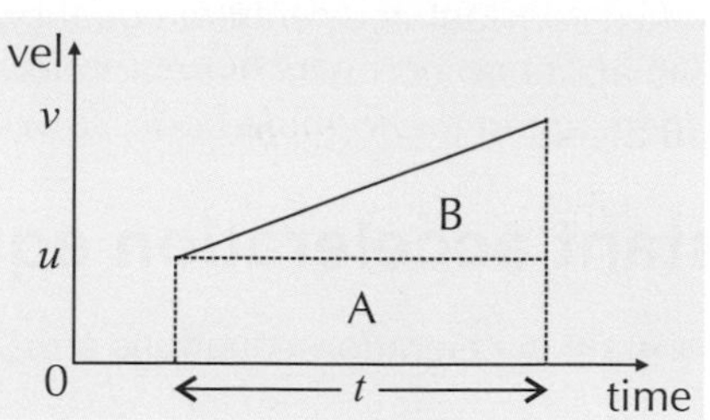

Now you can rearrange these two equations and make some substitutions to derive the remaining formulas.

- Substituting $v = u + at$ into $s = \left(\frac{u + v}{2}\right)t$ gives:

  $s = \left(\frac{u + u + at}{2}\right)t = \left(u + \frac{1}{2}at\right)t$

  $\Rightarrow$ $\boldsymbol{s = ut + \frac{1}{2}at^2}$

- Substituting $t = \left(\frac{v - u}{a}\right)$ into $s = \left(\frac{u + v}{2}\right)t$ gives:

  $s = \left(\frac{u + v}{2}\right)\left(\frac{v - u}{a}\right)$

  $2as = (u + v)(v - u) = v^2 - u^2$

  $\Rightarrow$ $\boldsymbol{v^2 = u^2 + 2as}$

- Substituting $u = v - at$ into $s = \left(\frac{u + v}{2}\right)t$ gives:

  $s = \left(\frac{v - at + v}{2}\right)t = \left(v - \frac{1}{2}at\right)t$

  $\Rightarrow$ $\boldsymbol{s = vt - \frac{1}{2}at^2}$

Example 1

A jet ski travels in a straight line along a river. It passes under two bridges 200 m apart and is observed to be travelling at 5 ms^{-1} under the first bridge and at 9 ms^{-1} under the second bridge. Calculate its acceleration.

- List the variables:

  $u = 5$ $\quad v = 9$ $\quad a = a$ $\quad s = 200$

You have to work out a.

- Choose the equation with u, v, s and a in it: $v^2 = u^2 + 2as$
- Substitute the values you're given: $9^2 = 5^2 + (2 \times a \times 200)$

  $81 = 25 + 400a$

  $400a = 81 - 25 = 56$

  $a = 56 \div 400 =$ 0.14 ms^{-2}

Tip: You're not told or asked for t, so don't bother writing it down.

Example 2

A particle accelerates from rest for 8 seconds at a rate of 12 ms^{-2}. The particle's motion is restricted to a straight path.

a) Find the velocity of the particle at the end of the 8 seconds.

- List the variables:

  $u = 0$

  $v = v$

  $a = 12$

  $s = s$ ← You'll need to find s in part **b)**.

  $t = 8$

- Choose the equation with u, a, t and v in it: $v = u + at$
- Substitute the values you're given: $v = 0 + (12 \times 8) =$ 96 ms^{-1}

Tip: If a particle 'starts from rest', then $u = 0$.

b) Find the distance travelled by the particle during this time.

- Choose the equation with u, a, t and s in it: $s = ut + \frac{1}{2}at^2$
- Substitute the values you're given: $s = (0 \times 8) + \frac{1}{2}(12 \times 8^2) =$ 384 m

Example 3

A car decelerates at a rate of 16 kmh^{-2} for 6 minutes. It travels 1.28 km along a straight road during this time. Find the velocity of the car at the end of the 6 minutes.

- List the variables:

  $v = v$

  $a = -16$ ← a is negative because the car is decelerating.

  $s = 1.28$

  $t = 6 \div 60 = 0.1$

- Choose the equation with a, s, t and v in it: $s = vt - \frac{1}{2}at^2$
- Substitute the values you're given: $1.28 = 0.1v - \frac{1}{2}(-16 \times 0.1^2)$

  $0.1v = 1.2$

  $v = 12$ kmh^{-1}

Tip: Make sure you use consistent units throughout the question. Here, you should change the time from minutes to hours to match the units of acceleration.

Exercise 2.1

Exam Hint: Remember — always write out the *uvast* variables.

Q1 A car travels along a straight horizontal road. It accelerates uniformly from rest to a velocity of 12 ms^{-1} in 5 seconds.

a) Find the car's acceleration.

b) Find the total distance travelled by the car.

Q2 Hint: To convert from kmh^{-1} to ms^{-1}, multiply by 1000, then divide by 60^2.

Q2 A cyclist is travelling at 18 kmh^{-1}.
He brakes steadily, coming to rest in 50 m.

a) Calculate the cyclist's initial speed in ms^{-1} .

b) Find the time it takes him to come to rest.

c) Find his deceleration.

Q3 A skater accelerates uniformly between two posts 30 m apart.
Her speed on passing the second post is 12 ms^{-1}.
She takes 3 seconds to travel between the posts.

a) Find her speed on passing the first post.

b) Find her acceleration.

Q4 A train running at 20 ms^{-1} is brought steadily to rest in $2\frac{1}{2}$ minutes.
Find the distance covered by the train in coming to rest.

Q5 A skier increases her velocity from 5 ms^{-1} to 25 ms^{-1} over a distance of 60 m.

a) Find the skier's acceleration.

b) What modelling assumptions have you made?

Q6 A runner decelerates at a rate of 1 ms^{-2} for 50 m.
His final velocity is 4 ms^{-1}.

a) Find the runner's initial velocity.

b) Calculate the time the runner decelerates for.

Q7 Hint: Consider the motion between the first and second posts and the first and third posts separately to form a pair of simultaneous equations.

Q7 A car travels with uniform acceleration between three lamp posts, equally spaced at 30 m apart. It passes the second post 2 seconds after passing the first post, and passes the third post 1 second later.

a) Find the car's acceleration.

b) Calculate the car's velocity when it passes the first post.

Q8 A bus is approaching a tunnel. The driver slows down steadily from a speed of U ms^{-1} to 20 ms^{-1} in 15 seconds. The driver maintains this speed for the 25 seconds it takes to drive through the tunnel. After emerging from the tunnel, he accelerates steadily, reaching a speed of U ms^{-1} in 30 seconds.

a) Calculate the length of the tunnel.

b) Given that the total distance travelled by the coach is 1580 m, find the value of U.

Gravity

- An object moving through the air will experience an **acceleration** towards the earth due to **gravity**.
- Acceleration due to gravity is denoted by the letter g, where $g = 9.8 \text{ ms}^{-2}$.
- Acceleration due to gravity always acts **vertically downwards**.
- For an object moving freely under gravity, you can use the *uvast* equations to find information such as the **speed of projection**, **time of flight**, **greatest height** and **landing speed**.

Tip: You might be given a different value of g in a particular question. Use the one you're given, otherwise your answer might not match the examiner's.

Example 1

A pebble is dropped into an empty well 18 m deep and moves freely under gravity until it hits the bottom. Calculate the time it takes to reach the bottom.

- First, list the variables, taking downwards as positive:

  $u = 0$ $\quad a = 9.8$ $\quad s = 18$ $\quad t = t$

- You need the equation with u, a, s and t in it: $s = ut + \frac{1}{2}at^2$
- Substitute values: $18 = (0 \times t) + (\frac{1}{2} \times 9.8 \times t^2)$

$$18 = 4.9t^2$$

$$t^2 = \frac{18}{4.9} = 3.67...$$

$$t = \sqrt{3.67...} = 1.92 \text{ s (3 s.f.)}$$

Tip: Watch out for tricky questions like this — at first it looks like they've only given you one variable. You have to spot that the pebble was dropped (so $u = 0$) and that it's moving freely under gravity (so $a = g = 9.8 \text{ ms}^{-2}$).

Example 2

A ball is projected vertically upwards at 3 ms⁻¹ from a point 1.5 m above the ground.

a) How long does it take to reach its maximum height?

- First, list the variables, taking up as the positive direction:

  $u = 3$

  $v = 0$ ← When projected objects reach the top of their motion, they stop momentarily.

  $a = -9.8$ ← Because g always acts downwards and up was taken as positive, a is negative.

  $t = t$

- Use the equation with u, v, a and t in it: $v = u + at$

  Substitute values: $0 = 3 + (-9.8 \times t)$

$$0 = 3 - 9.8t$$

$$t = \frac{3}{9.8} = 0.306 \text{ s (3 s.f.)}$$

Tip: Make sure you decide which direction (upwards or downwards) you are going to take as being positive. This tells you whether each of your *uvast* variables is positive or negative.

b) How fast will the ball be travelling when it hits the ground?

Think about the complete path of the ball.

The ball lands on the ground, 1.5 m below the point of projection.

So $s = -1.5$

Using $v^2 = u^2 + 2as$ where $u = 3$, $v = v$, $a = -9.8$, $s = -1.5$:

$v^2 = u^2 + 2as = 3^2 + 2(-9.8 \times -1.5)$

$= 38.4$

So $v = \sqrt{38.4} = 6.20 \text{ ms}^{-1}$ (to 3 s.f.)

Tip: Remember that s is **displacement** — the object's final position relative to its starting point, not its total distance travelled. Here, the ball lands below its initial point, and since upwards is positive, s is negative.

Example 3

A particle is projected vertically upwards from ground level with a speed of u ms^{-1}. The particle takes 2.6 s to return to ground level.

a) Draw a velocity-time graph to show the particle's motion.

- The particle is projected with speed u, then decelerates due to gravity until it is momentarily at rest at its highest point.
- It then returns to earth, accelerating due to gravity and reaching its initial speed u (but in the opposite direction to before) when it lands.
- There are two possible graphs, depending on which direction is taken as being positive.
- If upwards is taken as positive, then the particle's initial velocity is positive (u ms^{-1}), and its velocity on the way back down will be negative.

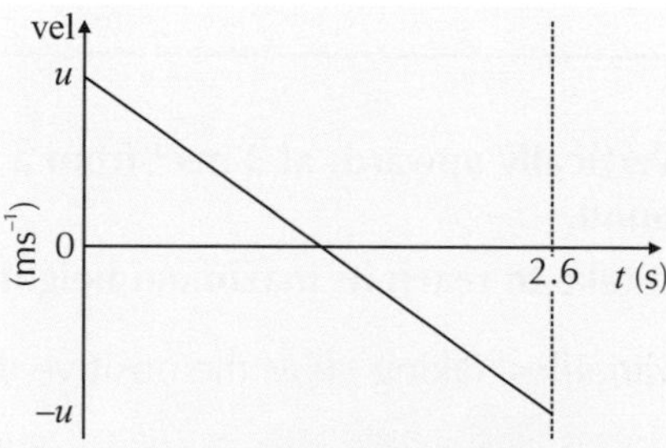

- If downwards is taken as positive, then the particle's initial velocity is negative ($-u$ ms^{-1}), and its velocity on the way back down will be positive.

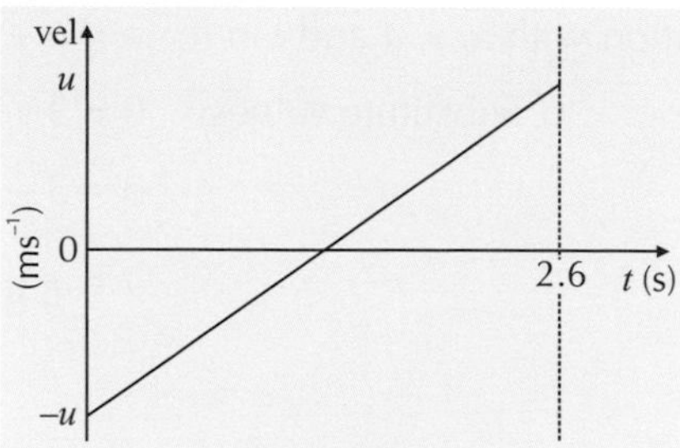

Tip: Remember that velocity takes into account the direction of motion, so can be positive or negative. Speed is all about the magnitude, so the direction doesn't matter.

b) Find u, the particle's speed of projection.

Think about the first half of the particle's motion, from ground level to its highest point. Taking upwards as positive:

$u = u$ $v = 0$ $a = -9.8$ $t = 2.6 \div 2 = 1.3$

Using $v = u + at$

$0 = u - 9.8 \times 1.3$

So $u = 9.8 \times 1.3 = 12.74 \text{ ms}^{-1}$

When it reaches its maximum height, the pebble will stop momentarily.

Tip: The particle reaches its maximum height halfway through its flight time.

Example 4

A particle is fired vertically upwards from ground level with speed 49 ms^{-1}. Assuming that air resistance can be ignored, find the amount of time that the particle is over 78.4 m above the ground.

- As the particle travels upwards, it will pass a height of 78.4 m.
- Once it has reached its highest point, it will start to fall, and will pass 78.4 m again, on the way back down.
- Use a constant acceleration equation to form a quadratic to find the two moments in time that the particle is at 78.4 m.
- The difference between these two times will be the length of time the particle is above that height.

- Taking up as the positive direction:

  $u = 49$ $a = -9.8$ $s = 78.4$ $t = t$

- Using $s = ut + \frac{1}{2}at^2$

  $78.4 = 49t - 4.9t^2$

  $\Rightarrow t^2 - 10t + 16 = 0$

  $(t - 2)(t - 8) = 0$

  $\Rightarrow t = 2, t = 8$

- So the particle is 78.4 m above the ground 2 seconds after being fired (on the way up), and 8 seconds after being fired (on the way back down).
- This means that the particle is above 78.4 m for $8 - 2 = 6$ seconds.

Example 5

A boot is thrown vertically upwards from a point x m above ground level. Its speed of projection is 4 ms^{-1}. The boot lands on the ground 2 seconds after being thrown.

a) Find the value of x.

> **Tip:** $s = -x$ because the boot lands x m below its point of projection.

Taking up as the positive direction:

$u = 4$ $a = -9.8$ $s = -x$ $t = 2$

Using $s = ut + \frac{1}{2}at^2$

$$-x = (4 \times 2) + \tfrac{1}{2}(-9.8 \times 2^2)$$

$$-x = -11.6$$

So $x =$ 11.6 m

b) Find the speed and direction of the boot 0.8 seconds after it is thrown.

Taking up as the positive direction:

$u = 4$ $v = v$ $a = -9.8$ $t = 0.8$

Using $v = u + at$

$$v = 4 + (-9.8 \times 0.8) = -3.84 \text{ ms}^{-1}$$

v is negative, so the boot is moving downwards at 3.84 ms^{-1}.

Exercise 2.2

> **Q1 Hint:** The pebble is dropped, so $u = 0$.

Q1 A pebble is dropped down a hole to see how deep it is. It reaches the bottom of the hole after 3 seconds. How deep is the hole?

Q2 A ball is dropped from a second floor window that is 5 metres from the ground.

a) How long will it take to reach the ground?

b) At what speed will it hit the ground?

Q3 An object is projected vertically upwards from ground level with a speed of 30 ms^{-1}.

a) Find the maximum height reached by the object.

b) Find the time it takes the object to land on the ground.

c) Find the object's speed and direction 2 seconds after launch.

Q4 A particle is projected vertically upwards with a speed u ms^{-1} from a point d metres above the ground. After 3 seconds the particle hits the ground with a speed of 20 ms^{-1}.

a) Calculate the value of u.

b) Calculate the value of d.

Q5 An apple is thrown vertically upwards with speed 8 ms^{-1} from a height of 5 metres above the ground.

a) Calculate the apple's maximum height above the ground.

b) For how long is the apple 8 m or more above the ground?

Q5 Hint: Remember that the apple is not thrown from ground level.

Q6 A decorator is painting the frame of a fifth floor window and catapults a brush up to his mate exactly three floors above him. He catapults it vertically with a speed of 12 ms^{-1}, and it is at its maximum height when his mate catches it.

a) Find the distance between the decorator and his mate.

b) For how long is the brush in the air?

He later catapults a tub of putty vertically at the same speed but his mate fails to catch it. The floors of the building are equally spaced apart, and the decorator is positioned at the base of the fifth floor.

c) At what speed does it hit the ground?

Q7 The displacement-time graph below shows the motion of an object fired vertically upwards with speed 24.5 ms^{-1} from the edge of a cliff. The object travels in a vertical line and hits the ground below (at x = 0).

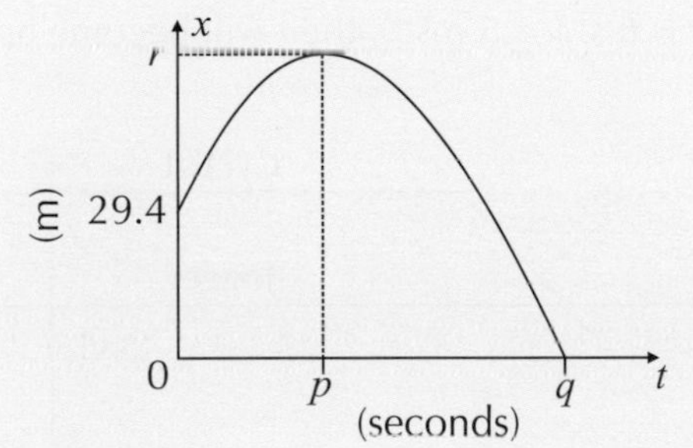

a) Find the value of p.

b) Find the value of q.

c) Find the value of r.

Q8 A projectile is fired from a point 50 m below ground level vertically upwards. It passes a target 100 m above ground level and 3 seconds later passes another target which is 220 m above ground level. Assume that air resistance can be ignored.

a) Find the speed of projection of the projectile.

b) Find the maximum height above the ground reached by the projectile.

c) Find the time taken by the projectile to reach the first target.

Q8 Hint: Work out part a) in two separate stages.

More complicated problems

Now you're nice and familiar with the constant acceleration equations, it's time to get your teeth into some trickier problems.

- Some questions will involve **motion graphs** — you may have to find areas and gradients as well as use the *uvast* equations.
- Some will involve **more than one** moving object. For these questions, t is often the same (or at least connected) because time ticks along for both objects at the same rate. The distance travelled might also be connected.

Example 1

A jogger and a cyclist are travelling along a straight path. Their movements are as follows:

- **The jogger runs with constant velocity.**
- **At the moment the jogger passes the cyclist, the cyclist accelerates from rest, reaching a velocity of 5 ms^{-1} after 6 seconds, and then continues at this velocity.**
- **The cyclist overtakes the jogger after 15 seconds.**

a) **Taking the time that the cyclist begins to accelerate as $t = 0$ s, draw a speed-time graph to show their motion.**

- The graph of the jogger's motion will be a horizontal line, as the speed is constant. Call the jogger's speed V.
- The graph of the cyclist's motion will increase from ($t = 0$ s, $v = 0$ ms^{-1}) to ($t = 6$ s, $v = 5$ ms^{-1}), then will become horizontal.

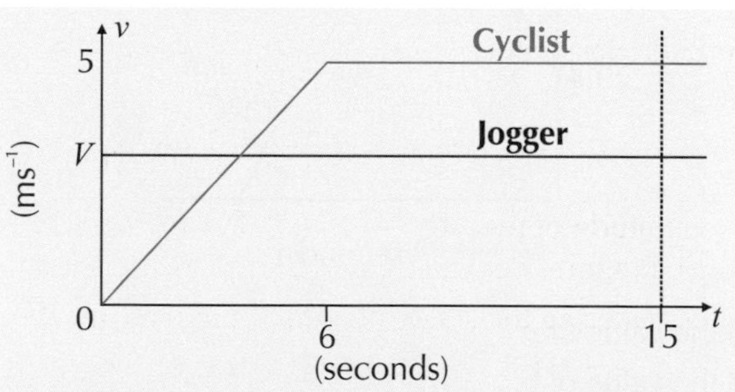

Tip: You know that the cyclist overtakes the jogger, so V must be less than 5 ms^{-1}.

b) **Find the speed of the jogger.**

- After 15 s the distances the jogger and cyclist have travelled are the same, so you can work out the area under the two graphs to get the distances:

Jogger: Distance = area = $15V$

Cyclist: Distance = area = $(6 \times 5) \div 2 + (9 \times 5) = 60$

So $15V = 60$

$V = 4$ ms^{-1}

Tip: Find the area under the cyclist's graph by splitting it into a triangle and a rectangle, or just use the formula for the area of a trapezium.

Example 2

A bus is travelling along a straight road at V ms^{-1}. When it reaches point A it accelerates uniformly for 4 s, reaching a speed of 21 ms^{-1} as it passes point B. At point B, the driver brakes uniformly until the bus comes to a halt 7 s later. The magnitude of the deceleration is twice the magnitude of the previous acceleration.

a) Draw a speed-time graph to show the motion of the bus.

- The graph will increase from ($t = 0$ s, $v = V$ ms^{-1}) to ($t = 4$ s, $v = 21$ ms^{-1}).
- It will then return to $v = 0$ ms^{-1} at time $t = 11$ s.

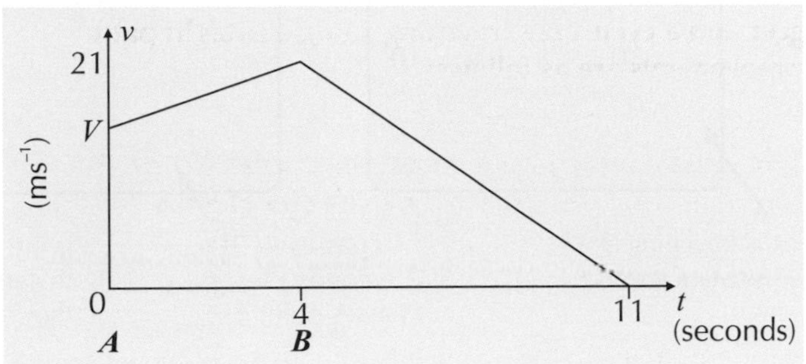

b) Find the value of V.

- Split the motion into two stages — 'between A and B', and 'after B'.
- First considering the stage 'after B', list the variables:

  $u = 21$ $\quad v = 0$ $\quad a = a$ $\quad t = 7$

- To find the deceleration use $a = \frac{(v - u)}{t}$ ← Just $v = u + at$ rearranged.

$$a = \frac{(0 - 21)}{7} = -3 \text{ ms}^{-2}$$

- The magnitude of the deceleration ('after B') is twice the magnitude of the acceleration ('between A and B'), so the acceleration is 1.5 ms^{-1}.
- Now considering the stage 'between A and B', list the variables:

  $u = V$ $\quad v = 21$ $\quad a = 1.5$ $\quad t = 4$

- Find V using $u = v - at$

$$V = 21 - (1.5 \times 4)$$

So, $V = 15$ ms^{-1}

c) Find the distance travelled by the bus during the measured time.

Find the area under the graph:

$$\text{Area} = (15 \times 4) + \tfrac{1}{2}(6 \times 4) + \tfrac{1}{2}(21 \times 7)$$

$$= 145.5 \text{ m}$$

Example 3

- **A car, A, travelling along a straight road at a constant 30 ms^{-1}, passes point R at time $t = 0$.**
- **Exactly 2 seconds later, a second car, B, passes point R with velocity 25 ms^{-1}, moving in the same direction as car A.**
- **Car B accelerates at a constant 2 ms^{-2}.**

a) Show that the two cars are level when $t^2 - 9t - 46 = 0$, for time t s.

- For each car, there are different *uvast* variables, so write separate lists and separate equations:

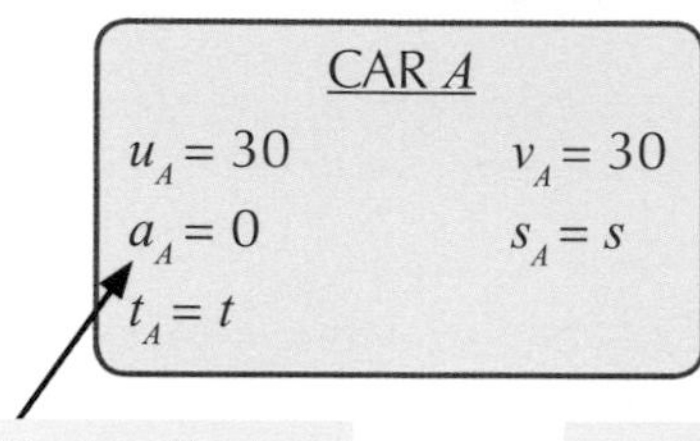

CAR B

$u_B = 25$ $\quad v_B = v$

$a_B = 2$ $\quad s_B = s$

$t_B = (t - 2)$

A is travelling at a constant speed.

B passes R 2 seconds after A passes point R.

s is the same for both cars because they're level.

Tip: Drawing a diagram can help if you're struggling to picture what's going on.

- When the two cars are level they will have travelled the same distance, so choose an equation with s in it: $s = ut + \frac{1}{2}at^2$

FOR CAR A:

$$s = 30t + (\tfrac{1}{2} \times 0 \times t^2)$$
$$\mathbf{s = 30t}$$

FOR CAR B:

$$s = 25(t - 2) + (\tfrac{1}{2} \times 2 \times (t - 2)^2)$$
$$s = 25t - 50 + (t - 2)(t - 2)$$
$$s = 25t - 50 + (t^2 - 4t + 4)$$
$$\mathbf{s = t^2 + 21t - 46}$$

- Make the equations for s equal to each other (because the cars have travelled the same distance):

$$30t = t^2 + 21t - 46$$
$$\Rightarrow \quad t^2 - 9t - 46 = 0$$

b) Find the time when the two cars are level.

Use the quadratic formula to solve for t:

$t^2 - 9t - 46 = 0$

$$t = \frac{-b \pm \sqrt{b^2 - 4ac}}{2a} = \frac{9 \pm \sqrt{9^2 - (4 \times 1 \times -46)}}{2 \times 1}$$

$\Rightarrow \quad t = 12.639...$ or $t = -3.639...$

So the cars are level 12.6 seconds after car A passes R (correct to 3 s.f.).

Tip: You can ignore the negative value of t, as time is always positive.

Example 4

Particle A is projected vertically upwards with speed 34.3 ms^{-1} from ground level. At the same time, particle B is dropped from a height of 686 m directly above the point that A is projected from. Assume that air resistance can be ignored.

Find the time that the two particles collide.

- Write down the different *uvast* variables for each particle, taking upwards as the positive direction:

PARTICLE A	
$u_A = 34.3$	$v_A = v_A$
$a_A = -9.8$	$s_A = s_A$
$t_A = t$	

PARTICLE B	
$u_B = 0$	$v_B = v_B$
$a_B = -9.8$	$s_B = s_B$
$t_B = t$	

- To find the time that the particles collide, you need to know how far they have moved. Use $s = ut + \frac{1}{2}at^2$:

FOR PARTICLE A: $s_A = 34.3t + (\frac{1}{2} \times -9.8 \times t^2)$
$\mathbf{s_A = 34.3t - 4.9t^2}$

FOR PARTICLE B: $s_B = 0 + (\frac{1}{2} \times -9.8 \times t^2)$
$\mathbf{s_B = -4.9t^2}$

- So, after t seconds, A is $(34.3t - 4.9t^2)$ m above the ground and B has moved $4.9t^2$ m downwards from a height of 686 m — i.e. B is $(686 - 4.9t^2)$ m above the ground.
- The particles collide when:

$$34.3t - 4.9t^2 = 686 - 4.9t^2$$

$$34.3t = 686$$

$$t = 686 \div 34.3 = 20$$

So the particles collide 20 seconds after being released.

Tip: t is the same for both particles, as they set off at the same time.

Tip: $a = -9.8$ for both particles because A is **decelerating** in the **positive** direction due to gravity, and B is **accelerating** in the **negative** direction due to gravity.

Tip: s_A is the displacement from the ground, and s_B is the displacement from the point B is dropped from.

Tip: They collide when they're the same distance above the ground.

Exercise 2.3

Q1 At time $t = 0$, an object passes point W with speed 2 ms^{-1}.
It travels at this constant speed for 8 seconds, until it reaches point X.
Immediately after passing X, the object accelerates uniformly to point Y, 28 m away. The object's speed at Y is 6 ms^{-1}.
Immediately after passing Y, the object decelerates uniformly to V ms^{-1} (where $V > 2$) in 5 seconds. The object travels a total distance of 67 m.

a) Find the time taken for the object to travel between X and Y.

b) Draw a speed-time graph to show the motion of the object.

c) Find the value of V.

Q2 A van is travelling at a constant speed of 14 ms^{-1} along a straight road. At time $t = 0$, the van passes a motorbike, which then sets off from rest and travels along the same road in the same direction as the van. The motorbike accelerates uniformly to a speed of 18 ms^{-1} in 20 seconds, then maintains this speed.

a) Draw a speed-time graph to show the motion of the two vehicles.

b) How long after setting off does the motorbike overtake the van?

Q3 Two remote-controlled cars, X and Y, lie on a straight line 30 m apart. At time $t = 0$, they are moving towards each other.
X has initial speed 15 ms^{-1} and accelerates at a rate of 1 ms^{-2}.
Y has initial speed 20 ms^{-1} and accelerates at a rate of 2 ms^{-2}.

a) Calculate the time taken for the cars to collide.

b) Calculate the speed of each car when they collide.

c) How far from the initial position of X do the two cars collide?

Q4 A particle travels between three points, P, Q and R.
At time $t = 0$, the particle passes P with speed 15 ms^{-1}.
Immediately after passing P, the particle accelerates uniformly at 3 ms^{-2} for 4 seconds, until it reaches Q with speed U ms^{-1}.
It then travels at this constant speed in a straight line for 6 seconds to point R. Immediately after passing R, the particle decelerates uniformly for T seconds until it comes to rest.

a) Draw a speed-time graph to show the particle's motion.

b) Find the value of U.

c) Given that the particle travels a total distance of 405 m, find how long after passing P the particle comes to rest.

d) Find the deceleration of the particle in coming to rest.

Q5 Hint: The second ball is rolled 3 seconds after the first ball, so if $t_1 = t$, then $t_2 = t - 3$.

Q5 At time $t = 0$, a ball is rolled across a mat with speed 5 ms^{-1}.
It decelerates at a rate of 0.5 ms^{-2} until it comes to rest.
3 seconds later, a second ball is rolled along a smooth floor, in a direction parallel to the first. This ball travels with a constant velocity of 4 ms^{-1}. The starting points of the two balls are side-by-side.

a) How long after the first ball is rolled does the second ball pass the first ball?

b) Find the distance travelled by each ball before the second ball passes the first ball.

c) How far ahead of the first ball is the second ball after 15 seconds?

Q6 At time $t = 0$, particle A is dropped from a bridge 40 m above the ground. One second later, particle B is projected vertically upwards with speed 5 ms^{-1} from a point 10 m above the ground.

a) Find the distance travelled by A when B is at the highest point in its motion.

b) How long after A is dropped do the two particles become level?

c) How far from the ground are they at this time?

Review Exercise — Chapter 2

Q1 The start of a journey is shown on the speed-time graph.

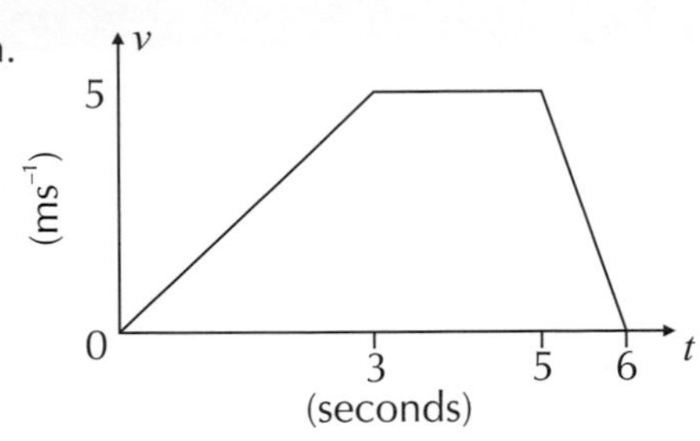

a) Find the acceleration during the first 3 seconds of motion.

b) Find the deceleration during the final 1 second of motion.

c) Find the distance travelled between $t = 3$ and $t = 6$.

Q2 The displacement-time graph on the right shows a motorcycle journey. Find the velocity of the motorcycle during each stage of the journey.

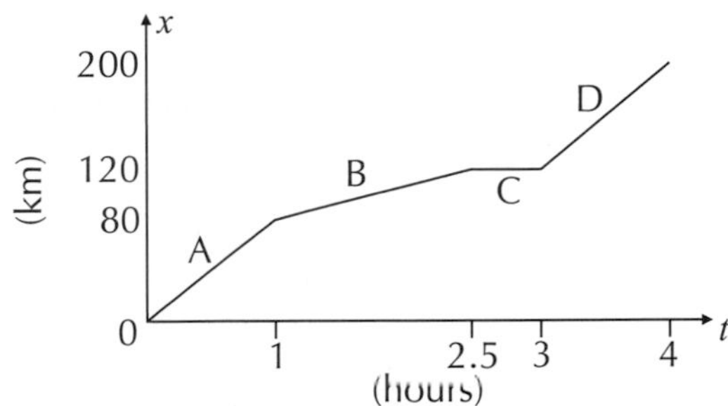

Q3 A runner starts from rest and accelerates at 0.5 ms^{-2} for 5 seconds. She then maintains a constant velocity for 20 seconds before decelerating to a stop at 0.25 ms^{-2}. Draw a velocity-time graph to show the motion and find the distance the runner travels.

Q4 A motorcyclist accelerates uniformly from 3 ms^{-1} to 9 ms^{-1} in 2 seconds. What is the distance travelled by the motorcyclist during this acceleration?

Q5 A runner accelerates at a rate of 0.2 ms^{-2} along a straight road. At the start of the road, her speed is 6 ms^{-1}. It takes her 20 seconds to run the length of the road.

a) How long is the road?

b) What is her speed as she reaches the end of the road?

Q6 A particle is projected vertically upwards with velocity 35 ms^{-1}.

a) Find the maximum height reached by the particle.

b) Find the time the particle is in the air before it lands again.

Q7 A horse runs towards the edge of a cliff with speed 11 ms^{-1}. The horse begins to decelerate at a rate of 3.8 ms^{-1} when it is a distance of 25 m from the cliff edge. Will the horse stop before it reaches the cliff edge?

Q8 A swimmer and a fish set off from the same place at the same time. The swimmer swims in a straight line with constant velocity 1 ms^{-1}. The fish accelerates uniformly from rest to U ms^{-1} in 2 seconds, then maintains this speed. It moves in a straight line throughout its motion, and overtakes the swimmer 5 seconds after they set off.

a) Draw a velocity-time graph to show the motion of the swimmer and the fish.

b) Use your graph to find the value of U.

Exam-Style Questions — Chapter 2

1 A window cleaner of a block of flats accidentally drops his sandwich, which falls freely to the ground. The speed of the sandwich as it passes a high floor is u. After a further 1.2 seconds the sandwich is moving at a speed of 17 ms^{-1}. The distance between the consecutive floors of the building is h.

a) Find the value of u.

(3 marks)

b) It takes the sandwich another 2.1 seconds to fall the remaining 14 floors to the ground. Find h.

(4 marks)

2 A train starts from rest at station A and travels with constant acceleration for 20 s. It then travels with constant speed V ms^{-1} for 2 minutes. It then decelerates with constant deceleration for 40 s before coming to rest at station B. The total distance between stations A and B is 2.1 km.

a) Sketch a velocity-time graph for the train's motion between stations A and B. *(3 marks)*

b) Hence or otherwise find the value of V. *(3 marks)*

c) Calculate the distance travelled by the train while decelerating. *(2 marks)*

d) Sketch an acceleration-time graph for this motion. *(3 marks)*

3 A delivery van is travelling with velocity 21 ms^{-1}. As it nears its delivery destination, the driver brakes and the van decelerates uniformly to rest in 6 seconds. The van is stationary for 10 seconds, then sets back off in the direction it came, accelerating uniformly to a velocity of $-U$ ms^{-1} in 4 seconds. It maintains this speed for 5 seconds.

a) Taking the time that the driver starts to brake as $t = 0$ s, draw a velocity-time graph to show the motion of the van.

(3 marks)

b) Find the van's deceleration.

(2 marks)

c) In total, the van travels a distance of 161 m during the measured time. Find the value of U.

(3 marks)

d) Find the van's displacement at time $t = 25$ s from its position at time $t = 0$ s. *(2 marks)*

4 A body is projected vertically upwards from a point 8 m above the ground at a speed of u ms^{-1} and travels freely under gravity. The body hits the ground with speed 20 ms^{-1}.

Find:

a) the value of u, *(3 marks)*

b) the time it takes to hit the ground. *(3 marks)*

5 A ball is thrown vertically upwards with velocity 5 ms^{-1} from a point 2 m above the ground. The velocity-time graph below shows the motion of the ball.

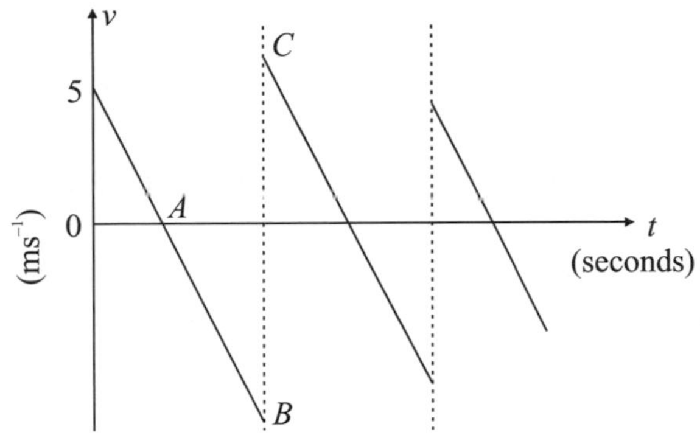

a) (i) Explain the significance of point A on the graph. *(1 mark)*

(ii) Find the time taken by the ball to reach point A. *(3 marks)*

b) (i) Explain the significance of point B on the graph. *(1 mark)*

(ii) Find the velocity of the ball when it is at point B. *(3 marks)*

c) Explain why there is a discontinuity between the points B and C on the graph. *(1 mark)*

6 At time $t = 0$ s, particle P is fired vertically upwards with speed 17.64 ms^{-1}. When P reaches its maximum height, particle Q is fired vertically upwards with speed 25 ms^{-1}. Both particles are fired from ground level.

a) Find the time between the two particles being fired. *(3 marks)*

b) Find the length of time after P is fired before the two particles become level. *(5 marks)*

c) Find the particles' vertical height above the ground when they are level. *(3 marks)*

Chapter 3 Vectors

1. Vectors

Learning Objectives:

- Understand the term 'vector' and use vector notation.
- Be able to perform vector calculations to find a resultant vector.
- Be able to find the magnitude and direction of a vector.
- Be able to use the unit vectors **i** and **j**.

Vectors crop up all over the place in Mechanics, so you really need to know how to handle them.

Vectors — the basics

- A **scalar** is a quantity which just has a **magnitude**. E.g. distance, speed, mass — you only need to know the size of the quantity.
- A **vector** is a quantity with a **magnitude** and a **direction**. E.g. displacement, velocity, force — you need to know the size of the quantity, and which way it is acting.
- The following is an example of how the direction of a vector makes it different to the corresponding scalar quantity.

A runner sprints 100 m along a track at a speed of 8 ms⁻¹. She then she jogs back 50 m at 4 ms⁻¹.

Average Speed

Speed = Distance ÷ Time

The runner takes (100 ÷ 8) + (50 ÷ 4) = 25 s to travel 150 m.

So her average speed is 150 ÷ 25 = **6 ms⁻¹**

Average Velocity

Velocity = Change in displacement ÷ Time

The runner travels 100 m, then 50 m back in the direction she came. So she ends up 50 m away from her start point. It takes her 25 s.

Her average velocity is 50 ÷ 25 = **2 ms⁻¹** in the direction of the sprint.

Tip: This is also an example of how displacement (a vector) can be different to distance travelled (a scalar).

- You can show the **magnitude** and **direction** of a vector with an arrow — the longer the arrow, the greater the magnitude:

A train travelling **due east at 16 ms⁻¹**.	A train travelling **due west at 8 ms⁻¹**.
⟶	⟵

Tip: The arrow pointing west is half the size since that vector has half the magnitude.

- Drawing the arrow on a **grid** can help show the vector's magnitude and direction (this is shown on the next page). Alternatively, you can state the vector's magnitude and the **angle** at which it acts.

- A **negative** vector acts in the **opposite** direction to a positive vector:

Taking right as positive:

A force of 30 N. → A force of –30 N. ←

- **Parallel** vectors have the **same direction**, but **not** necessarily the same **magnitude**.
- Vectors can be **multiplied by scalars**. This can **change** the **magnitude** of the vector, and, if the scalar is **negative**, **reverse** its **direction**.

Tip: There's loads more about vectors and forces in Chapter 4.

Example 1

The vector a is shown on the grid below.
On the same grid, draw the vectors 2a, –a and –1.5a.

- 2**a** is parallel to **a**, but will have twice the magnitude (i.e. length).
- –**a** has the same magnitude as **a**, but acts in the opposite direction.
- –1.5**a** acts in the opposite direction to **a**, and is one and a half times greater in magnitude.

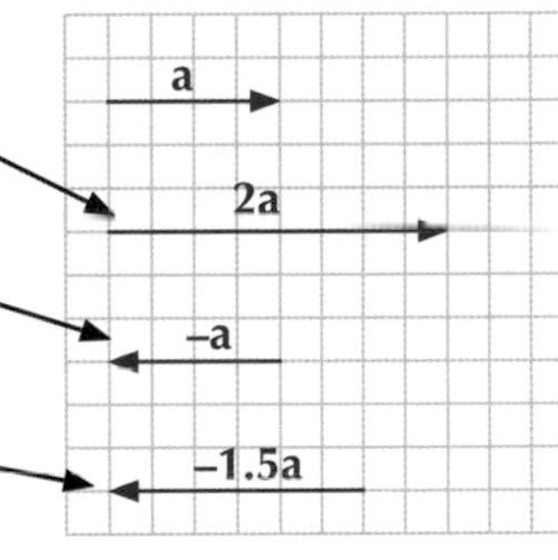

Tip: Vectors are often denoted by **bold letters**.

Tip: Use the grid lines to measure the length, or magnitude, of each vector.

Example 2

The vectors w, x, y and z are shown on the grid below.
Write the vectors x, y and z in terms of w.

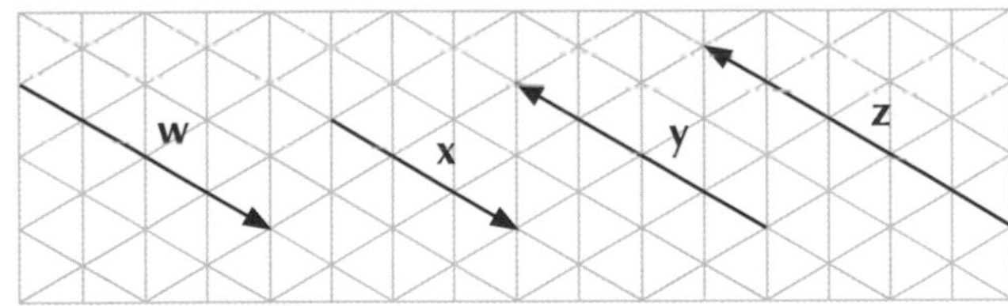

- **x** is parallel to **w**, but is three-quarters the length of **w**.
So **x = 0.75w**.
- **y** acts in the opposite direction to **w**, and is the same length as **w**.
So **y = –w**.
- **z** acts in the opposite direction to **w**, and is one-and-a-quarter times the length of **w**.
So **z = –1.25w**.

Tip: The vectors are shown on an isometric grid. It's made up of a pattern of equilateral triangles — so you can measure lengths by counting triangles. The grid lines show whether or not the vectors are parallel.

Exercise 1.1

Q1 Hint: Think about whether each quantity has a direction.

Q1 State whether each of the following are vector or scalar quantities:

a) time
b) acceleration
c) energy
d) temperature
e) weight
f) area

Q2 The vectors **p**, **q**, **r** and **s** are shown below.

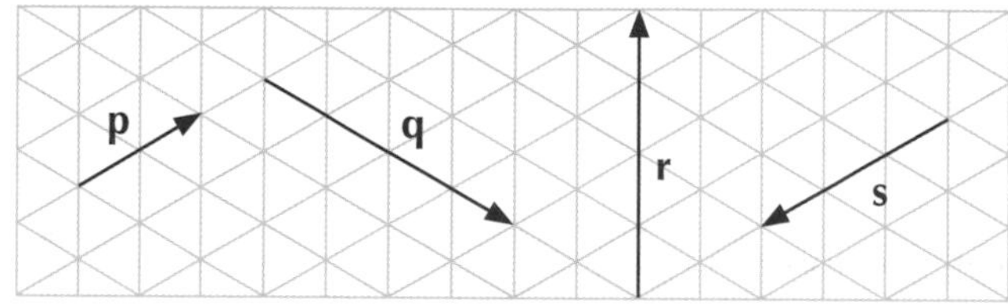

Q2 Hint: Use isometric paper (or measure angles).

Draw the following vectors:

a) 3**p**
b) –**p**
c) –2**q**
d) 0.75**q**
e) 0.5**r**
f) –1.5**r**
g) $-\frac{1}{3}\mathbf{s}$
h) $\frac{4}{3}\mathbf{s}$

Q3 a) Identify the pairs of parallel vectors from the grid shown.

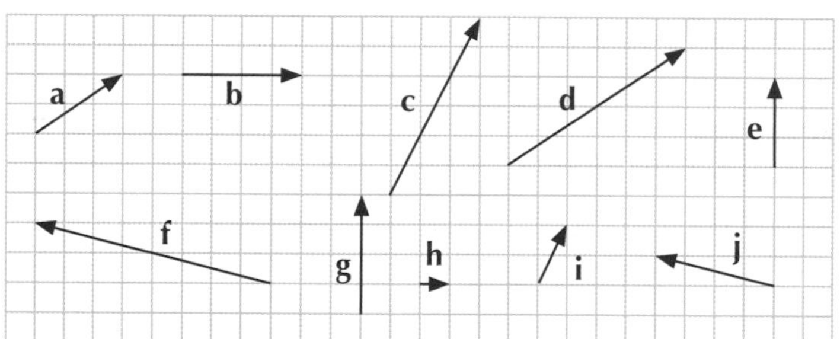

b) For each pair of parallel vectors, write one vector as a multiple of the other.

Q4 State which of the following vectors are parallel to the vector **a** + 3**b**.

Q4 Hint: Remember that parallel vectors are scalar multiples of each other.

2**a** + 6**b**   3**a** + 5**b**   –**a** – 5**b**   –**a** + 3**b**

3**a** + **b**   0.6**a** + 1.8**b**   1.5**a** + 0.5**b**

Resultant vectors

- You can **add** and **subtract** vectors to give a new vector — the **resultant vector**.
- The resultant is the single vector that has the same effect as **all the other vectors together**. It goes from the start of the first vector to the end of the last vector when they're drawn nose to tail.
- Drawing two vectors nose to tail to find the resultant is known as the **Triangle Law of Addition**.

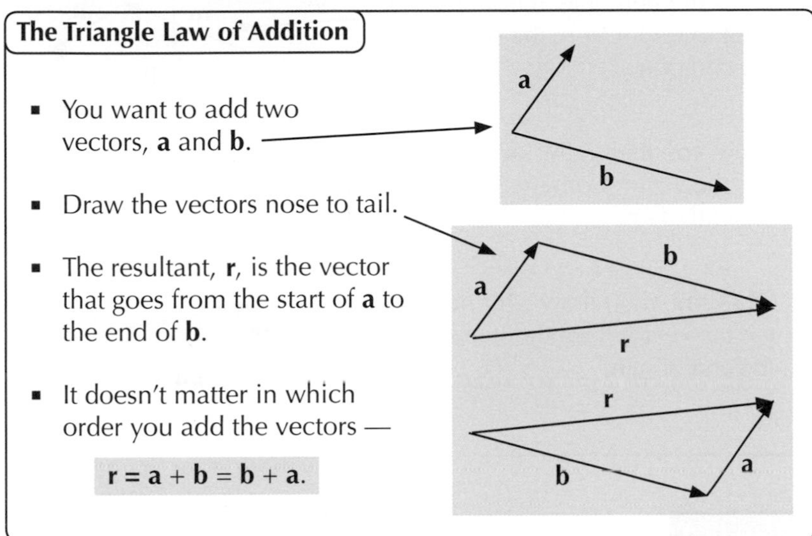

The Triangle Law of Addition

- You want to add two vectors, **a** and **b**.
- Draw the vectors nose to tail.
- The resultant, **r**, is the vector that goes from the start of **a** to the end of **b**.
- It doesn't matter in which order you add the vectors — **r = a + b = b + a.**

Tip: The resultant of two vectors can be thought of as the diagonal of a parallelogram.

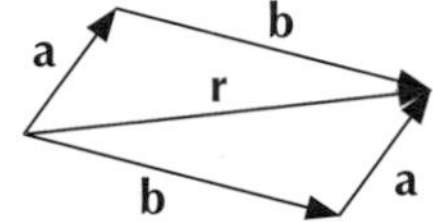

This is the Parallelogram Rule — it is a good way of showing that the order of addition doesn't matter.

- **Subtracting** a vector is the same as adding a **negative** vector.
- Draw the vector you're subtracting so that it acts in the **opposite direction**.
- Then draw it nose to tail with the vector you're subtracting it from.

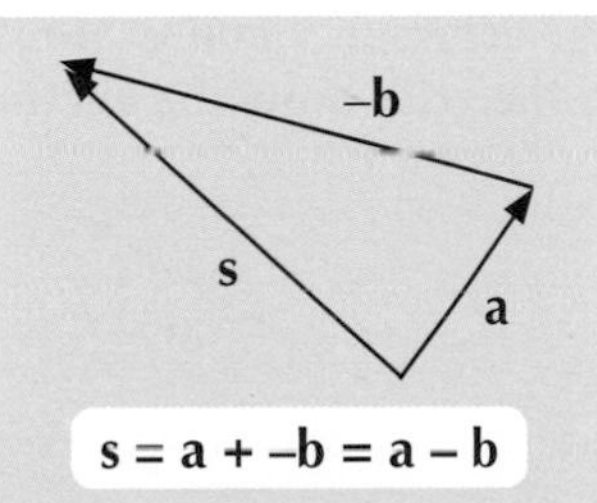

s = a + –b = a – b

Vector Polygons

- Now you're adding three vectors, **a**, **b** and **c**.
- Draw the vectors nose to tail as before.
- The resultant, **t**, is the vector that completes the polygon — it goes from the start of the first vector to the end of the last vector.
- Again, it doesn't matter in which order you add them — **a** + **b** + **c** = **b** + **a** + **c** = **c** + **a** + **b** and so on...

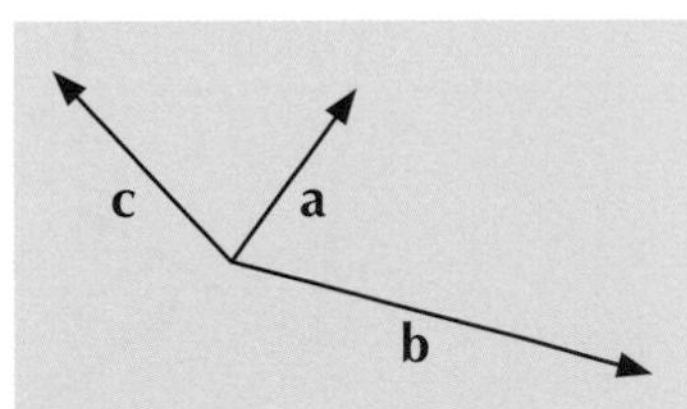

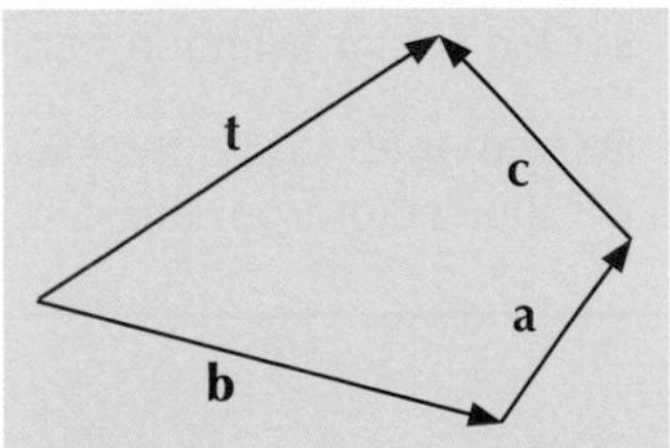

Example 1

The vectors m and n are shown on the grid below.
On the grid, draw the vectors p = m + n, q = 2m – n and r = –m – 2n.

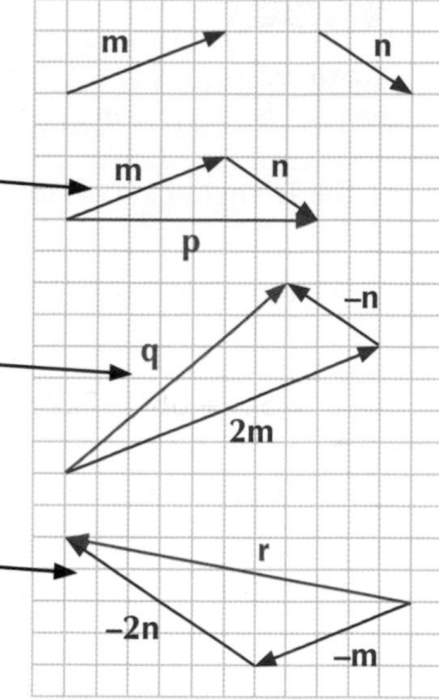

- Draw **m**, then draw **n** from its end. **p** is the vector from the start of **m** to the end of **n**.
- Draw 2**m**, then draw –**n** from its end. **q** is the vector from the start of 2**m** to the end of –**n**.
- Draw –**m**, then draw –2**n** from its end. **r** is the vector from the start of –**m** to the end of –2**n**.

Example 2

The vectors u, v and w are shown on the grid below.
On the grid, draw the vectors x = u + v + w and y = u – 2.5v + w.

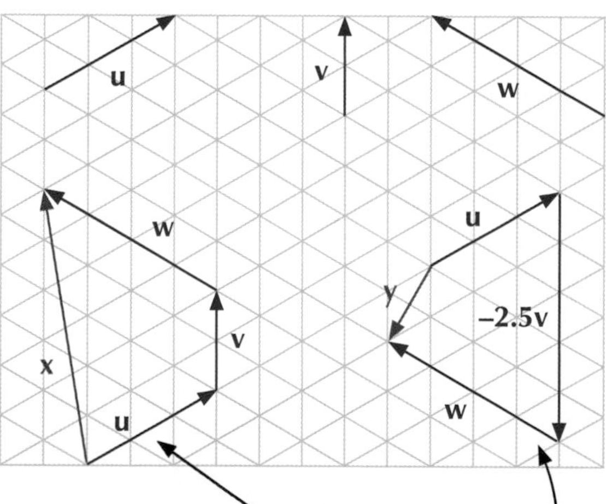

- Draw **u**, then **v**, then **w**, nose to tail. **x** is the vector from the start of **u** to the end of **w**.
- Draw **u**, then –2.5**v**, then **w**, nose to tail. **y** is the vector from the start of **u** to the end of **w**.

- If you join two vectors and their resultant to form a **triangle**, then you can use **Pythagoras' theorem** and **trigonometry** to find the **magnitudes** and **directions** of the vectors.

Example 3

A man walks 51 m east, then 68 m south.
How far is he from his starting point, and on what bearing?

Tip: '51 m east' and '68 m south' are vectors. The magnitude of the resultant vector is the man's distance from his starting point.

- Draw a diagram to show the man's journey — drawing the resultant vector **r** creates a right-angled triangle.

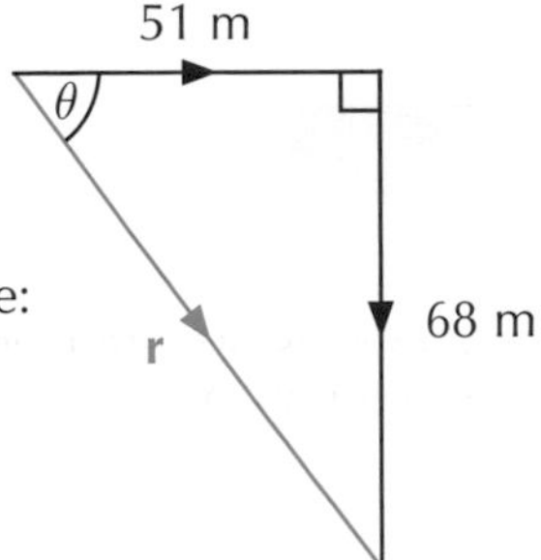

- Use Pythagoras' theorem to find the distance:
  $|\mathbf{r}|^2 = 51^2 + 68^2 = 7225$
  $\Rightarrow |\mathbf{r}| = \sqrt{7225} = 85$
  So he is 85 m from his starting point.

Tip: The magnitude of a vector **a** is often denoted $|\mathbf{a}|$ or a.

- Use trigonometry to find the angle θ:
  $\tan\theta = \frac{68}{51}$
  $\Rightarrow \theta = \tan^{-1}\left(\frac{68}{51}\right) = 53.13...°$
- θ is the angle below the horizontal, so the bearing of the man's final position from his original position is:
  $090° + 53.13...°$
  $= 143.13...° = 143°$

Tip: Remember — bearings are given as three digits and are measured clockwise from north.

Example 4

The vectors e and f are shown on the grid below.
The angle between e and f is 120°.
Find the magnitude of the resultant vector, g.

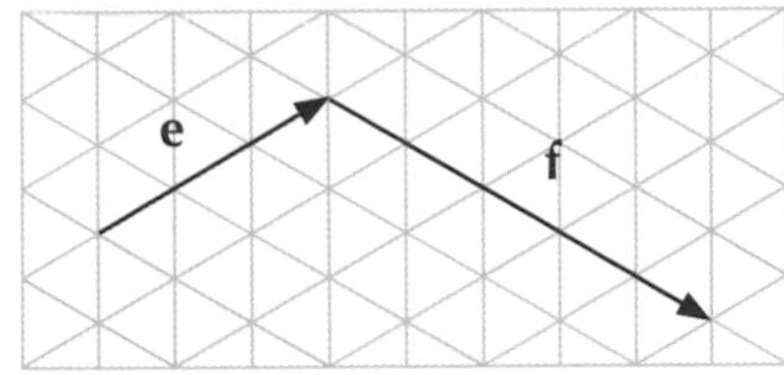

- Draw the resultant vector **g**.

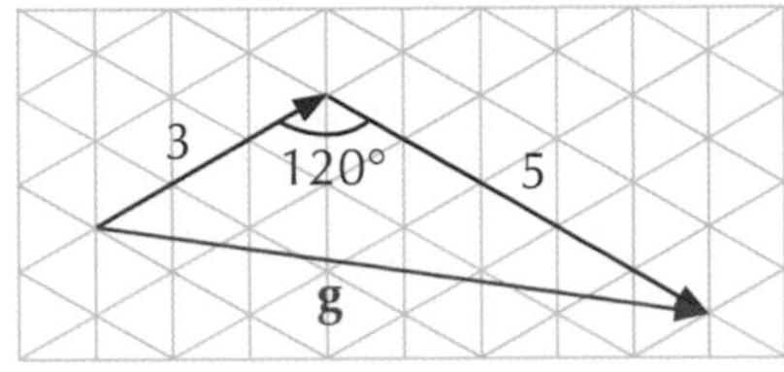

- You can find the relative magnitudes of **e** and **f** by measuring their lengths — **e** has length 3 units and **f** has length 5 units.

- Use the cosine rule on the vector triangle to find the magnitude of **g**:
  $a^2 = b^2 + c^2 - 2bc\cos A$
  $|\mathbf{g}|^2 = 3^2 + 5^2 - (2 \times 3 \times 5)\cos 120°$
  $|\mathbf{g}|^2 = 49$
  $|\mathbf{g}| = 7$
  So the magnitude of vector **g** is 7 units.

Tip: There's plenty more about forces as vectors in Chapter 4.

Example 5

The diagram shows two forces, A and B, of magnitudes 18 N and 24 N respectively. The angle between A and B is 129°. Their resultant has magnitude 38 N and acts horizontally.

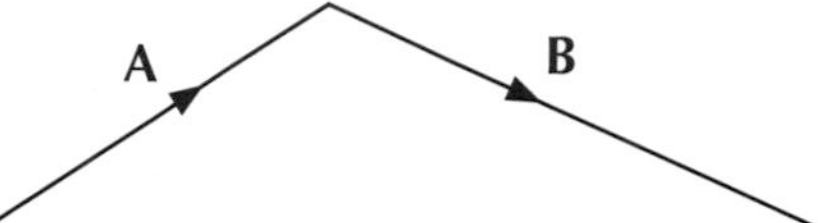

Find the directions of A and B to the horizontal.

- Draw a diagram to show the forces and their resultant:

- Use the sine rule to find θ and φ:

$$\frac{\sin 129°}{38} = \frac{\sin\theta}{24} = \frac{\sin\varphi}{18}$$

$\sin\theta = 24\left(\frac{\sin 129°}{38}\right)$
$\sin\theta = 0.490...$
$\Rightarrow \theta = 29.4°$ (3 s.f.)

$\sin\varphi = 18\left(\frac{\sin 129°}{38}\right)$
$\sin\varphi = 0.368...$
$\Rightarrow \varphi = 21.6°$ (3 s.f.)

- So **A** acts 29.4° above the horizontal and **B** acts 21.6° below the horizontal.

Tip: By the alternate angle theorem, φ is equal to the angle between **B** and the positive horizontal:

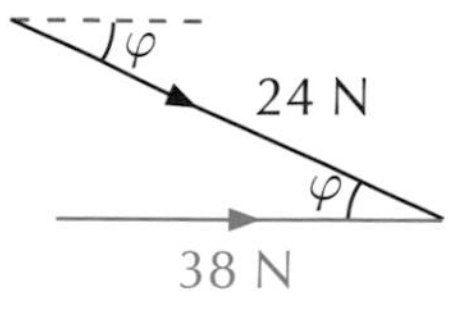

Example 6

A canoe is paddled at 4 ms^{-1} in a direction perpendicular to the seashore. The sea current has a velocity of 1 ms^{-1} parallel to the shore.

Find the resultant velocity, v, of the canoe.

- Draw a diagram to show the motion of the canoe and the current.
- The resultant velocity, **v**, is the hypotenuse of the right-angled triangle.
- Use Pythagoras' theorem to find the magnitude of **v**:
  $|\mathbf{v}|^2 = 4^2 + 1^2 = 17$
  $\Rightarrow |\mathbf{v}| = 4.12$ ms^{-1} (3 s.f.)
- Use trigonometry to find θ:
  $\tan\theta = \frac{1}{4}$
  $\Rightarrow \theta = 14.0°$ (3 s.f.)

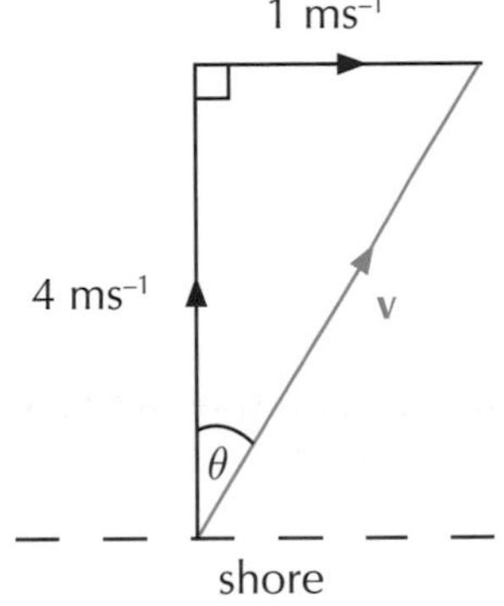

- So the resultant velocity of the canoe is 4.12 ms^{-1} at an angle of 14.0° from the perpendicular to the shore, in the direction of the current.

Tip: It's really important to draw a diagram to help you picture what's going on in these questions.

Example 7

A canoe is paddled at 4 ms^{-1} in still water. The sea current has a velocity of 1 ms^{-1} parallel to the shore.

Find the angle at which the canoe must be paddled in order to travel in a direction perpendicular to the shore, and the magnitude of the resultant velocity.

- Again, draw a diagram to show the motion of the canoe and the current.
- The resultant velocity **v** isn't the hypotenuse this time.
- Using trigonometry:
  $\sin\theta = \frac{1}{4}$
  $\Rightarrow \theta = \sin^{-1}(\frac{1}{4}) = 14.5°$ (3 s.f.)
- Using Pythagoras' theorem:
  $|\mathbf{v}|^2 = 4^2 - 1^2 = 15$
  $\Rightarrow |\mathbf{v}| = \sqrt{15} = 3.87$ ms^{-1} (3 s.f.)

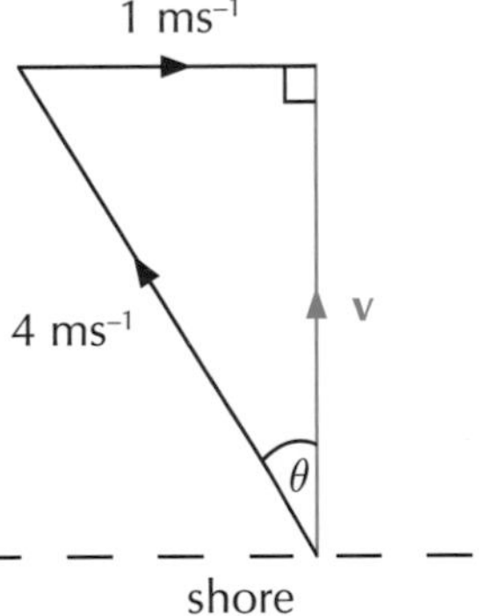

- So the canoe must be paddled at an angle of 14.5° from the perpendicular to the shore, in the opposite direction to the current. The magnitude of the resultant velocity is 3.87 ms^{-1}.

Tip: Make sure you set up the triangle correctly — like in this example, the resultant won't always be the hypotenuse.

Exercise 1.2

Q1 The grid below shows the vectors **a**, **b**, **c** and **d**.

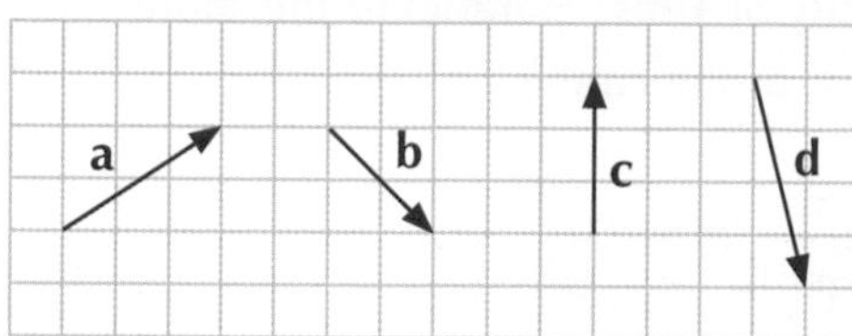

Draw each of the following resultant vectors:

a) $\mathbf{a} + \mathbf{b}$ b) $\mathbf{c} + \mathbf{d}$

c) $2\mathbf{b} + \mathbf{c}$ d) $\mathbf{d} - \mathbf{a}$

e) $3\mathbf{b} - 2\mathbf{c}$ f) $\mathbf{a} + \mathbf{b} + \mathbf{c}$

g) $2\mathbf{a} - 3\mathbf{b}$ h) $\mathbf{c} + \mathbf{d} - \mathbf{a}$

Q2 The grid below shows the vectors **p**, **q**, **r** and **s**.

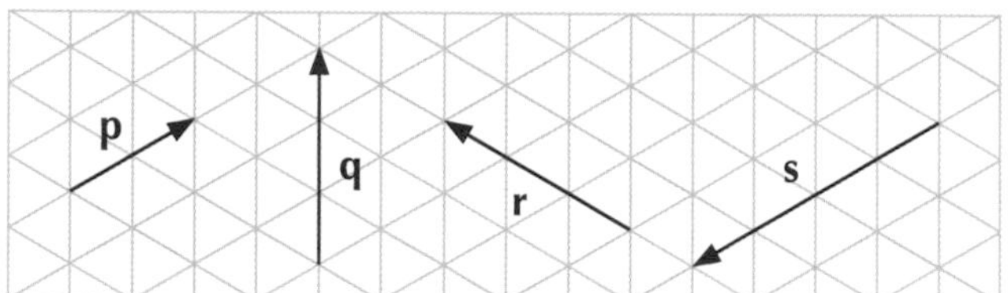

Draw each of the following resultant vectors:

a) $\mathbf{p} + \mathbf{q}$ b) $\mathbf{q} + 2\mathbf{r}$

c) $\mathbf{s} - 2\mathbf{q}$ d) $\mathbf{p} - \mathbf{q} + \mathbf{r}$

e) $\mathbf{s} + \mathbf{p} - \mathbf{r}$ f) $\mathbf{p} + \mathbf{q} + 0.5\mathbf{s}$

g) $1.5(\mathbf{p} + \mathbf{s})$ h) $0.5\mathbf{p} + \mathbf{r} - 1.25\mathbf{s}$

Exam Hint: Remember to draw a vector diagram to show what's going on in wordy questions.

Q3 A man leaves a car park and walks 4 miles due east. He then turns and walks due south for a distance of 6 miles. How far, and on what bearing, is he from the car park at the end of his journey?

Q4 A boat sets sail at 5 ms^{-1} to cross a lake. If there is a wind blowing at 3 ms^{-1} at right angles to the boat's initial direction of motion, find the boat's resultant speed and direction of motion.

Q5 A pilot is flying a small plane due north at 50 kmh^{-1}. The plane is blown off course by a steady wind blowing from east to west. After 2 hours, the plane is 120 km from its starting point.

Find:

a) the resultant speed of the plane,

b) the speed of the wind,

c) the bearing of the resultant path of the plane.

Q6 A salesman travels 30 km on a bearing of 060° from town *A* to town *B*. He then travels 50 km on a bearing of 130° from town B to town *C*. Find the distance and bearing along which the salesman would have to travel to get directly from town *A* to town *C*.

Unit vectors

Rather than drawing arrows to represent vectors, you can describe them in terms of the **unit vectors i and j**.

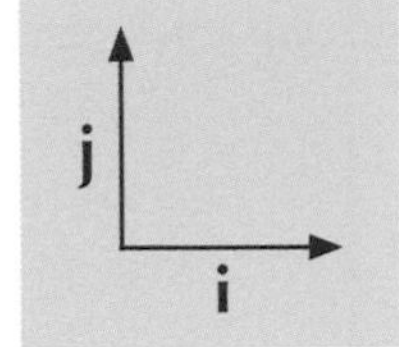

- **i** and **j** are called unit vectors because they each have a **magnitude of 1 unit**.
- **i** and **j** are perpendicular to each other — **i** is in the direction of the ***x*-axis** (horizontal or east), **j** is in the direction of the ***y*-axis** (vertical or north).
- You can write **any 2D vector** as a combination of scalar multiples of **i** and **j**.
- The **i** bit is called the '**horizontal component**' of the vector — i.e. how many units the vector is 'across'.
- The **j** bit is called the '**vertical component**' of the vector — i.e. how many units 'up or down' the vector is.

Tip: A horizontal vector is written in terms of **i** only — its **j**-component is zero. Similarly, a vertical vector is written in terms of **j** only — its **i**-component is zero.

Tip: You can also use column vectors. The horizontal component of the vector is written above the vertical component:
$x\mathbf{i} + y\mathbf{j} = \begin{pmatrix} x \\ y \end{pmatrix}$

Tip: $\overrightarrow{AB}$ is another way of writing a vector — it means 'the displacement of B from A'.

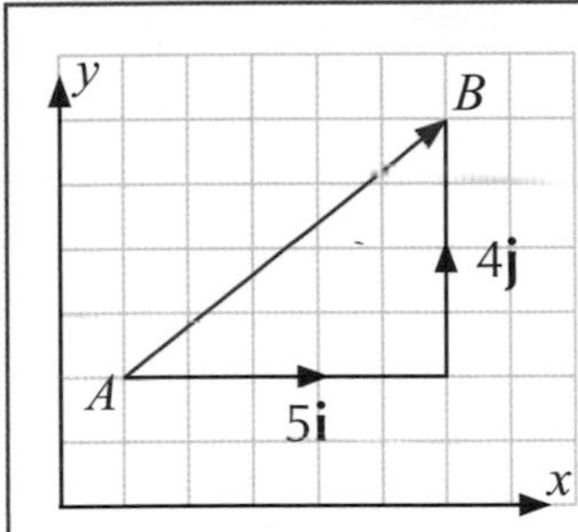

$\overrightarrow{AB}$ is '5 units across' and '4 units up', so it can be written as:

$\overrightarrow{AB} = 5\mathbf{i} + 4\mathbf{j}$

- Perform calculations with **i** and **j** vectors by treating the horizontal and vertical components separately.
- You can find the resultant of two vectors written in terms of **i** and **j** by finding the sum of the **i** components and the sum of the **j** components.

Example 1

a) The diagram shows the vectors $\overrightarrow{AB} = 3\mathbf{i} + 2\mathbf{j}$ and $\overrightarrow{BC} = 5\mathbf{i} - 3\mathbf{j}$. Find the resultant vector $\overrightarrow{AC}$.

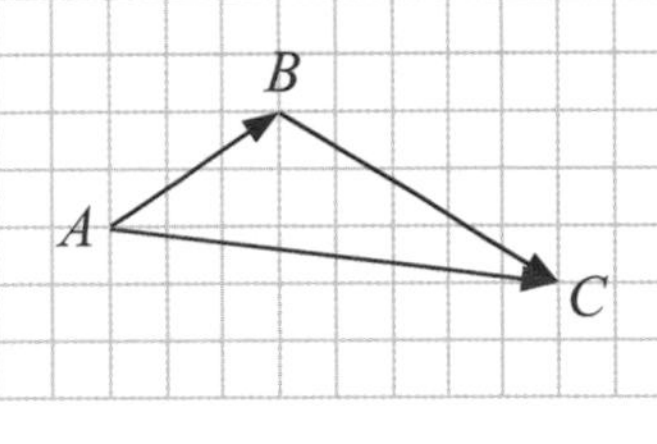

Add the horizontal and vertical components separately:

$\overrightarrow{AC} = \overrightarrow{AB} + \overrightarrow{BC} = (3\mathbf{i} + 2\mathbf{j}) + (5\mathbf{i} - 3\mathbf{j})$
$= (3 + 5)\mathbf{i} + (2 - 3)\mathbf{j}$
$= 8\mathbf{i} - \mathbf{j}$

Tip: Adding column vectors is the same — just treat the components separately:
$\begin{pmatrix} 3 \\ 2 \end{pmatrix} + \begin{pmatrix} 5 \\ -3 \end{pmatrix} = \begin{pmatrix} 3+5 \\ 2-3 \end{pmatrix} = \begin{pmatrix} 8 \\ -1 \end{pmatrix}$

b) Given the vectors p = 4i – j and q = –i + 6j, work out p – q.

Subtract the horizontal and vertical components separately:

$\mathbf{p} - \mathbf{q} = (4\mathbf{i} - \mathbf{j}) - (-\mathbf{i} + 6\mathbf{j})$
$= [4 - (-1)]\mathbf{i} + (-1 - 6)\mathbf{j}$
$= 5\mathbf{i} - 7\mathbf{j}$

Tip: When multiplying a column vector by a scalar, again just treat the components separately:

$2\begin{pmatrix}1\\4\end{pmatrix} = \begin{pmatrix}2 \times 1\\2 \times 4\end{pmatrix} = \begin{pmatrix}2\\8\end{pmatrix}$

c) Given the vectors u = –3i + 2j and v = i + 4j, work out –5u + 2v.

Multiply the components of the two vectors by their respective scalars, then add the horizontal and vertical components separately, as before:

$$\begin{aligned}-5\mathbf{u} + 2\mathbf{v} &= -5(-3\mathbf{i} + 2\mathbf{j}) + 2(\mathbf{i} + 4\mathbf{j})\\ &= (15\mathbf{i} - 10\mathbf{j}) + (2\mathbf{i} + 8\mathbf{j})\\ &= (15 + 2)\mathbf{i} + (-10 + 8)\mathbf{j}\\ &= 17\mathbf{i} - 2\mathbf{j}\end{aligned}$$

- You can find the **magnitude** (size) of a vector in **i** + **j** notation using **Pythagoras' theorem**, and the **direction** of the vector using **trigonometry**.

Example 2

The diagram shows the vector a = –2i + 3j. Find the magnitude of the vector and the angle, θ, it makes with the negative horizontal.

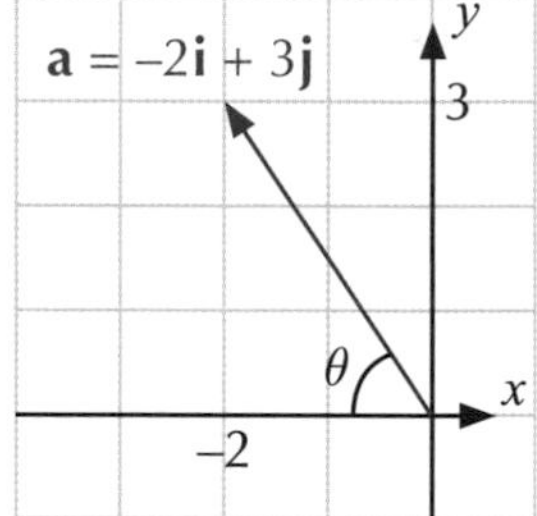

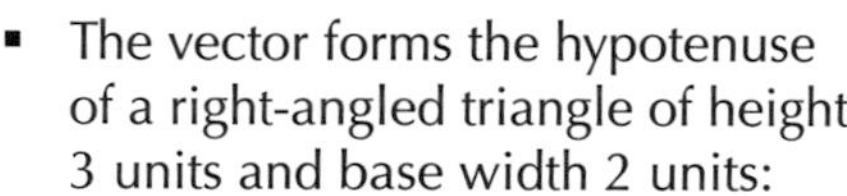

- The vector forms the hypotenuse of a right-angled triangle of height 3 units and base width 2 units:

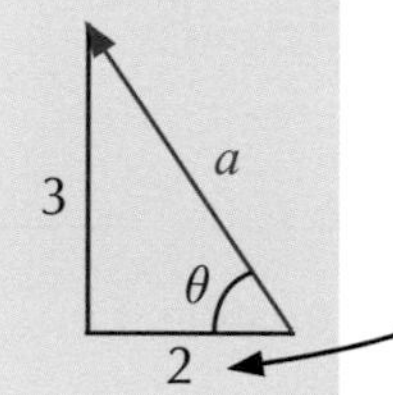

Once you've drawn the triangle, you're only really worried about the magnitudes of the components, so the **i**-component of –2 becomes a distance of 2.

- Use Pythagoras' theorem to find the magnitude:
  $a^2 = 3^2 + 2^2 = 13$
  $\Rightarrow a = \sqrt{13} = 3.61$ (3 s.f.)

- Use trigonometry to find the angle θ:
  $\tan\theta = \frac{3}{2}$
  $\Rightarrow \theta = \tan^{-1}\left(\frac{3}{2}\right) = 56.3°$ (3 s.f.)

- In general:

The vector $\mathbf{r} = x\mathbf{i} + y\mathbf{j}$ has magnitude $r = |\mathbf{r}| = \sqrt{x^2 + y^2}$ and direction $\theta = \tan^{-1}\left(\frac{y}{x}\right)$.

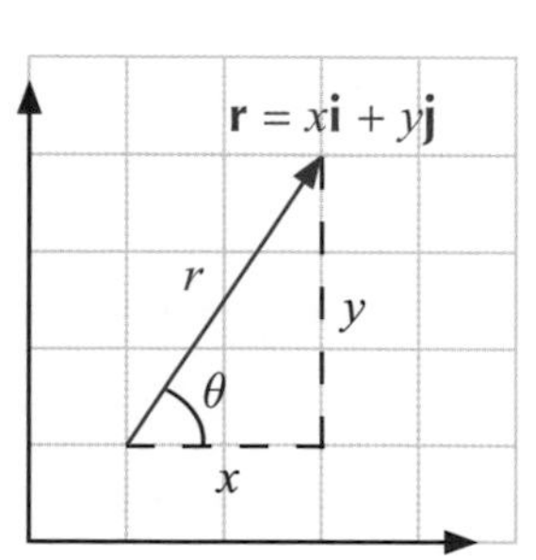

Example 3

The acceleration of a body is given by the vector a = (6i – 2j) ms^{-2}. Find the magnitude and direction of the acceleration.

- Start with a diagram — remember, the y-component "–2" means "down 2".

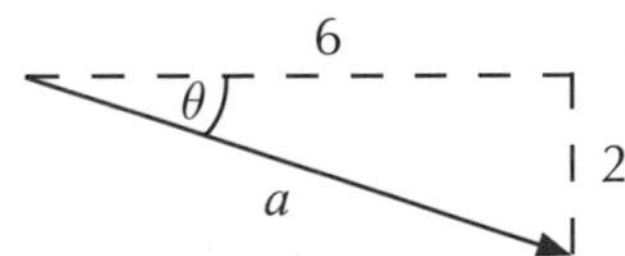

- Use Pythagoras' theorem to find the magnitude:
  $a^2 = 6^2 + 2^2 = 40$
  $\Rightarrow a = \sqrt{40} =$ 6.32 ms^{-2} (3 s.f.)

- Use trigonometry to find the angle θ:
  $\tan\theta = \frac{2}{6}$
  $\Rightarrow \theta = \tan^{-1}(\frac{2}{6}) =$ 18.4° (3 s.f.)

- So the acceleration has magnitude 6.32 ms^{-2} and direction 18.4° below the horizontal.

Tip: Make sure you pay attention to whether the components are positive or negative — this tells you which direction the vector acts in.

Example 4

The vector c is parallel to vector d. Given that d = 8i – 6j and |c| = 70, find vector c.

- Find the magnitude of **d**:
  $|\mathbf{d}| = \sqrt{8^2 + (-6^2)}$
  $= \sqrt{100} = 10$

- The magnitude of **c** is seven times the magnitude of **d**.
  So $\mathbf{c} = 7\mathbf{d}$
  $= 7(8\mathbf{i} - 6\mathbf{j})$
  $= 56\mathbf{i} - 42\mathbf{j}$

Tip: You can check your answer by finding the magnitude of **c** (it should be 70) and the directions of **c** and **d** (they should be the same).

Exercise 1.3

Q1 Write each of the following vectors (i) in **i** + **j** form, and (ii) as a column vector. (The grid is divided up into unit squares.)

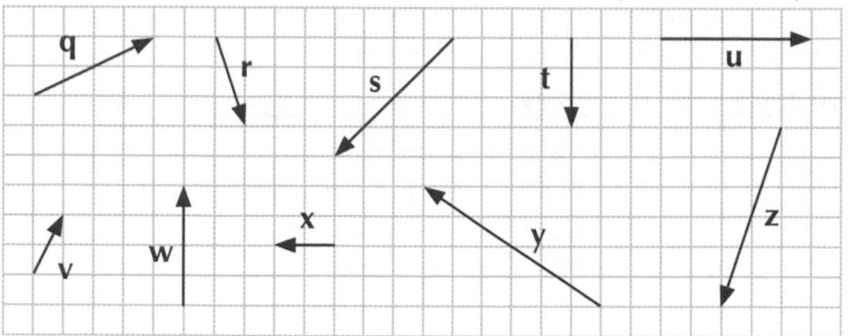

Q2 Draw each of the following vectors on a grid:

$\mathbf{a} = 3\mathbf{i} + \mathbf{j}$	$\mathbf{b} = 4\mathbf{i} - 3\mathbf{j}$	$\mathbf{c} = -\mathbf{i} - 2\mathbf{j}$	$\mathbf{d} = -5\mathbf{i} + 4\mathbf{j}$
$\mathbf{e} = -3\mathbf{j}$	$\mathbf{f} = 2\mathbf{i}$	$\mathbf{g} = 2\mathbf{i} - 3\mathbf{j}$	$\mathbf{h} = -6\mathbf{i} + \mathbf{j}$

Q3 Find the resultant of each of the following pairs of vectors:

a) $\mathbf{p} = 2\mathbf{i} - 6\mathbf{j}$ and $\mathbf{q} = -7\mathbf{i} + 11\mathbf{j}$

b) $\mathbf{u} = -9\mathbf{i} - 13\mathbf{j}$ and $\mathbf{v} = 7\mathbf{i} - 8\mathbf{j}$

c) $\mathbf{w} = -19\mathbf{i} - 14\mathbf{j}$ and $\mathbf{z} = -12\mathbf{i} - 20\mathbf{j}$

Q4 Given the following vectors:

$\mathbf{a} = 2\mathbf{i} + \mathbf{j}$	$\mathbf{b} = \mathbf{i} - 3\mathbf{j}$	$\mathbf{c} = 5\mathbf{i} + 2\mathbf{j}$
$\mathbf{d} = -\mathbf{i} + \mathbf{j}$	$\mathbf{e} = -4\mathbf{i} + 2\mathbf{j}$	$\mathbf{f} = -6\mathbf{i} - 5\mathbf{j}$

Find:

a) $3\mathbf{b}$	b) $4\mathbf{e}$	c) $-2\mathbf{a}$	d) $\mathbf{f} + \mathbf{c}$
e) $\mathbf{d} - \mathbf{a}$	f) $\mathbf{b} - 2\mathbf{f}$	g) $0.5\mathbf{c}$	h) $0.5\mathbf{e} + 2\mathbf{d} - \mathbf{a}$

Exam Hint: You may be asked to find 'the angle made with **i**' — this is just another way of saying 'the angle made with the positive horizontal axis'.

Q5 Find (i) the magnitude of each of the following vectors, and (ii) the direction each vector acts in.

a) $5\mathbf{i} + 12\mathbf{j}$	b) $4\mathbf{i} - 5\mathbf{j}$	c) $-2\mathbf{i} + 3\mathbf{j}$	d) $-0.5\mathbf{i} - 1.5\mathbf{j}$

Q6 A force of $(7\mathbf{i} + 9\mathbf{j})$ N acts on a body. Find the magnitude of the force and the direction it acts in.

Q7 Hint: The speed of a moving object is the magnitude of its velocity.

Q7 A body moves with velocity $(-3\mathbf{i} + 5\mathbf{j})$ ms^{-1}. Taking the horizontal axis to be due east and the vertical axis to be due north, find the speed of the body and the bearing along which it moves.

Q8 The vector **a** is parallel to vector **b**. If $\mathbf{b} = 3\mathbf{i} + 4\mathbf{j}$ and **a** has magnitude 15, find vector **a**.

Q9 A force **P** is acting parallel to another force **Q**. If **P** has magnitude $2\sqrt{5}$ N and $\mathbf{Q} = (-4\mathbf{i} + 8\mathbf{j})$ N, find the force **P**.

2. Resolving Vectors

Resolving a vector means splitting it up into components — then you can work things out using one component at a time. Resolving also tells you the effect of a vector in a particular direction.

Learning Objectives:

- Be able to resolve a vector into components.
- Be able to write a vector in terms of unit vectors **i** and **j**.
- Be able to resolve multiple vectors to find the resultant vector.

Resolving a vector horizontally and vertically

- To resolve a vector horizontally and vertically means to split it into its **horizontal** and **vertical components**.
- To split a vector into its horizontal and vertical components, consider the vector as the **hypotenuse** of a right-angled triangle, where the other two sides are horizontal and vertical.
- You can then use **trigonometry** to find the horizontal and vertical sides (or components).

Example 1

A vector, v, has magnitude 36 and acts at an angle of 60° above the positive horizontal direction. Find the horizontal and vertical components of v.

- Draw a diagram — x is the horizontal component of the vector and y is the vertical component.
- Use trigonometry to find the components.

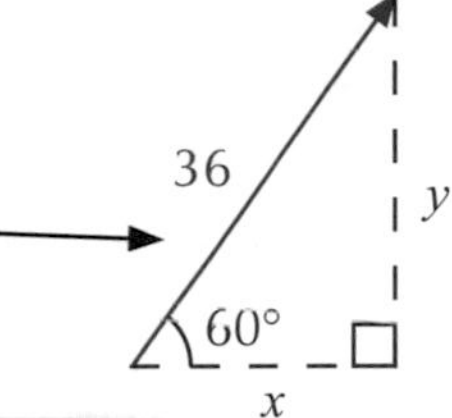

Horizontal component:
$\cos 60° = \frac{x}{36}$
$\Rightarrow x = 36\cos 60° = 18$

Vertical component:
$\sin 60° = \frac{y}{36}$
$\Rightarrow y = 36\sin 60° = 18\sqrt{3}$

Tip: It's a good idea to give the components in their exact form if you can, rather than as rounded decimals. These should help:

	sin	cos
30°	$\frac{1}{2}$	$\frac{\sqrt{3}}{2}$
45°	$\frac{1}{\sqrt{2}}$	$\frac{1}{\sqrt{2}}$
60°	$\frac{\sqrt{3}}{2}$	$\frac{1}{2}$

- Resolving a vector into its horizontal and vertical components lets you write the vector in terms of **i** and **j**. The horizontal component goes in front of the **i** and the vertical component goes in front of the **j**.
- It's really important that you know **which direction** a vector is acting in — this tells you whether the **horizontal** and **vertical components** are **positive** or **negative**.

Tip: Look back at page 43 for a reminder about the unit vectors **i** and **j**.

Vectors acting 'up and left' have negative **i**-components and positive **j**-components.

Vectors acting 'up and right' have positive **i**-components and **j**-components.

j, +ve, –ve, **i**, +ve, –ve

Vectors acting 'down and left' have negative **i**-components and **j**-components.

Vectors acting 'down and right' have positive **i**-components and negative **j**-components.

Example 2

The speed of a ball is 5 ms^{-1} at an angle of 30° below the positive horizontal direction.
Find v, the velocity of the ball. Give your answer in terms of i and j.

- As always, draw a diagram.
- Using trigonometry:

$\cos 30° = \frac{x}{5} \Rightarrow x = 5\cos 30° = \frac{5\sqrt{3}}{2}$

$\sin 30° = \frac{y}{5} \Rightarrow y = 5\sin 30° = \frac{5}{2}$

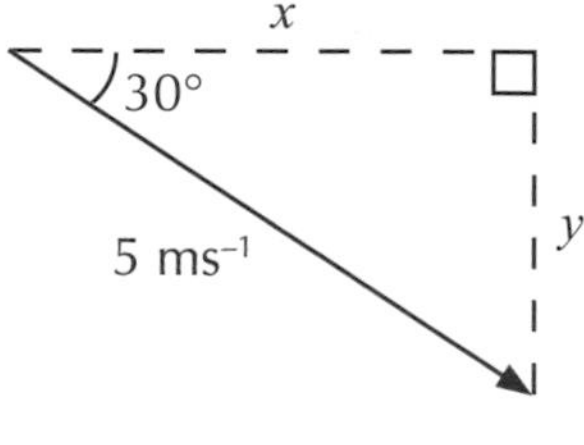

- The force acts diagonally downwards and to the right.
  In this direction, **i** is positive and **j** is negative, so $\mathbf{v} = x\mathbf{i} - y\mathbf{j}$:

$\mathbf{v} = \left(\frac{5\sqrt{3}}{2}\mathbf{i} - \frac{5}{2}\mathbf{j}\right)$ ms^{-1} or $\mathbf{v} = \frac{5}{2}(\sqrt{3}\,\mathbf{i} - \mathbf{j})$ ms^{-1}

Tip: Another way of doing these questions would be to rewrite the angle so that it's measured from the positive horizontal direction.
E.g. in this example, you could rewrite the 30° angle as 330° (or –30°):

330° –30°

and the y-component will come out negative.

Example 3

A particle moves with an acceleration of magnitude 55 ms^{-2}, directed at an angle of 25° below the negative horizontal direction.
Find the particle's acceleration, a, in terms of i and j.

- Using trigonometry:

$\cos 25° = \frac{x}{55} \Rightarrow x = 55\cos 25° = 49.8$ (3 s.f.)

$\sin 25° = \frac{y}{55} \Rightarrow y = 55\sin 25° = 23.2$ (3 s.f.)

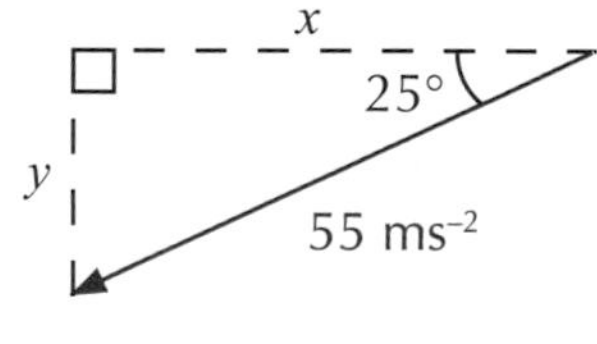

- The acceleration acts diagonally downwards and to the left.
  In this direction, **i** and **j** are both negative, so $\mathbf{a} = -x\mathbf{i} - y\mathbf{j}$:

$\mathbf{a} = (-49.8\mathbf{i} - 23.2\mathbf{j})$ ms^{-2} (3 s.f.)

Tip: Again, you could rewrite the 25° angle as 205° (or –155°):

205° 25° –155°

and both the x- and y-components will come out negative.

- In general:

The vector **r** with magnitude r and direction θ can be written as:

$\mathbf{r} = r\cos\theta\mathbf{i} + r\sin\theta\mathbf{j}$

(Where θ is measured from the positive horizontal direction.)

Exercise 2.1

Q1 Find the horizontal and vertical components of each of these vectors. Hence write each vector in **i** + **j** form.

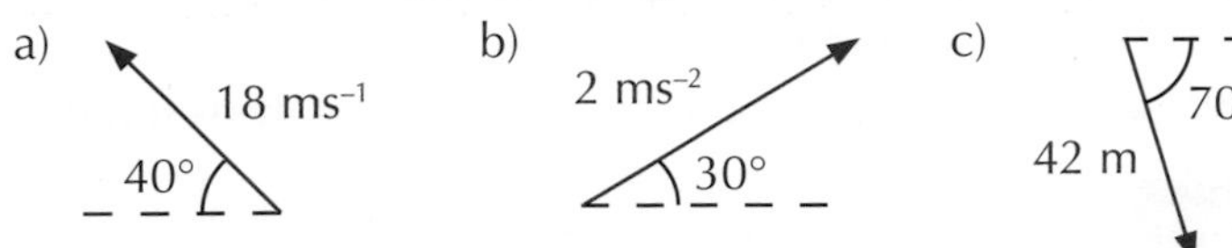

Q2 Find the horizontal and vertical components of each of the following vectors. Hence write each vector in **i** + **j** form.

a) Vector **a** of magnitude 3 N at an angle of 60° above the positive horizontal direction.

b) Vector **p** of magnitude 8 ms^{-2} at an angle of 45° below the positive horizontal direction.

c) Vector **d** of magnitude 17 ms^{-1} at an angle of 70° above the negative horizontal direction.

d) Vector **k** of magnitude 12 kmh^{-1} at an angle of 15° below the negative horizontal direction.

Q2 Hint: Make sure you get the direction of the vector right — this tells you whether the components are positive or negative.

Q3 A man walks 3 km on a bearing of 110°. Find the horizontal and vertical components of his final displacement from his starting point.

Q4 The speed of a particle is 13 ms^{-1} on a bearing of 050°. Find the velocity of the particle, giving your answer in **i** + **j** form, where **i** and **j** are the unit vectors acting due east and due north respectively.

Q5 A vector of magnitude 24 acts at an angle of 30° above the negative horizontal direction. Write the vector in terms of **i** and **j**.

Q6 A ship leaves a port and sails 50 km on a bearing of 350°. Find the boat's final displacement from the port in terms of **i** and **j**, where **i** and **j** are the unit vectors acting due east and due north respectively.

Q7 The wind blows a small boat along at a speed of 2.5 ms^{-1} on a bearing of 245°. Find the velocity of the boat in **i** + **j** form, where **i** and **j** are the unit vectors acting due east and due north respectively.

Q8 A ball is thrown through the air. At a certain point, it is travelling with velocity 2 ms^{-1}, at an angle of 42° to the horizontal, as shown.

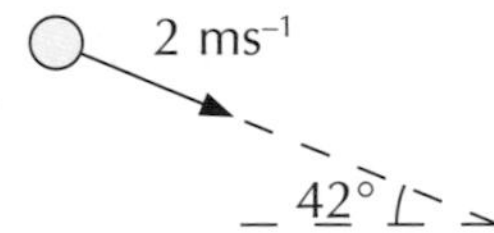

Find the ball's velocity in terms of **i** and **j**.

Resolving to find a resultant vector

You can find the **resultant** of multiple vectors using the following method:

- **Resolve** each vector into its **horizontal** and **vertical components**.
- Find the **sum** of the **horizontal components** and the **sum** of the **vertical components**.
- This gives the horizontal and vertical components of the **resultant vector**.

> **Tip:** Remember — the resultant is the single vector that has the same effect as all the other vectors together.

> **Tip:** You could find the resultant by drawing the vectors nose-to-tail to form a vector polygon, like on page 37:
>
> 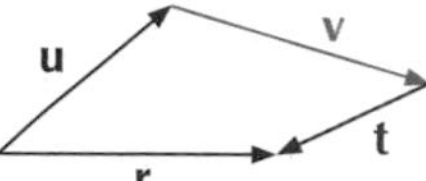
>
>
> then working **r** out geometrically, but resolving is a lot easier.

Example 1

The vectors t, u and v have magnitude 8, 11 and 13 respectively. t acts at an angle of 25° below the negative horizontal, u acts at an angle of 40° above the positive horizontal, and v acts at an angle of 16° below the positive horizontal.

a) Find the resultant vector r. Give your answer in terms of i and j.

- Draw a vector diagram.

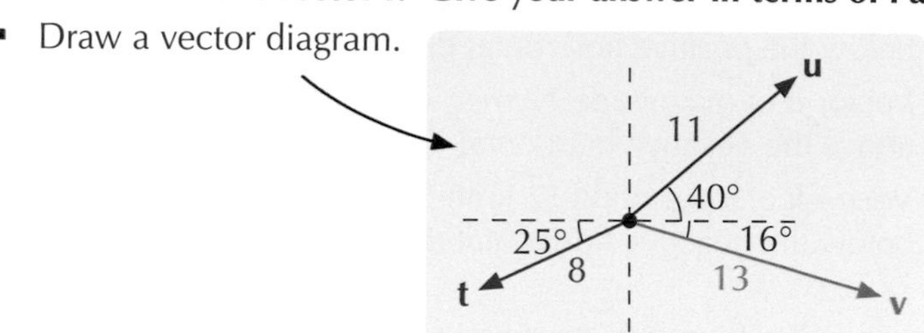

- Resolve each vector horizontally, taking right as positive:
  $\mathbf{u}_x$: 11cos40°
  $\mathbf{v}_x$: 13cos16°
  $\mathbf{t}_x$: –8cos25° ← $\mathbf{t}_x$ is negative because it acts to the left.

- Resolve each vector vertically, taking up as positive:
  $\mathbf{u}_y$: 11sin40°
  $\mathbf{v}_y$: –13sin16°
  $\mathbf{t}_y$: –8sin25° ← $\mathbf{v}_y$ and $\mathbf{t}_y$ are negative because they act downwards.

> **Tip:** **i** and **j** are defined as the unit vectors in the direction of the positive x- and y-axis respectively, so take these directions as positive when resolving.

- Add the components to find the components of the resultant:
  Horizontal: 11cos40° + 13cos16° – 8cos25° = **13.67...**
  Vertical: 11sin40° – 13sin16° – 8sin25° = **0.1064...**

- Now use these components to write the resultant in terms of **i** and **j**:
  r = 13.7**i** + 0.106**j** (3 s.f.)

b) Find the magnitude and direction of r.

- Draw a right-angled triangle using the components of **r**. (r, θ, 0.1064..., 13.67...)

- Using Pythagoras' theorem:
  $|\mathbf{r}| = \sqrt{13.67...^2 + 0.1064...^2} = 13.7$ (3 s.f.)

- Using trigonometry:
  $\theta = \tan^{-1}\left(\frac{0.1064...}{13.67...}\right) = 0.446°$ (3 s.f.)

- So **r** has magnitude 13.7 and acts at an angle of 0.446° above the positive horizontal.

> **Tip:** Finding the magnitude and direction of a vector given its horizontal and vertical components was covered on page 44.

Example 2

A ship travels 100 km at a bearing of 025°, then 75 km at 140° before going 125 km at 215°.
What is the displacement of the ship from its starting point?

- Draw a diagram of the ship's journey — remember that bearings are measured clockwise from north.
- The resultant vector, **r**, is the ship's final displacement.
- Use your diagram to draw the right-angled triangles whose hypotenuses are the different stages of the ship's journey.
- Find the 'vertical' and 'horizontal' components of the different stages.

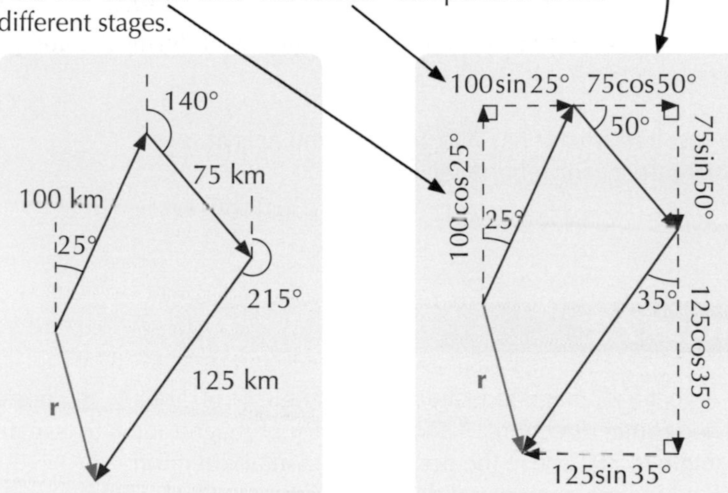

Tip: In this example, finding the components that act east and north is just the same as finding horizontal and vertical components respectively. And the ship's final displacement is just the resultant of the three vectors.

Tip: The 50° and 35° angles come from subtracting 90° and 180° from the bearings given in the question.

- Find the sum of the 'horizontal' components (taking east as positive):
  $100\sin 25° + 75\cos 50° - 125\sin 35° =$ **18.77... km**
- Find the sum of the 'vertical' components (taking north as positive):
  $100\cos 25° - 75\sin 50° - 125\cos 35° =$ **–69.21... km**
- So the horizontal component of the resultant is 18.77... km and the vertical component is –69.21... km.

18.77...
θ
r
69.21...

- Using Pythagoras' theorem:
  $|\mathbf{r}| = \sqrt{18.77...^2 + (-69.21...)^2}$
  $= 71.7$ km (3 s.f.)
- Using trigonometry:
  $\theta = \tan^{-1}\left(\frac{69.21...}{18.77...}\right) = 74.82...°$
  Writing this as a bearing:
  $090° + 74.82...° = 164.82...° = 165°$
- So the ship's final displacement is 71.7 km on a bearing of 165°.

- You can resolve vectors in **any two perpendicular directions** — not just horizontally and vertically.
- Choose whichever directions make the calculation easier.

Example 3

Find the resultant of the vectors shown in the diagram.

Tip: You could resolve horizontally and vertically, but it makes sense to resolve in the directions that the vectors are acting — that way, you don't need to worry about the 30° angles.

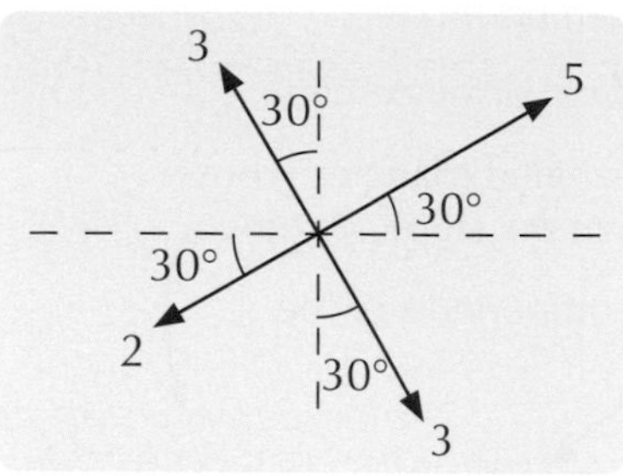

Resolving in ↖ direction:

$3 - 3 = 0$

Resolving in ↗ direction:

$5 - 2 = 3$

So the resultant vector has magnitude 3 and acts at 30° above the positive horizontal.

Exercise 2.2

Exam Hint: Draw a vector diagram to help you answer these questions.

Q1 A vector of magnitude 4 acts at an angle of 60° below the positive horizontal direction. A second vector of magnitude 8 acts at an angle of 70° above the positive horizontal direction.
Find the magnitude and direction of the resultant vector.

Q2 Three vectors act as follows: Magnitude 6 at 40° above the positive horizontal, magnitude 7 at 80° above the negative horizontal, and magnitude 5 at 30° below the positive horizontal.
Find the magnitude and direction of the resultant vector.

Q3 A girl cycles 4 km on a bearing of 060°, then 7 km on a bearing of 150°, then 2 km on a bearing of 270°.
Find the girl's final displacement from her starting point.

Q4 A hiker walks 7.5 km on a bearing of 350°, then 5 km on a bearing of 240°, then 4 km on a bearing of 165°.

a) Find the hiker's final distance from his starting point.

b) Find the bearing he needs to walk on to return to his starting point.

3. Applications of Vectors

You can use vectors to describe the position of an object, as well as information about the object's movement — for example, its velocity, acceleration and displacement over a period of time.

Learning Objectives:

- Be able to describe the position of a point using vectors.
- Be able to describe the displacement, velocity and acceleration of a moving particle using vectors.
- Be able to use the constant acceleration equations in vector form.

Position vectors

- A **position vector** describes the **position** of a point relative to the **origin**, O.

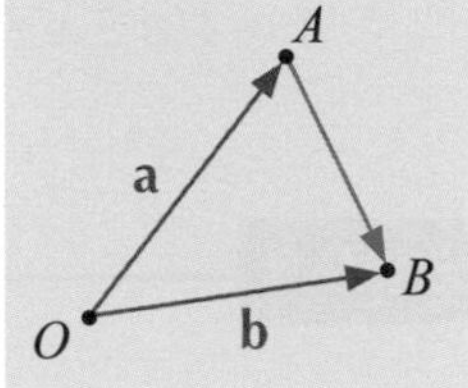

- The position vector of point A is $\overrightarrow{OA}$ — it's usually called vector **a**.
- The position vector of point B is $\overrightarrow{OB}$ — it's usually called vector **b**.
- You can write other vectors in terms of position vectors:

$$\overrightarrow{AB} = -\overrightarrow{OA} + \overrightarrow{OB} = \overrightarrow{OB} - \overrightarrow{OA} = \mathbf{b} - \mathbf{a}$$

This is the position vector of B **relative** to A.

- You can write the position of a point as a vector in **i** and **j** notation — just find the horizontal and vertical components of the position vector.
- The **distance** of a point from the origin is given by the **magnitude** of that point's position vector.

Example

The diagram shows the position vectors m = $\overrightarrow{OM}$ and n = $\overrightarrow{ON}$.

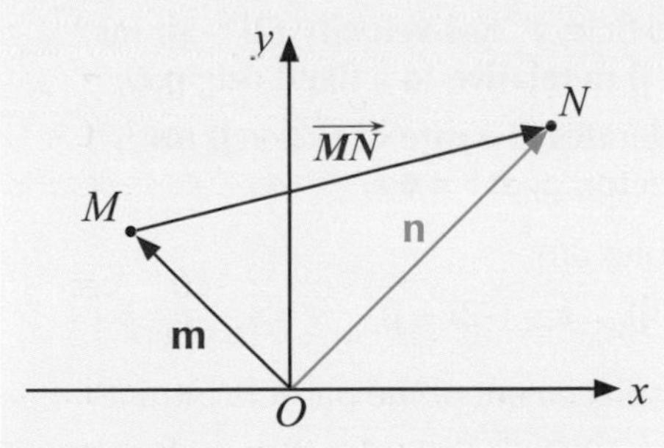

Given that m = –3i + 3j and n = 5i + 5j, find $\overrightarrow{MN}$, the position vector of N relative to M.

$\overrightarrow{MN} = \mathbf{n} - \mathbf{m} = (5\mathbf{i} + 5\mathbf{j}) - (-3\mathbf{i} + 3\mathbf{j})$

$= 8\mathbf{i} + 2\mathbf{j}$

So, to get from M to N, you go 8 units to the right, and 2 units up.

Displacement, velocity and acceleration vectors

Tip: Take a look back at Chapter 2 for a reminder about the *uvast* equations.

Tip: There's no equivalent to $v^2 = u^2 + 2as$ because you can't really square a vector.

Displacement, **velocity** and **acceleration** are all **vector quantities** (i.e. they have both magnitude and a direction).

So it makes sense that you can use the ***uvast*** **equations** in **vector form**.

These are:

$$\mathbf{v} = \mathbf{u} + \mathbf{a}t \qquad \mathbf{s} = \mathbf{u}t + \frac{1}{2}\mathbf{a}t^2$$

$$\mathbf{s} = \frac{1}{2}(\mathbf{u} + \mathbf{v})t \qquad \mathbf{s} = \mathbf{v}t - \frac{1}{2}\mathbf{a}t^2$$

Example 1

At $t = 0$ a particle has position vector (6i + 8j) m relative to a fixed origin O. The particle is travelling at constant velocity (2i – 6j) ms^{-1}. Find its position vector, p, at $t = 4$ s.

Tip: $\mathbf{s} = \mathbf{v}t$ is just $\mathbf{s} = \mathbf{v}t - \frac{1}{2}\mathbf{a}t^2$ with $\mathbf{a} = \mathbf{0}$.

- First find its displacement from its start point using $\mathbf{s} = \mathbf{v}t$:
  $\mathbf{s} = 4(2\mathbf{i} - 6\mathbf{j})$
  $= (8\mathbf{i} - 24\mathbf{j})$ m
- Then add this to its original position vector to find the final position vector relative to the origin:
  $\mathbf{p} = (6\mathbf{i} + 8\mathbf{j}) + (8\mathbf{i} - 24\mathbf{j})$
  $= (14\mathbf{i} - 16\mathbf{j})$ m

Example 2

At time $t = 0$, a particle, P, has velocity (2i – 5j) ms^{-1} and position (3i + j) m relative to a fixed origin O. Given that P accelerates at a rate of (–2i + j) ms^{-2}, find its position vector, p, at $t = 6$ s.

- The *uvast* variables are:
  $\mathbf{u} = (2\mathbf{i} - 5\mathbf{j}), \quad \mathbf{a} = (-2\mathbf{i} + \mathbf{j}), \quad \mathbf{s} = \mathbf{s}, \quad t = 6$
- First find the displacement of the particle from its start point after 6 seconds using $\mathbf{s} = \mathbf{u}t + \frac{1}{2}\mathbf{a}t^2$:
  $\mathbf{s} = 6(2\mathbf{i} - 5\mathbf{j}) + \frac{1}{2}(6^2)(-2\mathbf{i} + \mathbf{j})$
  $= (12\mathbf{i} - 30\mathbf{j}) + (-36\mathbf{i} + 18\mathbf{j})$
  $= (-24\mathbf{i} - 12\mathbf{j})$ m
- Then add this to its original position vector to find the final position vector relative to O:
  $\mathbf{p} = (3\mathbf{i} + \mathbf{j}) + (-24\mathbf{i} - 12\mathbf{j})$
  $= (-21\mathbf{i} - 11\mathbf{j})$ m

Example 3

A particle is moving with constant velocity. At $t = 0$, the particle has position vector $(-2\mathbf{i} + 6\mathbf{j})$ m relative to a fixed origin, O. 24 seconds later, the particle has position vector $(10\mathbf{i} - 54\mathbf{j})$ m.

a) Find the velocity of the particle.

- First find the particle's displacement from its start point after 24 seconds:
  $\mathbf{s} = (10\mathbf{i} - 54\mathbf{j}) - (-2\mathbf{i} + 6\mathbf{j})$
  $= (12\mathbf{i} - 60\mathbf{j})$ m
- Then use $\mathbf{v} = \frac{\mathbf{s}}{t}$ to find the velocity:
  $\mathbf{v} = \frac{1}{24}(12\mathbf{i} - 60\mathbf{j})$
  $= (0.5\mathbf{i} - 2.5\mathbf{j})\ \text{ms}^{-1}$

b) Find an expression for the position, p, of the particle at time t.

- Use $\mathbf{s} = \mathbf{v}t$ to find the particle's displacement form its start point at time t:
  $\mathbf{s} = \mathbf{v}t = [(0.5\mathbf{i} - 2.5\mathbf{j})t]$ m
- Then add this to the particle's position at $t = 0$ to find its position at time t:
  $\mathbf{p} = [(-2\mathbf{i} + 6\mathbf{j}) + (0.5\mathbf{i} - 2.5\mathbf{j})t]$ m

c) A second particle is moving with constant velocity $(0.3\mathbf{i} - 1.9\mathbf{j})\ \text{ms}^{-1}$. At $t = 0$, the particle is at O. How long after $t = 0$ do the particles collide?

- The second particle is at O at $t = 0$, so its position vector at time t is given by:
  $\mathbf{s} = \mathbf{v}t = [(0.3\mathbf{i} - 1.9\mathbf{j})t]$ m
- The particles will collide when they have the same position vector:
  $(-2\mathbf{i} + 6\mathbf{j}) + (0.5\mathbf{i} - 2.5\mathbf{j})t = (0.3\mathbf{i} - 1.9\mathbf{j})t$
- Equate the horizontal components ('**i** terms') to find t:
  $-2 + 0.5t = 0.3t$
  $0.2t = 2$
  $\Rightarrow t = 10$ seconds

Tip: It's a good idea to check you get the same value of t by equating the vertical components — that way you can be sure they actually collide.

d) Find the distance of the particles from O at this time.

- From part c), the position vector of the second particle at time t is $[(0.3\mathbf{i} - 1.9\mathbf{j})t]$ m. The particles collide at $t = 10$ s, so the position vector of both particles is:
  $(0.3\mathbf{i} - 1.9\mathbf{j}) \times 10 = (3\mathbf{i} - 19\mathbf{j})$ m
- The distance from O is given by the magnitude of the position vector:
  Distance $= \sqrt{3^2 + (-19)^2} = 19.2$ m (3 s.f.)

Tip: You could also find their position vector using the expression from part b) — the answer's the same.

Exercise 3.1

Q2 Hint: If you have an equation like $(a\mathbf{i} + b\mathbf{j}) = t(c\mathbf{i} + d\mathbf{j})$, then you can equate horizontal and vertical components to give $a = tc$ and $b = td$.

Q1 At time $t = 2$ s, a particle has position vector $(4\mathbf{i} - 3\mathbf{j})$ m relative to O. The particle moves with constant velocity $\mathbf{v} = (\mathbf{i} + 2\mathbf{j})$ ms^{-1}. Find the position vector of the particle at time $t = 6$ s.

Q2 A runner travels between points P and Q with constant velocity $(-2\mathbf{i} + 10\mathbf{j})$ kmh^{-1}. If P has position vector $(6\mathbf{i} - 3\mathbf{j})$ km and Q has position vector $(3\mathbf{i} + 12\mathbf{j})$ km, find the time taken.

Q3 A particle travels with uniform velocity from point S, with position vector $(4\mathbf{i} - 7\mathbf{j})$ m, to point R, with position vector $(-5\mathbf{i} + 2\mathbf{j})$ m, in 3 seconds. Find:

a) the velocity of the particle,

b) the speed of the particle,

c) the direction of motion of the particle.

Q4 A particle sets off from the origin with velocity $(4\mathbf{i} + 5\mathbf{j})$ ms^{-1} and travels for 6 seconds with constant acceleration until it reaches point A, with position vector $(33\mathbf{i} + 48\mathbf{j})$ m. Find the particle's acceleration.

Q5 A car leaves point P with velocity $(8\mathbf{i} + \mathbf{j})$ ms^{-1}, and arrives at point Q with velocity $(-3\mathbf{i} + 2\mathbf{j})$ ms^{-1}. If its acceleration is $(-5.5\mathbf{i} + 0.5\mathbf{j})$ ms^{-2}, find the time taken to travel from P to Q.

Q6 At $t = 0$, particle P sets off from rest from a fixed origin O, and accelerates at a rate of $(2\mathbf{i} - 8\mathbf{j})$ ms^{-2}.

a) Find an expression for the position vector, $\mathbf{p}$, of particle P at time t.

At $t = 0$, particle Q, moving with constant velocity, has position vector $(-4\mathbf{i} + 6\mathbf{j})$ m, relative to O. 2 seconds later, Q has position vector $(2\mathbf{i} + 2\mathbf{j})$ m.

b) Find the velocity of Q.

c) Hence find an expression for the position vector, $\mathbf{q}$, of particle Q at time t.

d) Find the distance between P and Q at time $t = 8$ seconds.

Q7 At time 09 00, a snowmobile passes a fixed origin O with constant velocity $(8\mathbf{i} - 14\mathbf{j})$ kmh^{-1}, where $\mathbf{i}$ and $\mathbf{j}$ are unit vectors due east and due north respectively. An hour and a half later, the snowmobile changes velocity so that it is travelling due west with speed 20 kmh^{-1}.

a) At what time is the snowmobile due south of O?

At 11 00, another snowmobile passes O. It moves with constant velocity and meets the first snowmobile at 12 00.

b) Assuming that the first snowmobile is still travelling due west with speed 20 kmh^{-1}, find the velocity of the second snowmobile.

Review Exercise — Chapter 3

Q1 Find the average velocity of a cyclist who cycles at 15 kmh^{-1} north for 15 minutes and then cycles south at 10 kmh^{-1} for 45 minutes.

Q2 Find $\mathbf{a} + 2\mathbf{b} - 3\mathbf{c}$ where $\mathbf{a} = 3\mathbf{i} + 7\mathbf{j}$, $\mathbf{b} = -2\mathbf{i} + 2\mathbf{j}$, and $\mathbf{c} = \mathbf{i} - 3\mathbf{j}$.

Q3 a) On a grid, draw the vectors $\mathbf{u} = 2\mathbf{i} - \mathbf{j}$ and $\mathbf{v} = -\mathbf{i} - \mathbf{j}$.

b) Draw the following vectors:

(i) $2\mathbf{u}$

(ii) $-\mathbf{v}$

(iii) $\mathbf{v} - \mathbf{u}$

(iv) $2(\mathbf{u} + \mathbf{v})$

c) Find the magnitude of $\mathbf{u}$.

d) Find the direction of $2(\mathbf{u} + \mathbf{v})$.

Q4 If $\mathbf{p} = 5\mathbf{i} - 12\mathbf{j}$ and vector $\mathbf{q}$ is parallel to $\mathbf{p}$ with magnitude 65, find the vector $\mathbf{q}$.

Q5 A plane flies 40 miles due south, then 60 miles southeast before going 70 miles on a bearing of 020°. Find the distance and bearing on which the plane must fly to return to its starting point.

Q6 A man wants to swim across a river. The current is flowing at 1.8 ms^{-1} parallel to the riverbank. Find the speed and direction that he needs to swim at for his resultant speed to be 1.2 ms^{-1} perpendicular to the riverbank.

Q7 A girl cycles along a bearing of 171° with speed 16 kmh^{-1}. Find her velocity in terms of $\mathbf{i}$ and $\mathbf{j}$, where $\mathbf{i}$ and $\mathbf{j}$ are the unit vectors directed due east and due north respectively.

Q8 Find the magnitude and direction of the resultant vector in each of the following:

a)

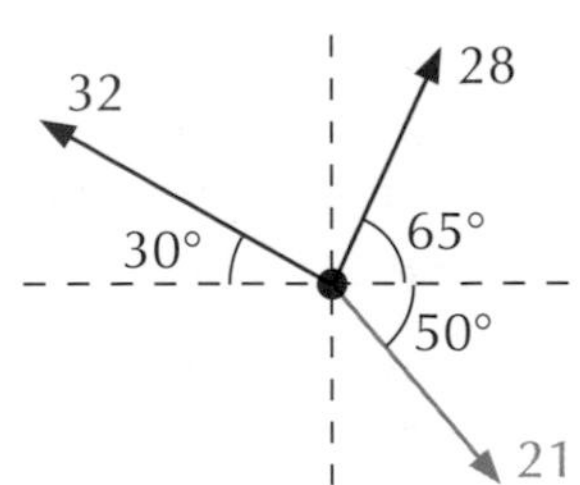

b)

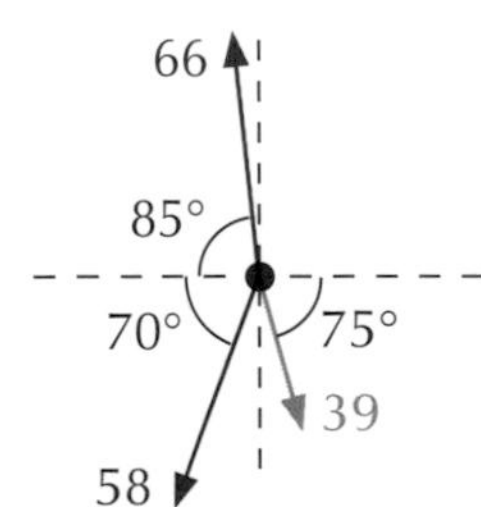

Q9 A dog walks 0.3 km due east, then 0.9 km on a bearing of 195°, then 0.4 km on a bearing of 260°.

a) Find the dog's final distance from its starting point.

b) Find the dog's final displacement from his starting point in terms of **i** and **j**, where **i** and **j** are the unit vectors directed due east and due north respectively.

Q10 A particle moves with constant velocity $\mathbf{v} = (3\mathbf{i} + 5\mathbf{j})$ ms^{-1} from a fixed origin O. Find its position vector and the distance travelled after 6 seconds.

Q11 An object travels from X to Y in 5 seconds with constant velocity $(7\mathbf{i} - 3\mathbf{j})$ ms^{-1}. If the position vector of Y is $\mathbf{y} = (2\mathbf{i} + 5\mathbf{j})$ m, find $\mathbf{x}$, the position vector of X.

Q12 Find the speed and direction of motion of a particle after 8 seconds if its initial velocity is $(5\mathbf{i} + 2\mathbf{j})$ ms^{-1} and its acceleration is $(\mathbf{i} + 2\mathbf{j})$ ms^{-2}.

Q13 A particle travels with constant acceleration from point A, with position vector $(3\mathbf{i} + 5\mathbf{j})$ m, to point B, with position vector $(-6\mathbf{i} + 3\mathbf{j})$ m, in a time of 5 seconds. If its initial velocity is $(2\mathbf{i} + \mathbf{j})$ ms^{-1}, find its final velocity.

Q14 A body leaves point A, with position vector $(4\mathbf{i} + 7\mathbf{j})$ m, with velocity $(2\mathbf{i} - 3\mathbf{j})$ ms^{-1}. It travels with constant acceleration to point B, with position vector $(8\mathbf{i} - 2\mathbf{j})$ m, arriving with velocity $-1.5\mathbf{j}$ ms^{-1}.

Find the time taken.

Q15 A train passes point C, with position vector $(9\mathbf{i} - 6\mathbf{j})$ m, with velocity $(\mathbf{i} + 2\mathbf{j})$ ms^{-1}. It travels with constant acceleration to point D, with position vector $(-5\mathbf{i} + 10\mathbf{j})$ m, in 4 seconds.

Find the magnitude of the acceleration of the train as it travels from C to D.

Q16 Particle P leaves the origin with velocity $(7\mathbf{i} - 2\mathbf{j})$ ms^{-1} and acceleration $(-3\mathbf{i} - 2\mathbf{j})$ ms^{-2}.

Find:

a) the position vector of P after 2 seconds,

b) the distance travelled by P in the first 2 seconds,

c) the velocity of P after 5 seconds.

Exam-Style Questions — Chapter 3

1 A girl is swimming across a river in a direction perpendicular to the riverbank. She swims at a speed of 2 ms^{-1} relative to the riverbank. The river is flowing at 3 ms^{-1} relative to the riverbank, and the current carries the girl downstream.

Find the magnitude of the resultant velocity of the girl and the angle it makes with the riverbank.

(4 marks)

2 A remote-controlled toy boat is powered across a loch with velocity $(4\mathbf{i} + 6\mathbf{j})$ ms^{-1} relative to the controller on land. There is a current flowing at $(\mathbf{i} - 2\mathbf{j})$ ms^{-1}, and there is a crosswind blowing at an effective speed of $-3\mathbf{j}$ ms^{-1}.

Find the magnitude and direction of the boat's resultant velocity.

(5 marks)

3 A vector of magnitude 7 acts vertically upwards. Another vector, of magnitude $4\sqrt{2}$, acts at an angle of 45° below the positive horizontal direction.
The resultant of the two vectors is $\mathbf{r}$.

a) Find $\mathbf{r}$ in terms of $\mathbf{i}$ and $\mathbf{j}$.

(2 marks)

b) The vector $\mathbf{s}$ acts parallel to $\mathbf{r}$, and has magnitude 35.
Find $\mathbf{s}$ in terms of $\mathbf{i}$ and $\mathbf{j}$.

(3 marks)

4 A particle initially has position vector $(\mathbf{i} + 2\mathbf{j})$ m and is travelling with constant velocity $(3\mathbf{i} + \mathbf{j})$ ms^{-1}. After 8 seconds it reaches point A. A second particle has constant velocity $(-4\mathbf{i} + 2\mathbf{j})$ ms^{-1} and takes 5 seconds to travel from point A to point B.

Find the position vectors of points A and B.

(5 marks)

5 The point P is 14 m from point O. The point Q is 11 m from O.
The angle between the position vectors $\overrightarrow{OP}$ and $\overrightarrow{OQ}$ is 105°.

a) Find the distance between the points P and Q.

(2 marks)

b) Find the angle between the position vectors $\overrightarrow{OP}$ and $\overrightarrow{PQ}$.

(2 marks)

[In questions 6 and 7, the unit vectors **i** *and* **j** *are directed due east and due north respectively.]*

6 At $t = 0$, a particle P is at position vector $(\mathbf{i} + 5\mathbf{j})$ m, relative to a fixed origin. P is moving with a constant velocity of $(7\mathbf{i} - 3\mathbf{j})$ ms^{-1}. After 4 s the velocity of P changes instantaneously to $(a\mathbf{i} + b\mathbf{j})$ ms^{-1}, where a and b are constants. After a further 3.5 seconds P reaches position vector $15\mathbf{i}$ m. Find:

a) the speed of P at $t = 0$, *(2 marks)*

b) the direction of motion of P at $t = 0$, giving your answer as a bearing, *(3 marks)*

c) the values of a and b. *(4 marks)*

7 A man, M, and a woman, W, start at point O. The man jogs 15 km on a bearing of 035°, then 9 km on a bearing of 120°, then 6 km on a bearing of 195°. The woman jogs 8 km on a bearing of 170°, then 10 km due east.

Find the distance and direction in which the woman has to travel to meet the man, giving the direction as a bearing. *(10 marks)*

8 At time $t = 0$, a particle sets off from rest at the point O and accelerates uniformly. At time $t = 3$ seconds, the particle has position vector $(9\mathbf{i} - 18\mathbf{j})$ m relative to O.

a) Find the acceleration of the particle. *(3 marks)*

b) Given that the particle continues to move with this constant acceleration, find an expression for the position vector, $\mathbf{p}$, of the particle at time t. *(3 marks)*

Also at time $t = 0$, a second particle moving with constant velocity $(3\mathbf{i} - 5\mathbf{j})$ ms^{-1} has position vector $(a\mathbf{i} + b\mathbf{j})$ m, where a and b are constants.

c) Given that the two particles collide at time $t = 8$ seconds, find the values of a and b. *(4 marks)*

d) Find the particles' distance from O at the point of collision. *(2 marks)*

e) Find the distance between the two particles at time $t = 11$ seconds, given that the trajectory of each particle is unchanged by the collision. *(4 marks)*

1. Forces

A force is an influence which can change the motion of a body (i.e. cause an acceleration). It can also be thought of as a 'push' or a 'pull' on an object. All forces are vectors — they have a direction and a magnitude. So all the stuff you learnt about vectors in Chapter 3 should come in useful in this chapter too.

Learning Objectives:

- Understand and use the fact that forces are vectors.
- Be able to resolve the forces acting on an object.
- Be able to calculate the resultant force on an object.
- Solve problems for objects in equilibrium.

Treating forces as vectors

You've done a fair amount of resolving vectors already in Chapter 3, so hopefully resolving forces should be pretty straightforward.

- A **component of a force** is the **magnitude** of the force in a **particular direction**.
- You can use trigonometry to **resolve** forces and find their components in a particular direction.
- Often it's very useful to resolve forces into their **horizontal** and **vertical** components. Together with the force vector, these components form a **right-angled triangle**.

Tip: As well as changing the motion of an object, forces can also change an object's shape, e.g. by squashing or stretching it. You don't need to know about this in M1 though.

You can find the horizontal and vertical components of a force, F, using **trigonometry**.

- Horizontal component, F_x:

$$\cos\theta = \frac{\text{adjacent}}{\text{hypotenuse}} = \frac{F_x}{F}, \text{ so } \boldsymbol{F_x = F\cos\theta}$$

- Vertical component, F_y:

$$\sin\theta = \frac{\text{opposite}}{\text{hypotenuse}} = \frac{F_y}{F}, \text{ so } \boldsymbol{F_y = F\sin\theta}$$

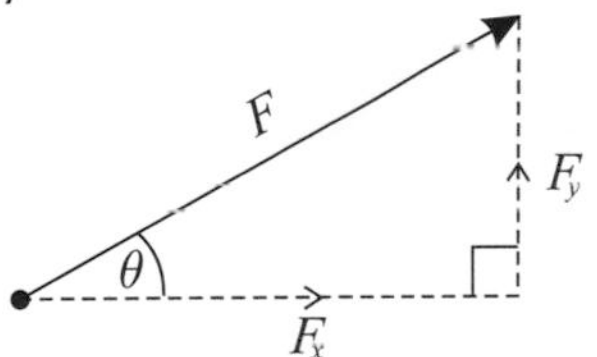

Example 1

A particle is acted on by a force of 15 N at 30° above the positive horizontal. Find the horizontal and vertical components of the force.

- Draw a vector triangle and use trigonometry to calculate the horizontal and vertical components.
- Vertical component = 15sin30°
  = 7.5 N upwards

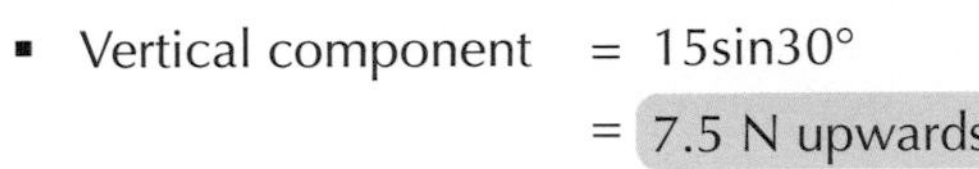

- Horizontal component = 15cos30°
  = 13.0 N (to 3 s.f.) to the right

Tip: For example, a force which acts horizontally has zero vertical component, and vice versa.

- If you're resolving in a direction which is **perpendicular** to the line of action of a force, then the component of the force in that direction will be **zero**.
- When you're resolving a force, you should state which direction you're taking as being positive. Then any components acting in the **opposite direction** will be **negative**.

Example 2

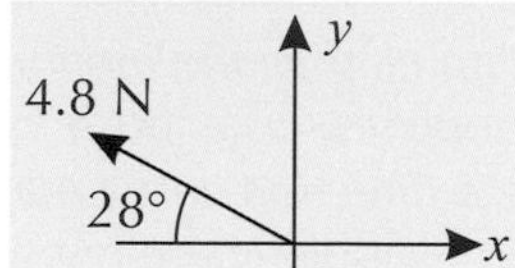

Find the horizontal and vertical components of the force shown.

Tip: Draw an arrow to show which direction you are taking as positive. Here, 'right' is positive, so the x-component of the force is negative, because it acts to the left.

- Resolving in the x-direction (→):

  $-4.8\cos 28° = -4.24$ N (to 3 s.f.)

- Resolving in the y-direction (↑):

  $4.8\sin 28° = 2.25$ N (to 3 s.f.)

- You can resolve forces in **any two perpendicular directions**, not just horizontally and vertically.
- For example, for an object on an **inclined plane**, you might want to resolve the forces in directions **parallel** and **perpendicular** to the plane.

Example 3

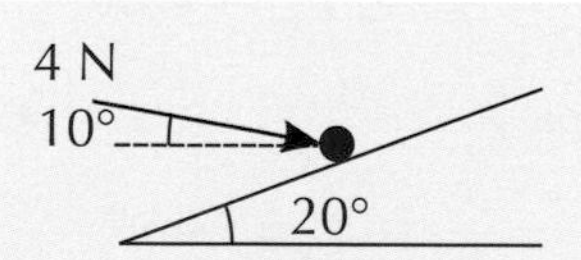

The diagram shows a particle at rest on a smooth inclined plane. A force of magnitude 4 N acts on the particle at an angle of 10° to the horizontal. Find the components of the force that act parallel and perpendicular to the plane.

- By the alternate angles theorem, the angle between the direction of the force and the slope of the plane is 20° + 10° = 30°.

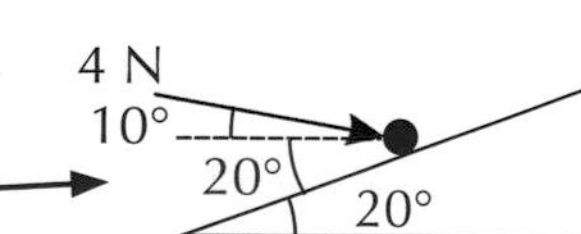

- Resolving parallel to the plane (↗):

  $F_{\text{parallel}} = 4\cos 30° = 3.46$ N (to 3 s.f.)

- Resolving perpendicular to the plane (↖):

  $F_{\text{perpendicular}} = -4\sin 30° = -2$ N

- You can describe forces using the **unit vectors i** and **j**. The number in front of the **i** is the horizontal force component, and the number in front of the **j** is the vertical force component.

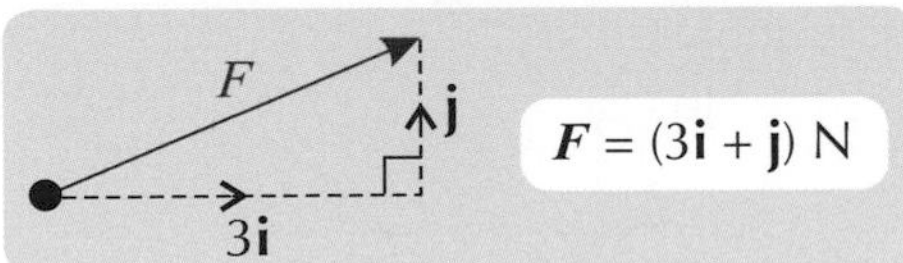

Tip: Unit vectors are a pair of perpendicular vectors, each of magnitude one unit. See page 43 for more information.

Example 4

A force F = (3i – 2j) N acts on particle P.
Find the magnitude of the force and the angle it makes with i.

- Draw a vector diagram of the force acting on the particle to get a clear idea of what's going on.

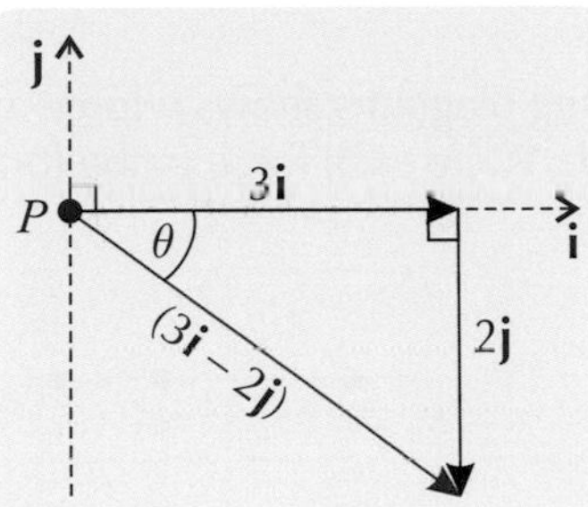

- The force and its **i** and **j** components form a right-angled triangle, so you can use Pythagoras' theorem to find the magnitude of the force:

Magnitude of $F = \sqrt{3^2 + 2^2}$
$= \sqrt{13}$
$=$ 3.61 N (to 3 s.f.)

- Use trigonometry to find θ, the angle the force makes with **i**.

$\tan\theta = \frac{2}{3}$
$\theta = \tan^{-1}\left(\frac{2}{3}\right)$
$=$ 33.7° (to 3 s.f.)

Tip: Examples 1 to 3 involved resolving a force into a pair of perpendicular components. In this example, you're given the components and you need to find the force itself.

Tip: It's always a good idea to draw a vector diagram if you're not given one in the question.

Exercise 1.1

Q1 Find the horizontal and vertical components of each of the forces shown.

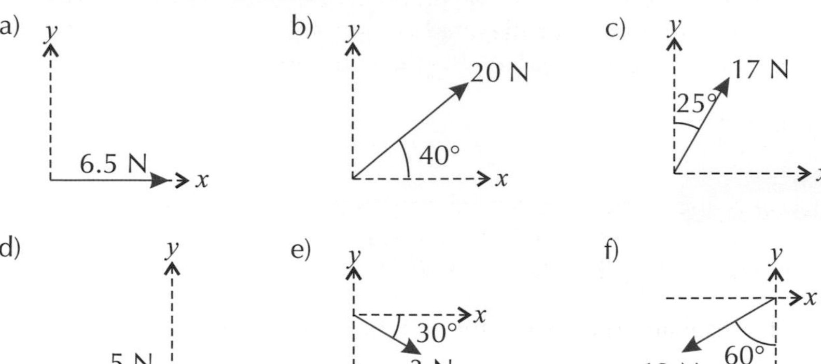

Q2 Each of the following diagrams shows a force and the angle it makes with the horizontal. Write each force in the form (a**i** + b**j**) N.

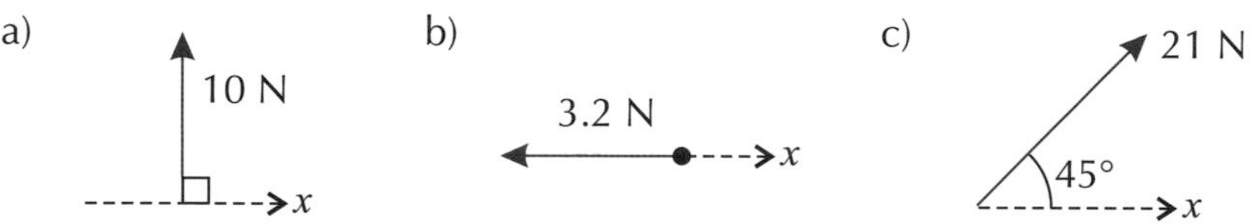

Q3 Hint: You might also see this question written as 'find the angle between the force and the horizontal'.

Q3 Find the angle the force (**i** + $\sqrt{3}$**j**) N makes with **i**.

Q4 The force (c**i** + 7**j**) N acts at 25° to **i**, where c is a positive constant.

a) Find the value of c.

b) Find the magnitude of this force.

Q5

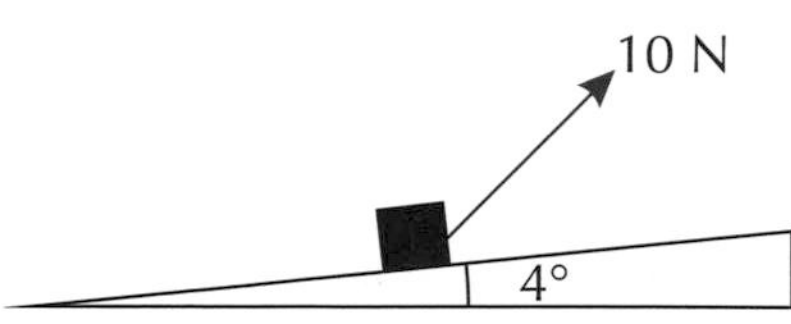

The diagram shows a force of magnitude 10 N acting on an object on an inclined plane. The component of the force in the direction parallel to the plane is 7.1 N.

a) Find the angle between the direction of the force and the incline of the plane.

b) Find the horizontal component of the force.

Q6 Hint: Find the angle each force makes with the horizontal first.

Q6 The forces (3**i** + 4**j**) N and (4**i** + 3**j**) N act at the same point. Find the angle between these two forces.

Resultant forces

The **resultant force** on an object is the **single** force that has the **same effect** as all the forces acting on the object.

You can find the resultant force on an object either by adding all the force vectors using a **vector diagram**, or by **resolving** the forces in two perpendicular directions and adding the components.

Tip: The resultant can also be thought of as the sum of all the forces acting on the object. You came across resultant vectors in Chapter 3. See page 37 for a reminder.

Example 1

Forces S and T, given by S = (6i + 2j) N and T = (8qi – qj) N, act on a particle. Given that the resultant of these two forces, R, is parallel to j, find the value of q.

- The resultant force is just the sum of forces S and T.

$$R = S + T$$
$$= [(6 + 8q)\mathbf{i} + (2 - q)\mathbf{j}]\text{ N}$$

- R is parallel to **j**, so the **i** component of R must be zero.

$$6 + 8q = 0\text{, therefore } q = -\frac{6}{8} = -\frac{3}{4}$$

Tip: Forces given in terms of **i** and **j** are already split into their components — to find the resultant you just need to add all the **i** terms together and all the **j** terms together.

Example 2

The diagram on the right shows a force of 15 N and a horizontal force of 20 N applied to a particle. Find the magnitude and direction of the resultant force on the particle.

- Draw a vector triangle to show the sum of the two forces.

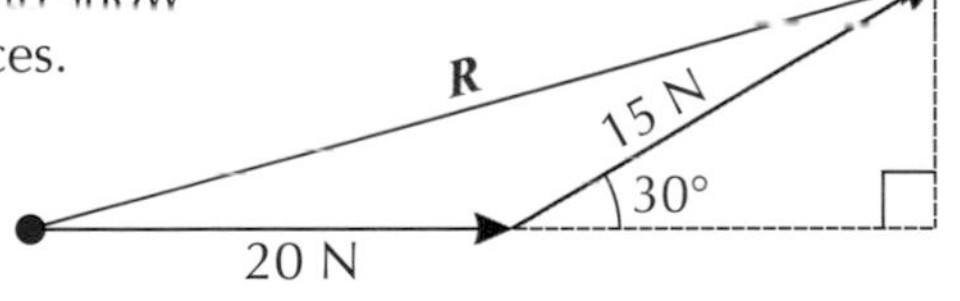

- Resolve to find the horizontal and vertical components of the 15 N force.

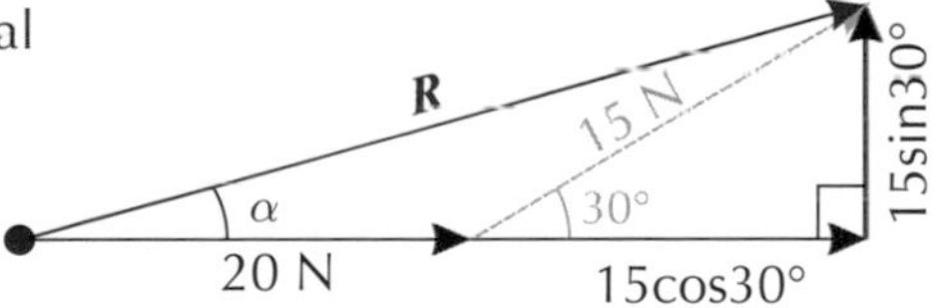

Tip: This example uses the vector diagram method. Remember to always put vector arrows 'nose to tail' when you draw vector diagrams.

- Use Pythagoras' theorem to find the magnitude of R.

$$R^2 = (20 + 15\cos30°)^2 + (15\sin30°)^2$$
$$R = \sqrt{(20 + 15\cos30°)^2 + (15\sin30°)^2}$$
$$= \sqrt{32.99...^2 + 7.5^2}$$
$$= 33.8\text{ N (to 3 s.f.)}$$

Tip: You could also use the cosine rule to find R.

- Use trigonometry to find α, the angle R makes with the horizontal.

$$\tan\alpha = \frac{7.5}{32.99...}$$
$$\alpha = \tan^{-1}\left(\frac{7.5}{32.99...}\right)$$
$$= 12.8° \text{ (to 3 s.f.) above the horizontal}$$

Example 3

Three forces of magnitude 9 N, 12 N and 13 N act on a particle *P* in the directions shown in the diagram.

Find the magnitude and direction of the resultant of the three forces.

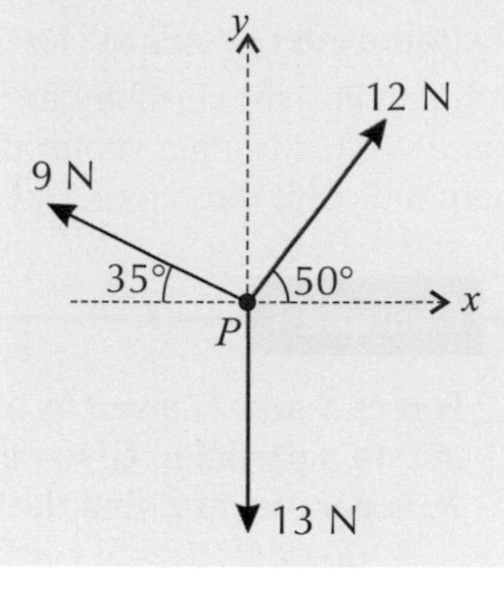

> **Tip:** This example uses the resolving method — it's the best method to use when you've got more than two forces to deal with.

- Resolving in the y-direction (↑):

  $9\sin35° + 12\sin50° - 13$
  $= 1.354... = 1.35$ N (to 3 s.f.)

- Resolving in the x-direction (→):

  $12\cos50° - 9\cos35°$
  $= 0.3410... = 0.341$ N (to 3 s.f.)

- Use the components to form a right-angled triangle. The resultant is the hypotenuse of the triangle.

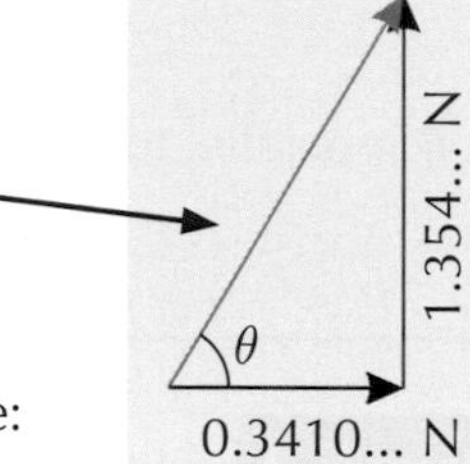

- Use Pythagoras' theorem to find the magnitude:

  $\sqrt{1.354...^2 + 0.3410...^2}$ = **1.40 N (to 3 s.f.)**

- Use trigonometry to find the required direction:

  $\theta = \tan^{-1}\left(\frac{1.354...}{0.3410...}\right)$ = **75.9° (to 3 s.f.)** above the positive x-axis.

Example 4

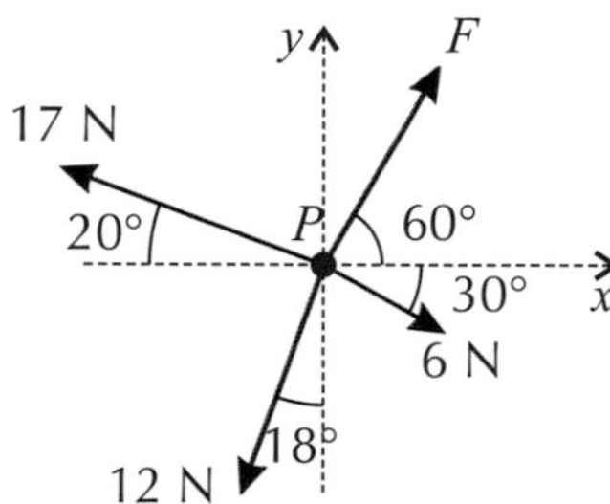

The diagram shows the forces acting on particle *P*. Find the magnitude of force *F*, given that the resultant force on the particle acts in the *x*-direction.

> **Tip:** You're told that the resultant force acts in the x-direction. This means that the vertical component of the resultant must be zero.

- Resolving in the y-direction (↑):

  $F\sin60° + 17\sin20° - 12\cos18° - 6\sin30° = 0$

- Rearrange and solve this equation to find the magnitude of F:

$$F = \frac{-17\sin 20° + 12\cos 18° + 6\sin 30°}{\sin 60°}$$

$= $ **9.93 N** (to 3 s.f.)

Exercise 1.2

Q1 Find the magnitude and direction of the resultants of each of these pairs of forces.

a) 8.2 N, 39°, 7 N

b) 4 N, 45°, 5 N, 30°

Q2 A force of magnitude 18 N acts on a particle at 60° above the positive horizontal. A force of magnitude 16 N also acts vertically upwards on the particle.

a) Draw a diagram to illustrate the forces acting on the particle.

b) Find the magnitude and direction of the resultant of the two forces.

Q3 Two forces of $(8\mathbf{i} + 5\mathbf{j})$ N and $(3\mathbf{i} - 2\mathbf{j})$ N act on a particle. Find the magnitude and direction of the resultant of these two forces.

Q4 Each of the diagrams below shows the forces acting on a particle. Find the magnitude and direction of the resultant force on each particle.

a)

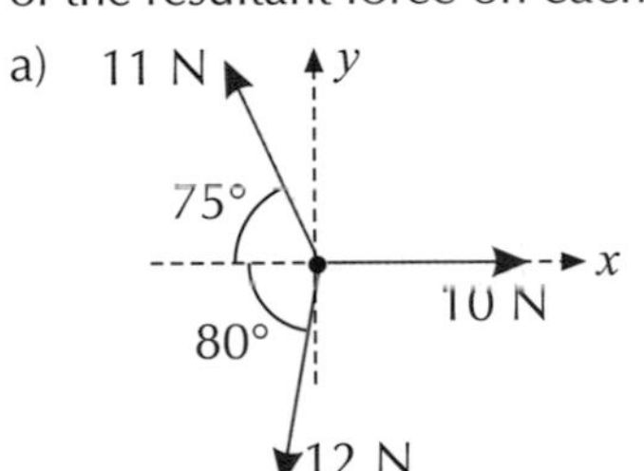

b) y, 6.5 N, 8 N, 61°, 69°, x, 47°, 10 N

Q5 Three forces act on a particle, as shown in the diagram. The resultant force on the particle acts in the x-direction only. Find T.

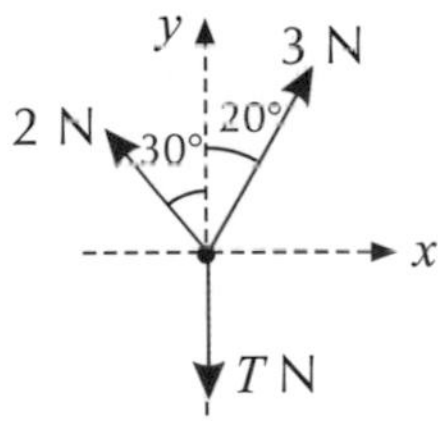

Q6 A particle is acted on by a force of magnitude 9 N in the positive horizontal direction and a force of magnitude 10 N at 30° above the positive horizontal. A third force of magnitude P N acts on the particle at 60° above the positive horizontal. Find P, given that the resultant of the three forces acts at 45° above the positive horizontal.

Q7 Forces of magnitude 1 N and 2 N act at angles of 10° and 35° above $\mathbf{i}$ respectively. A third force of magnitude 3 N acts at an angle of θ above $\mathbf{i}$, where $180° \leq \theta \leq 360°$. The resultant of the three forces has no horizontal component.

a) Find θ.

b) Calculate the magnitude of the resultant of the three forces.

Q7 Hint: Be careful — make sure the angle you calculate is in the range given for θ. Remember $\cos\theta = \cos(360° - \theta)$.

Forces in equilibrium

If an object is in **equilibrium**, all the forces acting on the object **cancel each other out**.

There is **no resultant force** on an object in equilibrium.

Equilibrium problems are an exam favourite.
There are two ways you can go about solving them:

- The first way is to use the fact that the forces acting on an object in equilibrium form a **closed loop** when you draw them nose to tail. (This is sometimes called a **vector triangle** or **vector polygon**.)

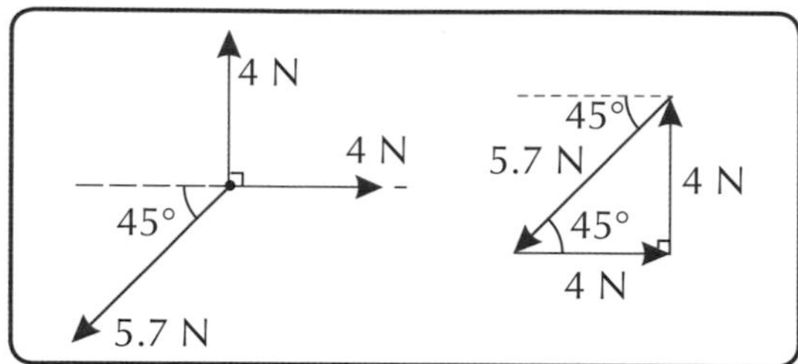

  Once you've formed the polygon of vectors, you can use geometry (usually Pythagoras' theorem and trigonometry) to work out the **direction** and **magnitude** of a missing force.

- The second way is to **resolve the forces** acting on the object in two perpendicular directions. The resultant force on an object in equilibrium is zero, which means that the sum of the components in any particular direction must also be zero.

Tip: In M1, you'll only really come across **static equilibrium** — this means that the object isn't moving. However, an object moving with constant velocity is also in equilibrium — the object is not accelerating, so there is no resultant force acting on it. See Chapter 5 for more about forces and acceleration.

Tip: More often than not, it's easiest to solve equilibrium problems by resolving forces — trying to solve problems geometrically can quickly get tricky when you have any more than three forces acting on an object.

Example 1

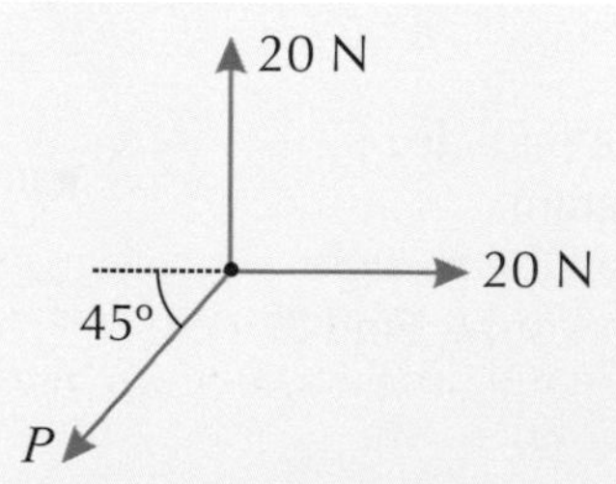

The diagram shows all the forces acting on a particle. Given that the particle is in equilibrium, find the magnitude of the missing force *P*.

- The particle is in equilibrium, so the forces will form a closed loop when drawn nose to tail.
- Use trigonometry to find the magnitude of P:

$$\cos 45° = \frac{20}{P}$$

$$P = \frac{20}{\cos 45°}$$

$$= 28.3 \text{ N} \text{ (to 3 s.f.)}$$

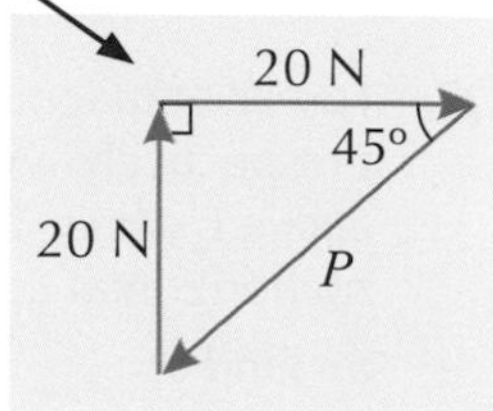

Tip: You could answer this question just as easily by resolving forces and knowing that the sum of the components in any given direction is zero.

Example 2

The diagram on the right shows all the forces acting on a particle. Given that the particle is in equilibrium, find the magnitudes of the missing forces *P* and *Q*.

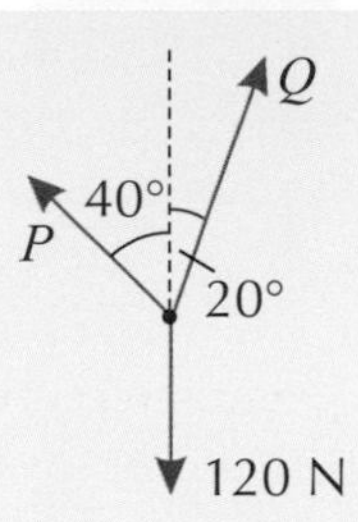

- Draw the vectors nose to tail to form a vector triangle:

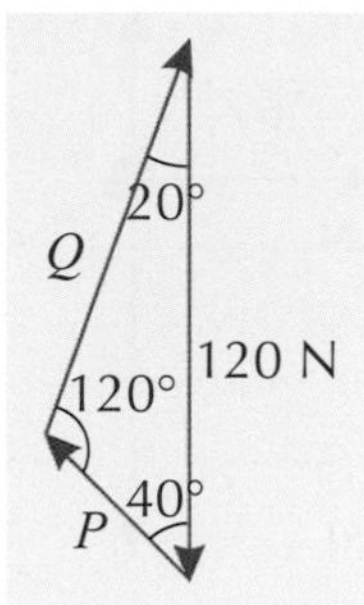

- Then use the sine rule to find *P* and *Q*:

$\frac{P}{\sin 20°} = \frac{120}{\sin 120°}$ So $P =$ 47.4 N (to 3 s.f.)

$\frac{Q}{\sin 40°} = \frac{120}{\sin 120°}$ So $Q =$ 89.1 N (to 3 s.f.)

Example 3

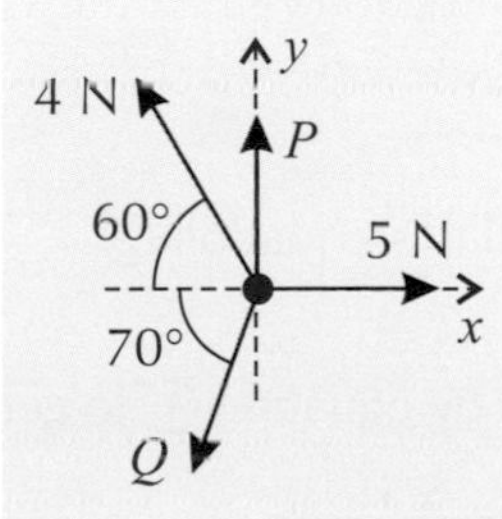

The diagram shows all the forces acting on a particle. Given that the particle is in equilibrium, find the magnitudes of the missing forces *P* and *Q*.

- The particle is in equilibrium, so the resultant force on the particle is zero.
- Resolve to find two perpendicular components of the resultant force, then make each component equal to zero.

Tip: There are a lot of forces acting on the particle, so it's easier to resolve the forces than to use vector polygons.

- Resolving in the *x*-direction (→): $5 - Q\cos 70° - 4\cos 60° = 0$
  $Q\cos 70° = 3$
  $\Rightarrow Q = 8.771... =$ 8.77 N (to 3 s.f.)

- Resolving in the *y*-direction (↑): $P + 4\sin 60° - Q\sin 70° = 0$
  $P = (8.771...)\sin 70° - 4\sin 60°$
  $= 4.778...$ N $=$ 4.78 N (to 3 s.f.)

Example 4

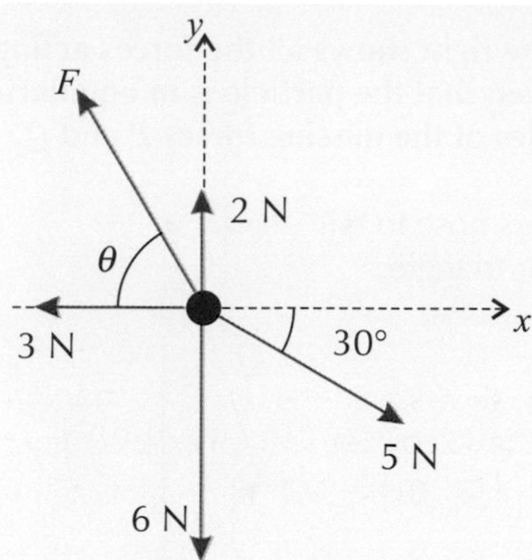

The diagram shows all the forces acting on a particle. Given that the particle is in equilibrium, find the magnitude of force F and the value of θ.

- Again, resolve in the x- and y-directions to find expressions for the horizontal and vertical components of the resultant, and make these equal zero.

  Resolving in the x-direction ($\rightarrow$):

  $5\cos 30° - 3 - F\cos\theta = 0$

  $F\cos\theta = 5\cos 30° - 3$ — call this equation ①

  Resolving in the y-direction ($\uparrow$):

  $2 + F\sin\theta - 6 - 5\sin 30° = 0$

  $F\sin\theta - 6.5 = 0$

  $F\sin\theta = 6.5$ — call this equation ②

- Divide equation ② by equation ① to get an equation for θ:

  $$\frac{F\sin\theta}{F\cos\theta} = \frac{6.5}{5\cos 30° - 3}$$

  $$\tan\theta = \frac{6.5}{5\cos 30° - 3}$$

  $$\theta = \tan^{-1}\left(\frac{6.5}{5\cos 30° - 3}\right)$$

  $$= 78.43...°$$

  $$= 78.4° \text{ (to 3 s.f.)}$$

- Substitute your value for θ into equation ② and solve to find F:

  $F\sin 78.43...° = 6.5$

  $$F = \frac{6.5}{\sin 78.43...°}$$

  $$= 6.63 \text{ N (to 3 s.f.)}$$

Tip: You could substitute your value for θ into equation 1 to find F instead — you'll get exactly the same answer.

Exercise 1.3

Q1

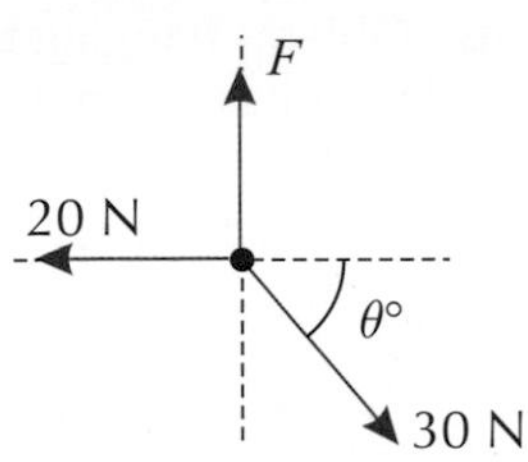

The diagram shows the three forces acting on a particle.
The particle is in equilibrium. By drawing a polygon of forces, find the magnitude of force F and angle θ.

Q2

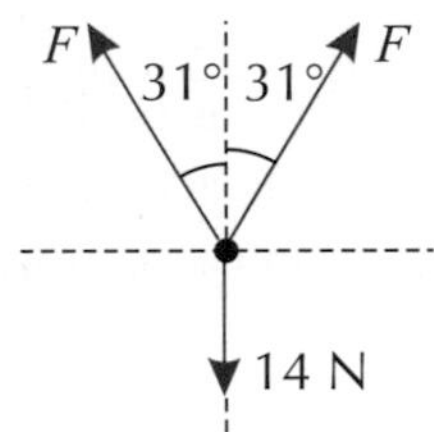

The diagram shows all the forces acting on a particle in equilibrium.
Find the magnitude of force F.

Q3

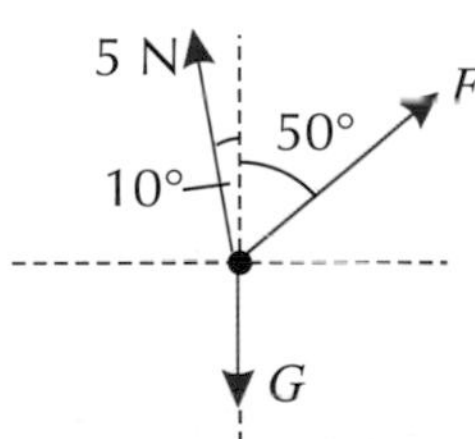

A downward force of magnitude G acts on a particle.
Two forces of magnitude 5 N and F also act on the particle, at 10° and 50° to the upward vertical, as shown in the diagram.
No other forces act on the particle. Given that the particle is in equilibrium, find the magnitude of forces F and G.

Q3 Hint: You could solve this question by resolving forces, or by using a polygon of vectors and the sine rule.

Q4

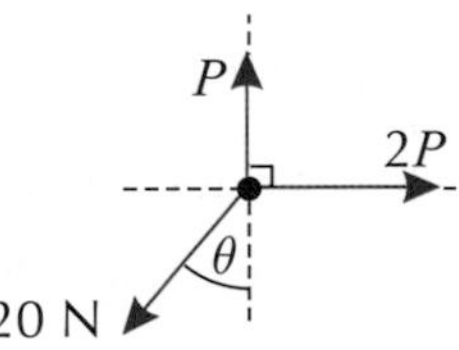

Forces of magnitude P N and $2P$ N act on a particle vertically upwards and horizontally, as shown in the diagram.
A third force of 20 N acts at an angle θ to the downward vertical.
No other forces act on the particle.
Given that the particle is in equilibrium, find the values of P and θ.

Equilibrium problems

You can use everything from the last few pages to answer questions about all sorts of **real-life situations**. Objects hanging from **strings**, and objects on **inclined planes** are particular favourites when it comes to exam questions.

Tip: The $8g$ force acting downwards is the body's weight. T_1 and T_2 are the tensions in the two strings. Look back at page 2 if you'd like a reminder about weight and tension.

Example

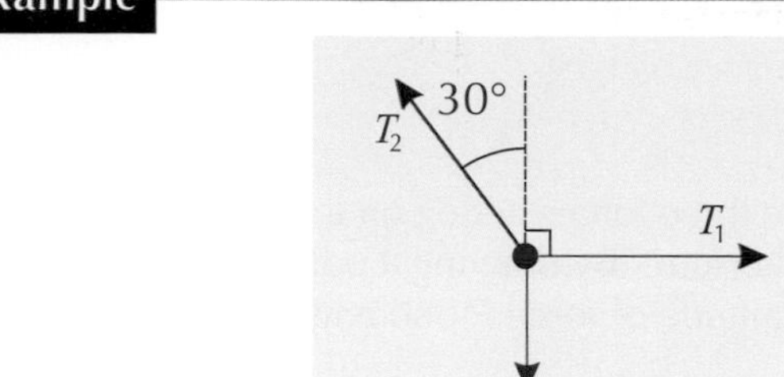

The diagram shows a body of mass 8 kg held in equilibrium by two light, inextensible strings. One string is horizontal, and the other string makes an angle of 30° with the vertical.

Find the magnitude of the tension in each string.

Tip: The components in each direction must sum to zero because the body is in equilibrium.

- Resolving vertically (↑):

$$T_2\cos30° - 8g = 0$$
$$T_2\cos30° = 8g$$
$$T_2 = 8g \div \cos30°$$
$$= 90.528... = 90.5 \text{ N (to 3 s.f.)}$$

Remember to use $g = 9.8 \text{ ms}^{-2}$ unless you're told otherwise.

- Resolving horizontally (→):

$$T_1 - T_2\sin30° = 0$$
$$T_1 = T_2\sin30°$$
$$= 90.528... \times \sin30°$$
$$= 45.264... = 45.3 \text{ N (to 3 s.f.)}$$

Inclined planes

Tip: You did a bit of resolving parallel and perpendicular to a plane earlier in the chapter, so this shouldn't be completely new.

Inclined planes come up all through M1. When you're resolving forces in inclined plane questions, it's pretty much always best to resolve **parallel** and **perpendicular to the slope**.

Mostly, you'll be resolving an object's **weight**, because weight always acts **vertically downwards**, and you'll need to use its **components parallel** and **perpendicular to the slope**.

These are:

- Component of weight **parallel** to the plane: $mg\sin\theta$
- Component of weight **perpendicular** to the plane: $mg\cos\theta$

Where mg is the weight of the object and θ is the angle of the incline of the slope.

Resolving an Object's Weight

- You want to find the **components** of an object's weight **parallel** and **perpendicular** to the plane.
- Using **right-angled triangles**, the angle between the object's weight and its component perpendicular to the plane is equal to θ.
- You can **resolve** as usual to find the components of the weight using **trigonometry**.
- You may have to resolve **other forces** as well as the weight, depending on their **direction**.

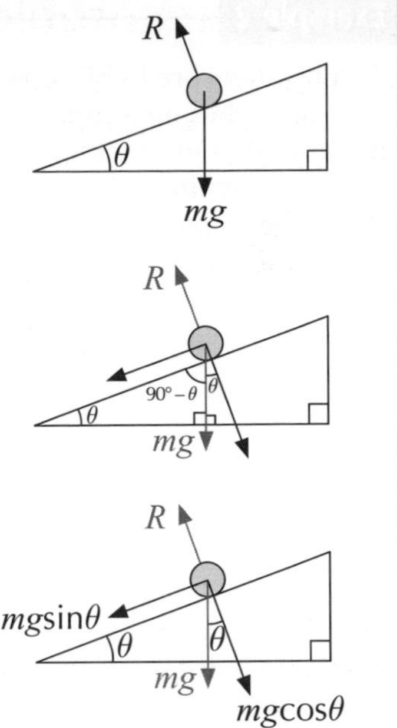

Example 1

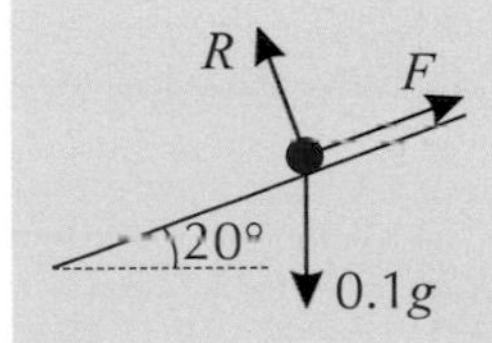

A stone of mass 0.1 kg rests on a smooth plane inclined at 20° to the horizontal. It is held in equilibrium by a force, *F*, acting parallel to the plane, as shown.

Find the magnitude of force *F* and the normal reaction, *R*, of the plane on the stone.

- Resolving parallel to the plane (↗):

$$F - 0.1g\sin 20° = 0$$
$$F = 0.1g\sin 20°$$
$$= 0.335 \text{ N} \quad \text{(to 3 s.f.)}$$

This is the component of the stone's weight acting down the plane.

Tip: The force F acts parallel to the plane already, so you don't need to resolve it into components.

- Resolving perpendicular to the plane (↖):

$$R - 0.1g\cos 20° = 0$$
$$R = 0.1g\cos 20°$$
$$= 0.921 \text{ N} \quad \text{(to 3 s.f.)}$$

Example 2

Two brothers are fighting over a sledge of weight 100 N. The sledge lies on a smooth slope inclined at an angle of 35° to the horizontal. One brother tries to pull the sledge up the slope with a force of magnitude 70 N, while the other tries to pull the sledge down the slope with a force of magnitude F.

a) Find the magnitude of the normal reaction force, R, on the sledge.

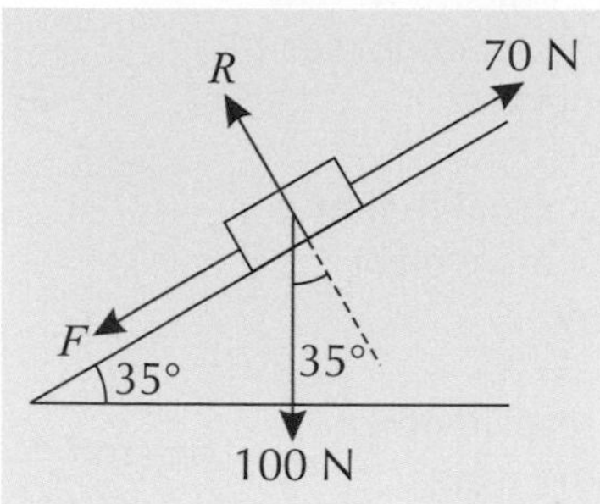

- Resolving perpendicular to the plane (↖):

$$R - 100\cos 35° = 0$$

$$\text{So, } R = 100\cos 35° = 81.9 \text{ N (to 3 s.f.)}$$

b) The sledge remains stationary. Find the magnitude of the force F.

- Resolving parallel to the plane (↗):

$$70 - F - 100\sin 35° = 0$$

$$F = 70 - 100\sin 35° = 12.6 \text{ N (to 3 s.f.)}$$

Example 3

A rock of mass 9 kg rests on a smooth plane inclined at 35° to the horizontal. A horizontal force of magnitude 10 N directed towards the plane and the tension in a string parallel to the plane keep the particle in equilibrium.

a) Find the normal reaction force, R, between the plane and rock.

Tip: You need to resolve the 10 N force into components parallel and perpendicular to the plane. Find the angle between the 10 N force and the slope of the plane using alternate angles.

- Draw a diagram showing all the forces acting on the rock.
- Resolving perpendicular to the plane (↖):

$$R - 10\sin 35° - 9g\cos 35° = 0$$

$$R = 10\sin 35° + 9g\cos 35° = 78.0 \text{ N (to 3 s.f.)}$$

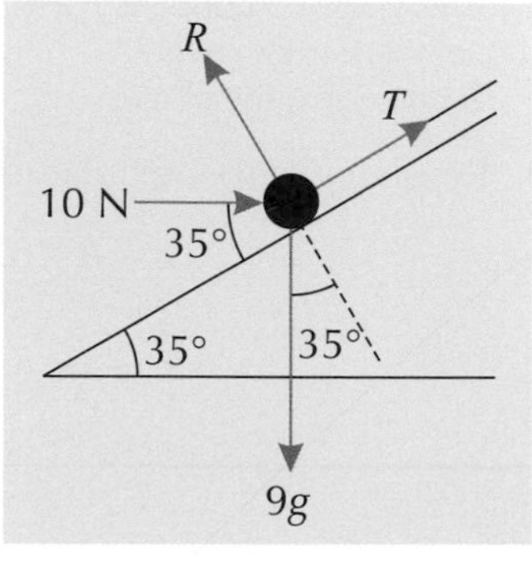

b) Find the magnitude of the tension in the string.

- Resolving parallel to the plane (↗):

$$T + 10\cos35° - 9g\sin35° = 0$$
$$T = 9g\sin35° - 10\cos35°$$
$$= 42.4 \text{ N (to 3 s.f.)}$$

Example 4

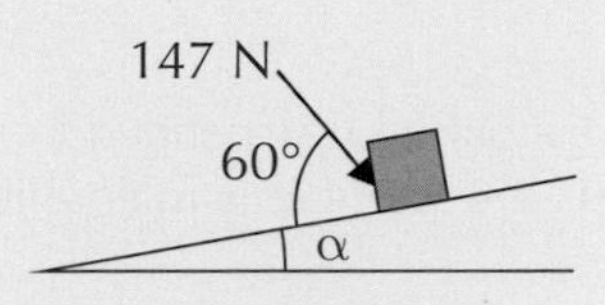

The diagram shows a block of mass 30 kg at rest on a smooth inclined plane. The plane is inclined at an angle α to the horizontal. The block is held in equilibrium by a force of 147 N, acting at an angle of 60° to the plane.

a) Show that $\sin\alpha = 0.25$.

- Draw a diagram showing all of the forces acting on the block:

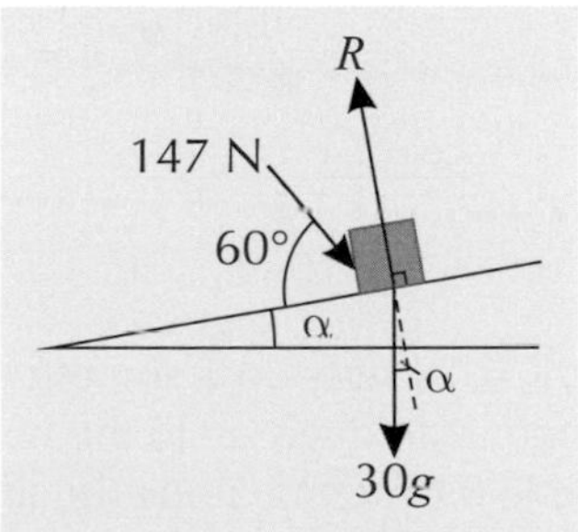

- Resolving parallel to the plane (↗):

$$147\cos60° - 30g\sin\alpha = 0$$
$$30g\sin\alpha = 147\cos60°$$
$$\sin\alpha = 147\cos60° \div 30g$$
$$= 0.25 \text{ as required}$$

Tip: This time you've got two different angles to deal with — make sure you use the correct one when resolving the different forces.

b) Find the normal reaction, R, of the plane on the block.

- First you need to find the value of α:

$$\alpha = \sin^{-1}(0.25) = 14.472...°$$

- Now resolving perpendicular to the plane (↖):

$$R - 147\sin60° - 30g\cos\alpha = 0$$
$$R = 147\sin60° + 30g\cos(14.472...°)$$
$$= 412 \text{ N (to 3 s.f.)}$$

Exercise 1.4

Q1 Each of the following diagrams shows a particle held in equilibrium by two light, inextensible strings. In each case, find the magnitude of the missing tension, T, and the mass of the particle, m.

Q1 Hint: Don't forget to include the weight of the particle.

a) b)

Q2 The diagram shows a particle suspended from two light, inextensible strings. The particle is in equilibrium.

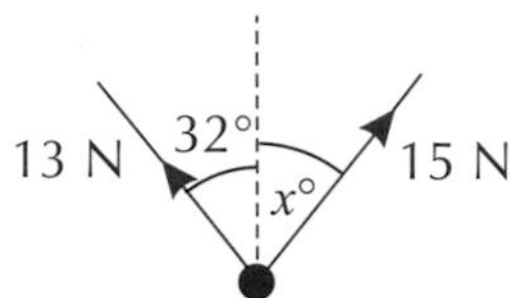

Find the weight of the particle, W, and the angle x.

Q3

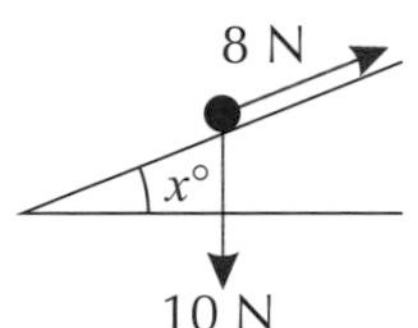

Q3 Hint: The 'line of greatest slope of the plane' just means straight down (or up) the slope of the plane.

A particle of weight 10 N rests on a smooth inclined plane. The plane is inclined at an angle $x°$ to the horizontal. A force of magnitude 8 N acting along the line of greatest slope of the plane holds the particle in equilibrium.

a) Calculate the size of the angle x.

b) Calculate the magnitude of the normal reaction force exerted by the plane on the particle.

Q4 Hint: Use the fact that cos45° = sin45°.

Q4 A particle rests on a smooth plane inclined at 45° to the horizontal. A force acting up the plane, parallel to the slope, holds the particle in equilibrium. The magnitude of the normal reaction force exerted by the plane on the particle is 25 N.

a) Find the magnitude of the force which holds the particle at rest.

b) Find the mass of the particle.

Q5

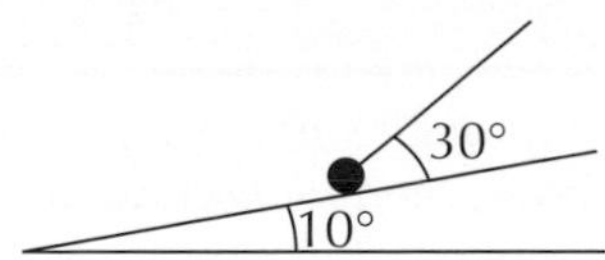

A particle with a mass of 5 kg rests on a smooth plane inclined at 10° to the horizontal, as shown. The particle is held in place by a light, inextensible string inclined at an angle of 30° to the plane.

a) Calculate the magnitude of the tension in the string.

b) Calculate the magnitude of the normal reaction of the plane on the particle.

Q6

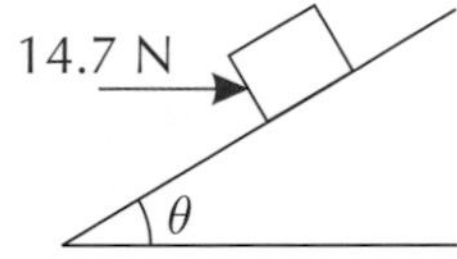

The diagram shows a 2 kg block held at rest on a smooth inclined plane by a horizontal force of 14.7 N.
The plane is inclined at an angle of θ to the horizontal.
Show that $\tan\theta = 0.75$

Q7 A particle of mass m is held at rest on a smooth plane inclined at 12° to the horizontal by a light, inextensible string. The string is inclined at 45° to the horizontal. The magnitude of the normal reaction force from the plane on the particle is 15 N. Find:

a) the magnitude of the tension, T, in the string,

b) the mass, m, of the particle in kg.

Q8 A particle is held in equilibrium on a smooth plane by a light, inextensible string. The plane is inclined at 50° to the horizontal and the string is inclined at 70° to the horizontal. The tension in the string has magnitude 5 N. A force, F, also acts on the particle, down the plane, parallel to the slope. Given that the magnitude of the normal reaction of the plane on the particle is four times the magnitude of F, find the weight of the particle.

2. Friction

Learning Objectives:

- Understand and use the relationship $F \le \mu R$.
- Understand the term 'limiting friction'.
- Use the formula for limiting friction to solve problems for a body in equilibrium.

If a body is in contact with a rough surface, and there is a force acting that could cause the body to move, then friction will act between the body and the surface to try and prevent motion. It comes up loads in M1 — pretty much any time you see the word 'rough', you know you're going to be dealing with it.

Friction

- If an object is in contact with a **rough** surface, then **friction** can act to try and **prevent it moving**.
- Friction will **only** act if there is a **force** acting on the object which could cause it to **move** along the surface.

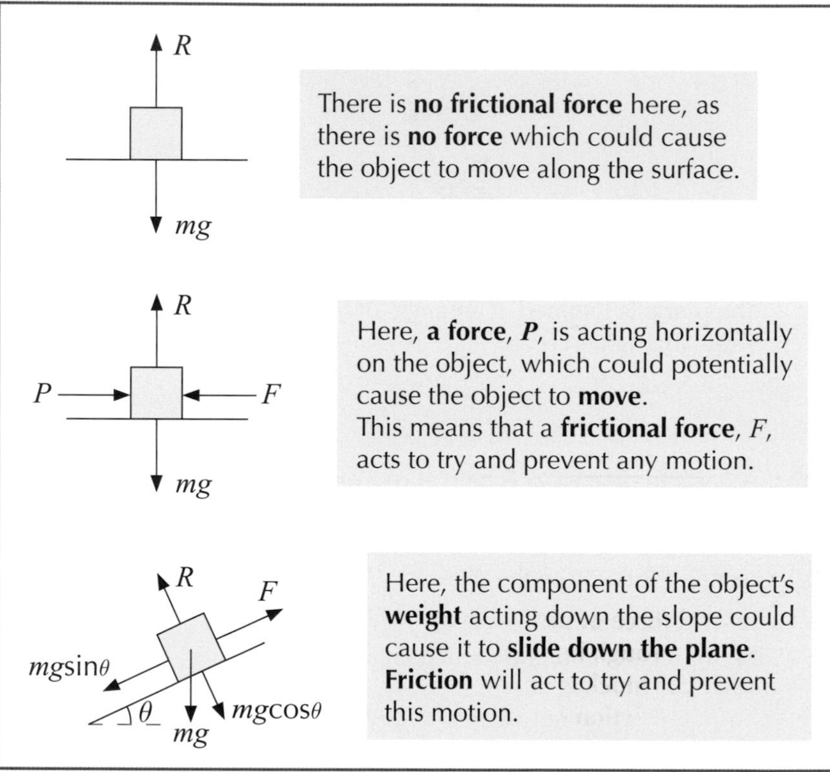

Tip: Remember — there will only be friction if the surface is rough. If the surface is smooth, no frictional force will act on the object.

- Friction always acts in the **opposite direction to motion** (or potential motion).
- The magnitude of the frictional force can take a **range of possible values**. As the magnitude of the force which is trying to move the object **increases**, the magnitude of the frictional force will **also increase**.
- Eventually, the frictional force will reach its **maximum possible value**. At this point, friction is **limiting**.
- If the force which is trying to move the object is **greater** than the maximum possible frictional force, the frictional force won't be large enough to prevent motion, and the object will **move**.
- The maximum possible magnitude of the frictional force depends on the **coefficient of friction**, μ, between the surface and the object.
- μ is a **number greater than or equal to 0**, and is a measure of the effect of friction between the object and the surface — the higher the number, the greater the effect of friction.

Tip: The magnitude of the frictional force will only be as big as is necessary to prevent motion.

- The frictional force, F, acting on an object is given by:

$$F \leq \mu R$$

where R is the **normal reaction** of the surface on the object.

- When the object starts to **move**, or is on the point of moving (i.e. friction is **limiting**), the frictional force takes its **maximum value**:

$$F_{max} = \mu R$$

Tip: An object which is on the point of moving is said to be in 'limiting equilibrium'. For friction problems involving a moving object, see pages 92-97.

Example 1

A horizontal force, P, acts on a particle Q, of mass 12 kg, which is at rest on a rough horizontal plane.
Find the range of values that the frictional force, F, can take, given that the coefficient of friction between the particle and the plane is 0.4.

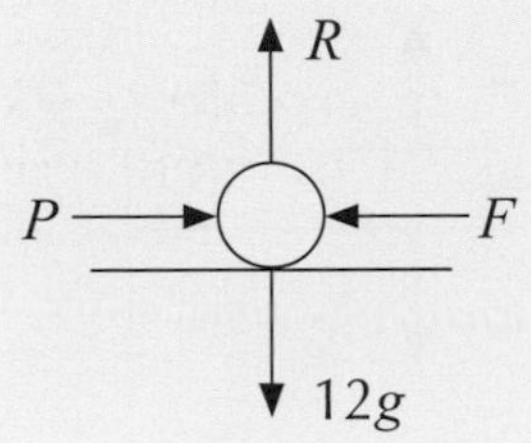

Resolving vertically (↑): $R = 12g$

This is just $R - 12g = 0$ rearranged.

So, using $F \leq \mu R$: $F \leq 0.4 \times 12g$

$F \leq 47.04$ N

Tip: So F can take any value up to 47.04 N, depending on the magnitude of P.
If $P \leq 47.04$ N, then the particle will remain at rest (and will be on the point of moving if $P = 47.04$ N).
If $P > 47.04$ N, then the particle will move and F will remain constant at 47.04 N.

Example 2

A horizontal force of 30 N acts on a 4 kg block which is at rest on a rough horizontal plane.
Given that the block is on the point of moving, find the coefficient of friction between the block and the plane.

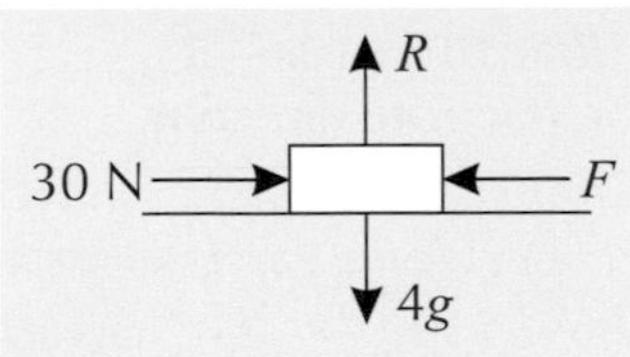

- Resolving horizontally: $F = 30$ N
- Resolving vertically: $R = 4g$
- The block is on the point of moving, so friction is limiting:

$$F = \mu R$$
$$30 = \mu \times 4g$$
$$\mu = 30 \div 4g$$
$$= 0.77 \text{ (to 2 d.p.)}$$

Tip: μ is usually given correct to 2 decimal places.

Example 3

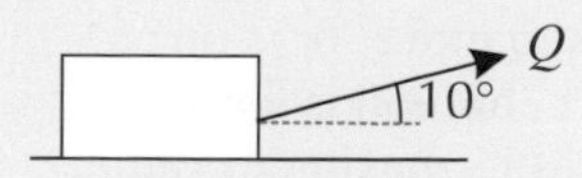

A box of mass 10 kg is on the point of slipping across a rough horizontal plane. A force, Q, acts on the box at an angle of 10° to the horizontal, as shown.

Given that the coefficient of friction between the box and the plane is 0.7, find the magnitude of Q.

- Draw a diagram to show all the forces acting on the box:

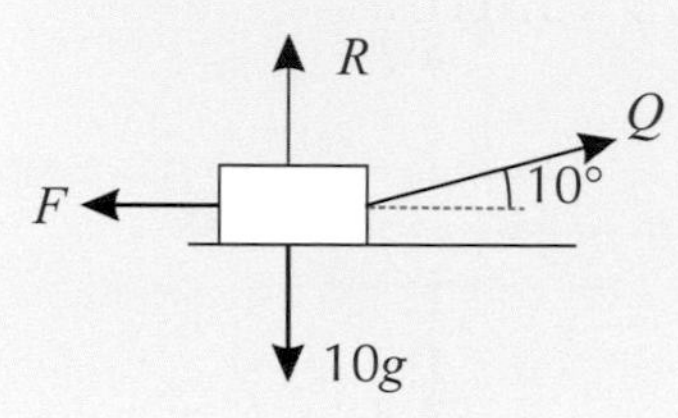

- Resolving vertically: $R + Q\sin 10° = 10g$

  $Q\sin 10° = 10g - R$ — call this equation ①

- Resolving horizontally: $Q\cos 10° = F$

  $Q\cos 10° = \mu R$

  $Q\cos 10° = 0.7R$ — call this equation ②

- Dividing equation ① by equation ②:

$$\frac{Q\sin 10°}{Q\cos 10°} = \frac{10g - R}{0.7R}$$

$$\tan 10° = \frac{10g - R}{0.7R}$$

$$0.7R\tan 10° = 10g - R$$

$$R = \frac{10g}{(1 + 0.7\tan 10°)}$$

$$= 87.232...$$

$$= 87.2 \text{ N (to 3 s.f.)}$$

- Substituting R into equation ②:

$$Q\cos 10° = 0.7 \times 87.232...$$

$$Q = 61.063... \div \cos 10°$$

$$= 62.0 \text{ N (to 3 s.f.)}$$

Tip: F always acts parallel to the surface, no matter what angle other forces act at.

Tip: You can assume that the box is about to slide horizontally in the direction of Q.

Tip: The box is on the point of sliding (i.e. in limiting equilibrium), so $F = \mu R$.

Example 4

A block of mass 3.2 kg lies at rest on a rough plane, inclined at an angle of θ to the horizontal. The block is on the point of sliding. Given that $\mu = 0.75$, find the value of θ.

- Draw a diagram.
- Resolving parallel to the plane:
  $F = 3.2g\sin\theta$
- Resolving perpendicular to the plane:
  $R = 3.2g\cos\theta$
- The block is on the point of moving, so, using $F = \mu R$:
  $3.2g\sin\theta = 0.75 \times 3.2g\cos\theta$
  $\frac{3.2g\sin\theta}{3.2g\cos\theta} = 0.75$
  $\tan\theta = 0.75$
  $\theta = 36.9°$ (to 3 s.f.)

Tip: Make sure you know in which direction friction is acting. Here, the block is on the point of sliding down the slope, because of its weight. Friction will therefore act up the slope, to oppose motion.

Example 5

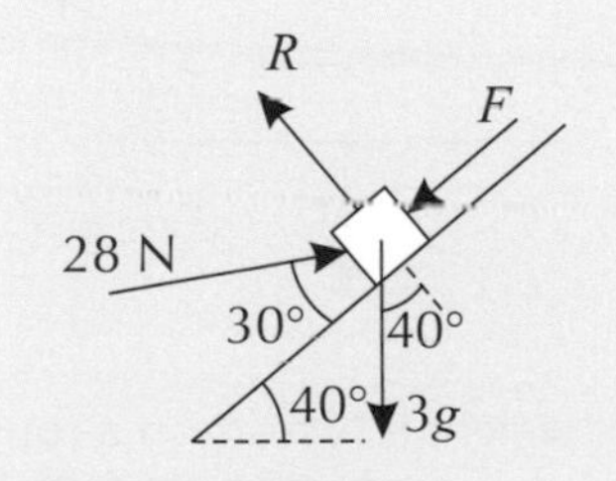

A block of mass 3 kg is on the point of sliding up a rough plane inclined at an angle of 40° to the horizontal.
A force of magnitude 28 N acts on the block, at an angle of 30° to the plane, as shown.
Find the coefficient of friction between the block and the plane.

- Resolving perpendicular to the plane:
  $R = 28\sin30° + 3g\cos40°$
- Resolving parallel to the plane:
  $28\cos30° = 3g\sin40° + F$
  $F = 28\cos30° - 3g\sin40°$
- Using $F = \mu R$:
  $28\cos30° - 3g\sin40° = \mu(28\sin30° + 3g\cos40°)$
  $\mu = (28\cos30° - 3g\sin40°) \div (28\sin30° + 3g\cos40°)$
  $= 0.15$ (to 2 d.p.)

Tip: In this example, the block is on the point of sliding up the plane, so friction acts down the plane.

Exercise 2.1

Q1 A particle of weight W rests on a rough horizontal surface with coefficient of friction μ. A horizontal force is applied to the particle such that the particle is on the point of slipping.

Find the magnitude of the frictional force, F, on the particle if:

a) $W = 5$ N, $\mu = 0.25$

b) $W = 8$ N, $\mu = 0.3$

c) $W = 15$ N, $\mu = 0.75$

Q2

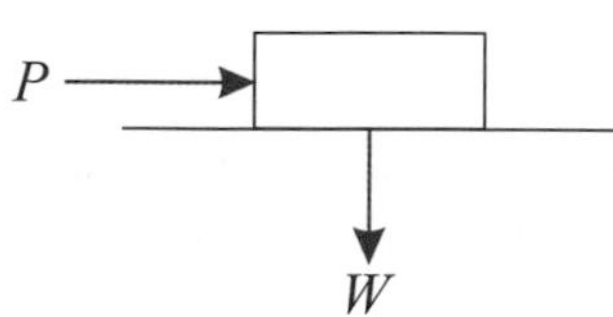

A particle of weight W is at rest on a rough horizontal surface. A horizontal force P acts on the particle. Given that the particle is on the point of moving, calculate the coefficient of friction if:

a) $W = 20$ N, $P = 5$ N b) $W = 15$ N, $P = 8$ N

Q3

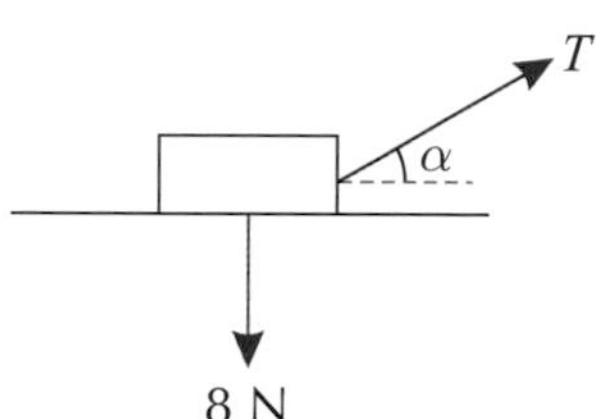

A pull-along toy of weight 8 N rests on a rough horizontal surface with coefficient of friction $\mu = 0.61$. A light, inextensible string is attached to the toy, at an angle of α to the horizontal, as shown.

Find the maximum possible tension in the string given that the toy remains stationary when:

a) $\alpha = 0°$ b) $\alpha = 35°$

Q3 Hint: You're looking for the tension in the string when the toy is on the point of sliding.

Q4

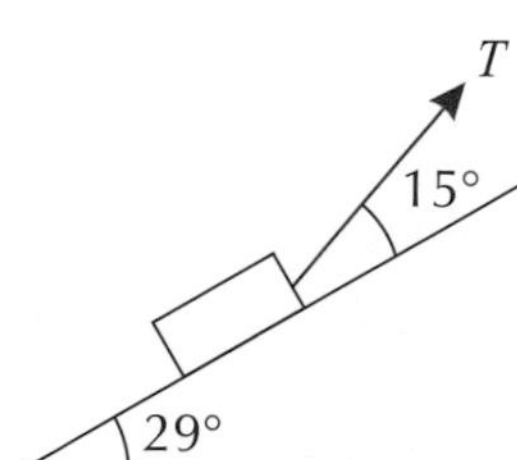

A sledge of mass 20 kg is at rest on a rough slope inclined at 29° to the horizontal. The coefficient of friction between the slope and the sledge is 0.1. A force, T, acts on the sledge at an angle of 15° to the slope, as shown.

Calculate the magnitude of T, given that this force is only just large enough to stop the sledge sliding down the slope.

Q4 Hint: Think carefully about which direction the frictional force will act in.

Q5 A particle of mass 12 kg is placed on a rough horizontal surface. A horizontal force of magnitude 50 N is applied to the particle. The coefficient of friction between the particle and the surface is 0.5.

a) Will the 50 N force cause the particle to move?

b) What is the maximum possible magnitude of force that can be applied horizontally to the particle, such that the particle will remain in equilibrium?

Q6

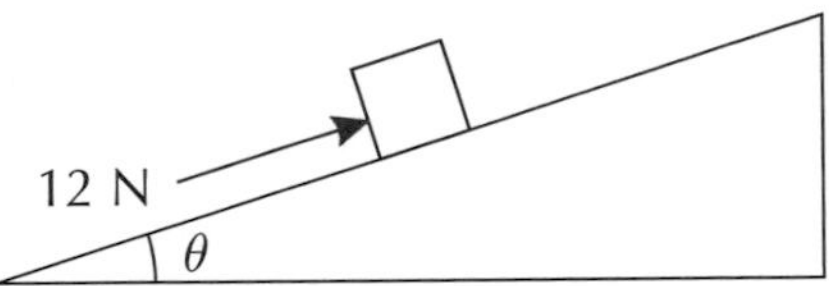

A box of mass 2 kg is at rest on a rough plane inclined at an angle of θ to the horizontal. A force of 12 N acts up the plane on the box, which is on the point of moving up the slope. Given that $\cos\theta = \frac{4}{5}$, find the coefficient of friction between the box and the plane.

Q6 Hint: To find $\sin\theta$ given $\cos\theta$, you can draw a right-angled triangle and use trigonometry and Pythagoras' theorem. Alternatively, you can use $\theta = \cos^{-1}(\frac{4}{5})$, as long as you don't round it.

Q7

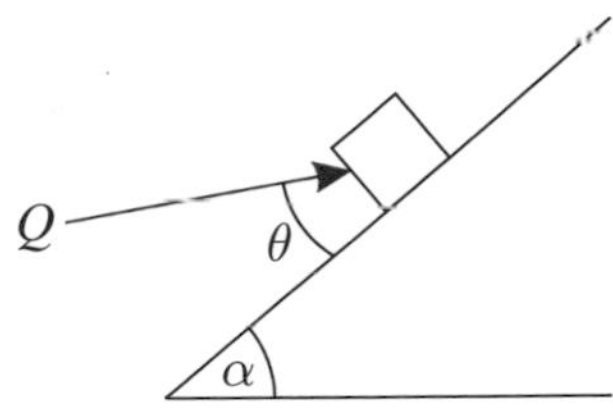

An object of weight W is at rest on a rough plane inclined at an angle α to the horizontal. A force, Q, is applied to the object at an angle of θ to the plane, as shown. Given that the object is on the point of sliding up the plane, find the coefficient of friction, μ, between the object and the plane when:

a) $\alpha = 30°$, $\theta = 0°$, $W = 8$ N and $Q = 10$ N

b) $\alpha = 25°$, $\theta = 30°$, $W = 6$ N and $Q = 5$ N

Q8

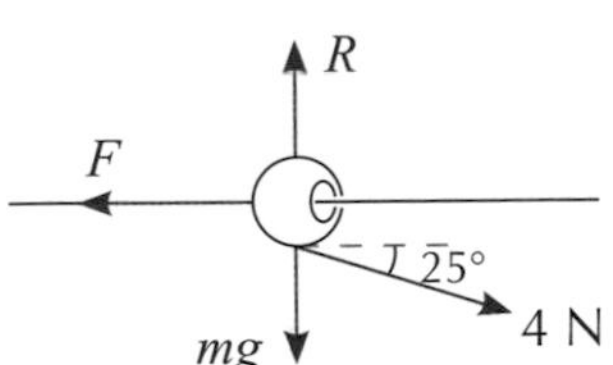

A horizontal wire is threaded through a bead of mass m kg. A force of magnitude 4 N is applied to the bead, at an angle of 25° to the horizontal, as shown. The bead is on the point of sliding along the wire. Given that the coefficient of friction between the wire and the bead is 0.15, find:

a) the magnitude of R, the normal reaction of the wire on the bead,

b) the value of m.

Q8 Hint: This question looks a bit different, but you just have to resolve forces horizontally and vertically as usual.

Q9 An object is placed on a rough plane inclined at an angle α to the horizontal. The coefficient of friction of the plane is μ. Show that the object will be at rest on the plane if $\tan\alpha \leq \mu$.

Review Exercise — Chapter 4

Q1 Find the magnitude and direction of the resultant force in each of the following:

a)

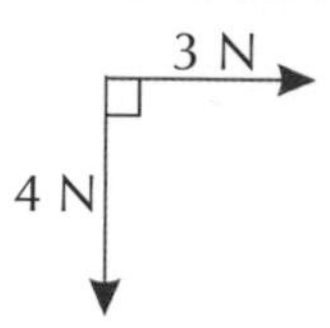

b)

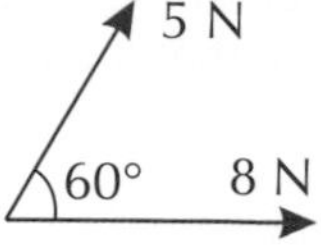

c)

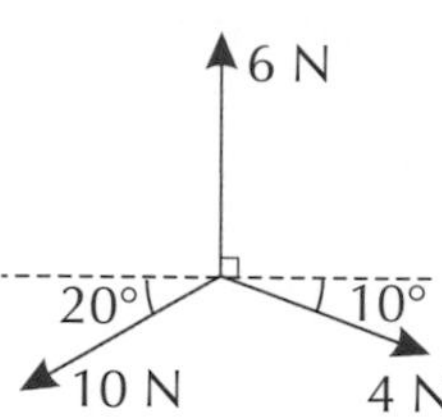

Q2 A force ($x\mathbf{i} + y\mathbf{j}$) N, acting in a direction which is parallel to the vector ($2\mathbf{i} + 7\mathbf{j}$) N, acts on a particle, P. Find the angle between the vector $\mathbf{j}$ and the force.

Q3

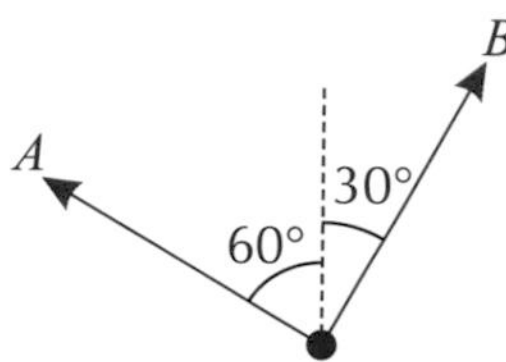

A particle of mass M kg is suspended in equilibrium by two light wires A and B, with angles 60° and 30° to the vertical, as shown. The tension in wire A is 20 N. Find:

a) the magnitude of the tension in wire B,

b) the value of M.

Q4

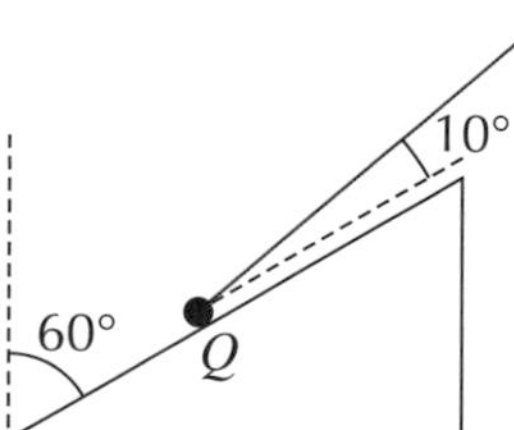

A particle, Q, of mass m kg, rests on a smooth plane which makes an angle of 60° to the vertical. It is held in equilibrium by a light, inextensible string angled at 10° to the plane, as shown. The magnitude of the tension in the string is 70 N.

Find the mass of Q and the normal reaction of the plane on Q.

Q5 The diagrams below show a particle on the point of slipping on a rough surface. Calculate the coefficient of friction, μ, between each particle and the surface shown.

a)

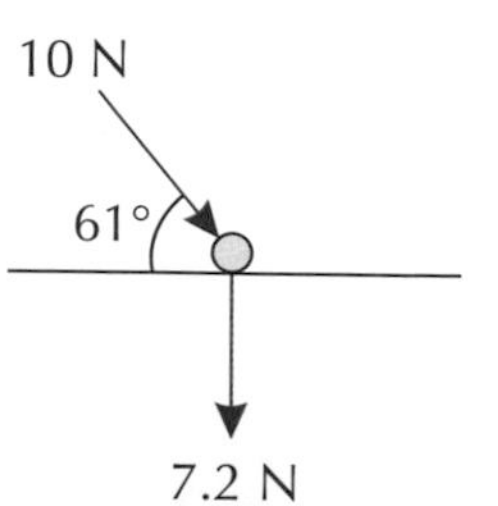

b)

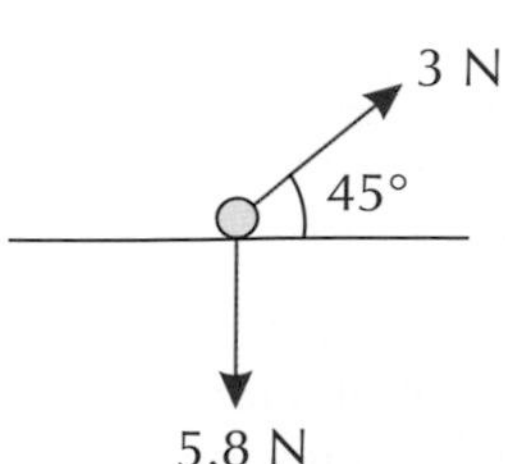

Exam-Style Questions — Chapter 4

1

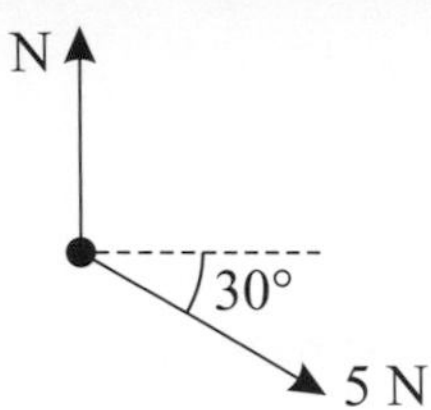

The diagram shows two forces acting on a particle.
Find the magnitude and direction of the resultant force.

(4 marks)

2 A box of mass 39 kg is at rest on a rough horizontal surface. A force of magnitude 140 N acts down on the box at an angle of 20° above the horizontal. The box remains stationary.

a) Draw a diagram to show the four forces acting on the box. *(2 marks)*

b) Calculate the magnitude of the normal reaction force and the frictional force on the box. *(4 marks)*

3 Two forces, $\mathbf{A} = (2\mathbf{i} - 11\mathbf{j})$ N and $\mathbf{B} = (7\mathbf{i} + 5\mathbf{j})$ N, act on a particle. Find:

a) the resultant of **A** and **B**, *(2 marks)*

b) the magnitude of the resultant force. *(2 marks)*

4 A force of magnitude 7 N acts horizontally on a particle. Another force, of magnitude 4 N, acts on the particle at an angle of 30° to the horizontal force. The resultant of the two forces has magnitude R and acts at an angle α above the horizontal. Find:

a) the force R, *(3 marks)*

b) the angle α. *(2 marks)*

5

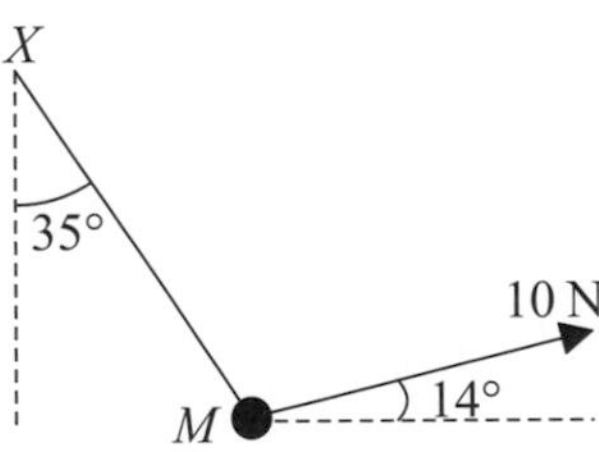

A particle, M, is attached to the end of a light, inextensible rod fixed at point X.
A force of magnitude 10 N is applied to M at an angle of 14° to the horizontal.
M is held in equilibrium such that the rod makes an angle of 35° to the vertical, as shown.

Find the mass of M.

(4 marks)

6 Three forces of magnitudes 15 N, 12 N and W act on a particle, as shown.
Given that the particle is in equilibrium, find:

15 N θ 12 N W

a) the value of θ, *(2 marks)*

b) the magnitude of force W. *(2 marks)*

The force W is now removed.

c) State the magnitude and direction of the resultant of the two remaining forces. *(2 marks)*

7 A sledge is held at rest on a smooth slope which makes an angle of 25° with the horizontal. The rope holding the sledge is at an angle of 20° above the slope. The normal reaction acting on the sledge due to contact with the surface is 80 N. Find:

a) the tension, T, in the rope, *(3 marks)*

b) the weight of the sledge. *(2 marks)*

8

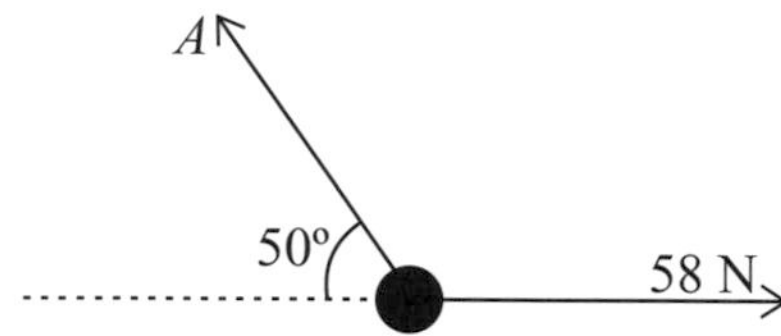

A particle of mass m kg is held in equilibrium by two light, inextensible strings. One string is attached at an angle of 50° to the horizontal, as shown, and has tension A. The other string is horizontal and has tension 58 N. Find:

a) the magnitude of A, *(2 marks)*

b) the mass, m, of the particle. *(2 marks)*

9

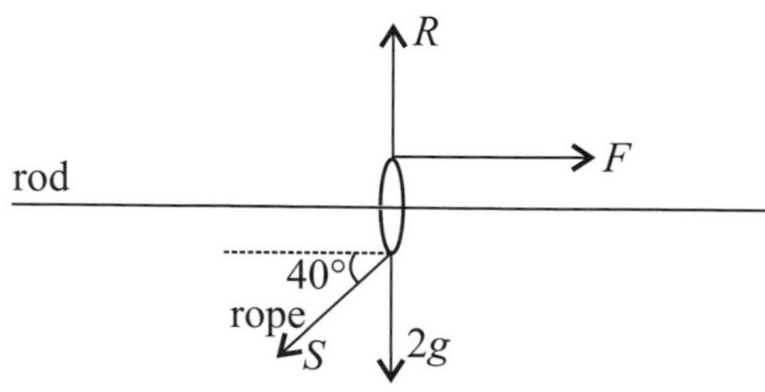

A 2 kg ring threaded on a rough horizontal rod is pulled by a rope with tension S and attached at 40° to the horizontal, as shown. The normal reaction of the rod on the ring is R and frictional force between the rod and the ring is F. The coefficient of friction between the rod and the ring is 0.3. Given that the ring is about to slide, find the magnitude of S.

(4 marks)

Chapter 5 Dynamics

1. Newton's Laws of Motion

In this section, you'll look at how the forces acting on a particle affect its motion, and whether or not they will cause the particle to accelerate.

Learning Objectives:

- Know and understand Newton's three laws of motion.
- Be able to apply Newton's laws of motion to simple constant acceleration problems (where acceleration may be a vector in **i** and **j** notation).
- Be able to solve problems involving friction when a particle is moving.

Newton's laws of motion

- **Newton's first law:**

A body will stay at **rest** or maintain a **constant velocity** unless a **resultant force** acts on the body.

- So if the forces acting on something are perfectly **balanced**, then it **won't accelerate**.
- If it's stationary, it'll **stay stationary** and if it's moving in a straight line with constant speed, it'll carry on moving in the **same straight line** with the same **constant speed**.

- **Newton's second law:**

The **overall resultant force** (F_{net}) acting on a body is equal to the **mass** of the body multiplied by the body's **acceleration**.

- So if the forces acting on a body **aren't** perfectly **balanced**, then the body will **accelerate** in the **direction** of the resultant force.
- The magnitude of the acceleration will be proportional to the magnitude of F_{net}.
- A body's mass, its acceleration and the resultant force acting on it are related by the following formula, sometimes called the **equation of motion**:

$$F_{net} = ma$$

Tip: $F_{net} = ma$ is often written as $F = ma$, but the F always means resultant force.

Tip: The formula for weight ($W = mg$) is derived from Newton's second law, where g is acceleration due to gravity.

- **Newton's third law:**

For **two bodies** in contact with each other, the force each applies to the **other** is **equal in magnitude** but **opposite in direction**.

- So for a particle sat on a horizontal surface, there is a force acting vertically **upwards** on the particle which has the **same magnitude** as the particle's **weight** (the weight acts vertically **downwards**).
- This is called the **reaction force**, and is normally labelled R.
- Newton's third law also applies to two **colliding particles** or a particle colliding with a **surface** (see page 122).

Tip: Newton's third law is often stated as: "Every action has an equal and opposite reaction".

Using Newton's laws

Newton's laws are a lot easier to understand once you start **using them**. If you're doing calculations, you'll probably use the second law ($F_{net} = ma$) more than the other two.

Example 1

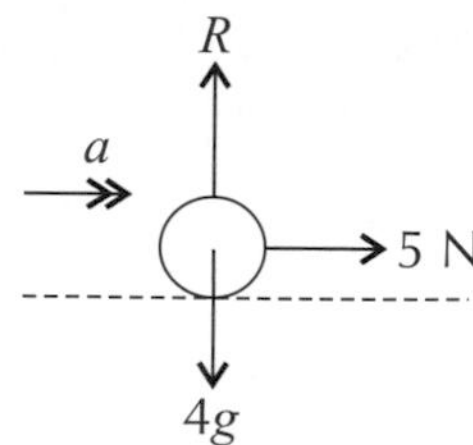

A mass of 4 kg, initially at rest on a smooth horizontal plane, is acted on by a horizontal force of 5 N. Find the magnitude of the acceleration of the mass and the normal reaction from the plane, *R*.

- Resolving forces horizontally (→), $F_{net} = 5$
  So use Newton's second law to find the acceleration, a:
  $$F_{net} = ma$$
  $$5 = 4a$$
  $$a = 1.25 \text{ ms}^{-2}$$

- Resolving forces vertically (↑), $F_{net} = R - 4g$
  There is no acceleration vertically, so using Newton's second law:
  $$F_{net} = ma$$
  $$R - 4g = 4 \times 0$$
  $$R = 4g$$
  $$= 39.2 \text{ N}$$

Tip: It's best to only resolve forces either in the direction of the acceleration, or perpendicular to it.

Tip: Remember — unless a question tells you otherwise, take $g = 9.8 \text{ ms}^{-2}$.

Example 2

A particle of mass 12 kg is attached to the end of a light, vertical string. The particle is accelerating vertically downwards at a rate of 7 ms^{-2}.

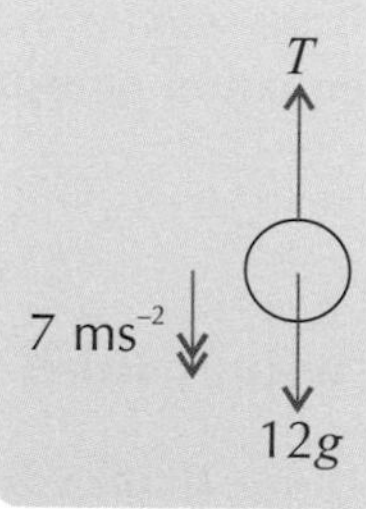

a) Find *T*, the tension in the string.

- Resolving vertically (↓):
  $$F_{net} = ma$$
  $$12g - T = 12 \times 7$$
  $$T = 12g - 84$$
  $$= 33.6 \text{ N}$$

b) Find the resultant force acting horizontally on the particle.

The particle is not accelerating horizontally, so from Newton's first law, there is no resultant force acting horizontally on the particle.

Tip: When you're resolving, draw an arrow to show which direction you're taking as positive.

Tip: You don't have to work out the resultant force separately before using $F = ma$. You can do the whole thing in one 'resolving' step.

Example 3

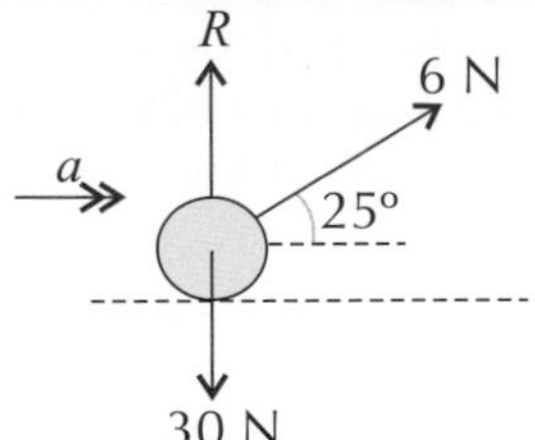

A particle of weight 30 N is being accelerated across a smooth horizontal plane by a force of 6 N acting at an angle of 25° to the horizontal, as shown. Given that the particle starts from rest, find its speed after 4 s.

- Resolving forces horizontally (→), $F_{net} = 6\cos 25°$
  Using Newton's second law to find the acceleration, a:
  $$F_{net} = ma$$
  $$6\cos 25° = \frac{30}{g}a$$
  $$a = 1.776...\ \text{ms}^{-2}$$
- Use one of the constant acceleration equations to find the speed:
  $u = 0,\quad v = v,\quad a = 1.776...,\quad t = 4$
  $$v = u + at$$
  $$= 0 + 1.776... \times 4$$
  $$= 7.11\ \text{ms}^{-1}\ \text{(to 3 s.f.)}$$

Tip: It always helps to draw a diagram showing the forces acting on a body and the direction of acceleration.

Tip: The constant acceleration equations are covered in Chapter 2.

Example 4

A particle of mass m kg is acted upon by two forces, (8i – j) N and (4i + 6j) N, resulting in an acceleration of magnitude 8 ms^{-2}.

a) Find the value of m.

- Resultant force, $\mathbf{R} = (8\mathbf{i} - \mathbf{j}) + (4\mathbf{i} + 6\mathbf{j}) = (12\mathbf{i} + 5\mathbf{j})$ N
  Magnitude of $\mathbf{R} = |\mathbf{R}| = \sqrt{12^2 + 5^2} = \sqrt{169} = 13$ N
- Now use Newton's second law to find m:
  $$F_{net} = ma$$
  $$13 = 8m$$
  $$m = 1.63\ \text{kg (to 3 s.f.)}$$

b) A third force of (pi + qj) N is applied to the particle and the particle now moves with acceleration (14i – 16j) ms^{-2}. Find p and q.

- Use Newton's second law to find the new resultant force acting on the particle:
  $$\mathbf{F} = m\mathbf{a}$$
  $$= 1.625(14\mathbf{i} - 16\mathbf{j}) = (22.75\mathbf{i} - 26\mathbf{j})\ \text{N}$$
- Finally subtract the two original forces from **F**, to find p and q.
  $$\mathbf{F} - (8\mathbf{i} - \mathbf{j}) - (4\mathbf{i} + 6\mathbf{j}) = (10.75\mathbf{i} - 31\mathbf{j})\ \text{N}$$
  So, $p = 10.8$ (to 3 s.f.) and $q = -31$.

Tip: You can still use Newton's second law when the force and acceleration are in vector form. Just write the formula as $\mathbf{F} = m\mathbf{a}$.

Exercise 1.1

Q1 A particle with mass 15 kg is accelerating at 4 ms^{-2}.
Find the magnitude of the resultant force acting on the particle.

Q2 A block of mass 5 kg is acted on by a resultant force of 10 N. Find:

a) the acceleration of the block,

b) the speed of the block after 8 s (given that it starts from rest).

Q3 A particle of mass 18 kg is attached to the end of a light, vertical string. Given that the particle is accelerating vertically upwards at 0.4 ms^{-2}, find T, the tension in the string.

Q4 A model car, initially at rest on a horizontal plane, is acted on by a resultant horizontal force of magnitude 18 N, causing it to accelerate at 5 ms^{-2}. Find:

a) the mass of the model car,

b) the car's speed after 4 seconds,

c) the magnitude of the normal reaction from the plane.

Q5

R

10 N

a

45°

$3g$

Q5 Hint: The normal reaction force always acts perpendicular to the surface.

A particle of mass 3 kg is being accelerated across a horizontal plane by a force of 10 N acting at an angle of 45° to the horizontal, as shown above. Find the magnitude of:

a) the acceleration of the particle,

b) the normal reaction with the plane.

Q6

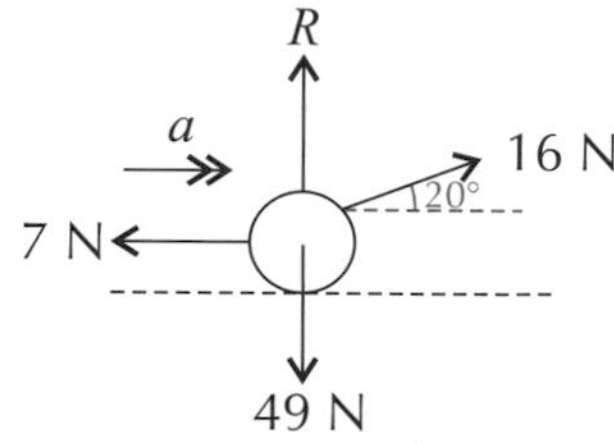

A particle of weight 49 N initially at rest on a horizontal plane is acted on by a constant horizontal resistive force of 7 N and a force of 16 N acting at an angle of 20° to the horizontal, as shown. Find:

a) the acceleration of the particle,

b) the speed of the particle after 7 seconds,

c) the magnitude of the normal reaction with the plane.

Q7 A sack of flour of mass 55 kg is attached to the end of a light vertical rope. The sack starts from rest and accelerates vertically upwards at a constant rate so that after 4 seconds it is moving with speed 2.5 ms^{-1}.

a) Find the magnitude of the acceleration of the sack of flour.

b) Assuming that the sack experiences a non-gravitational constant resistance to motion of magnitude 120 N, find the tension in the rope.

Q8 A stone of mass 300 g is dropped from the top of a mine shaft and falls vertically down the shaft. It hits the bottom 12 seconds after being released from rest. Assuming that the stone experiences a constant resistance of 1.5 N, find the depth of the mine shaft.

Q8 Hint: Use Newton's second law to find the acceleration of the stone first.

Q9 A particle of mass 10 kg is acted on by two forces, $(5\mathbf{i} + 2\mathbf{j})$ N and $(3\mathbf{i} - 4\mathbf{j})$ N.

a) Find the acceleration of the particle in vector form.

b) Find the magnitude of the acceleration.

c) Assuming that the particle is initially at rest, find the speed of the particle after 6 seconds have elapsed.

Q10 Two constant forces are acting on a body of mass 2 kg. 10 seconds after starting to accelerate from rest, the velocity of the body is given by $(30\mathbf{i} + 20\mathbf{j})$ ms^{-1}.

a) Calculate the resultant force acting on the body. Give your answer in vector form.

b) If one of the forces is given by $(10\mathbf{i} - 3\mathbf{j})$ N, what is the magnitude of the other force?

Q11 A particle of mass m kg is acted on by two forces, $(6\mathbf{i} + 3\mathbf{j})$ N and $(2\mathbf{i} + 3\mathbf{j})$ N. Given that the particle is initially at rest and accelerates to a speed of 6ms^{-1} in 2 seconds, find the value of m.

Q12 A particle of mass 5 kg is acted on by two forces, $(6\mathbf{i} - 10\mathbf{j})$ N and $(4\mathbf{i} + 5\mathbf{j})$ N.

a) Find the magnitude of the acceleration of the particle.

b) A third force, of $(-6\mathbf{i} + 2\mathbf{j})$ N, begins to act on the particle.
Describe the effect this has on the magnitude of the acceleration of the particle.

Q13 Three forces are acting on a particle of mass m kg.

a) Two of the forces are given by $(6\mathbf{i} - 2\mathbf{j})$ N and $(5\mathbf{i} + 5\mathbf{j})$ N and the resultant force is $(7\mathbf{i} + \mathbf{j})$ N. Find the third force in vector form.

b) Given that the particle accelerates from 2 ms^{-1} to 6 ms^{-1} in 8s, find the mass of the particle.

c) A fourth force, of $(-7\mathbf{i} - \mathbf{j})$ N, begins to act on the particle. Describe the effect this has on the particle's motion.

Friction and inclined planes

Inclined planes

- For objects moving up or down an inclined plane, resolve forces **parallel** and **perpendicular** to the plane, rather than horizontally and vertically.
- Remember that weight always acts **vertically downwards**, so you need to find the **components** of the weight parallel and perpendicular to the plane.

Example

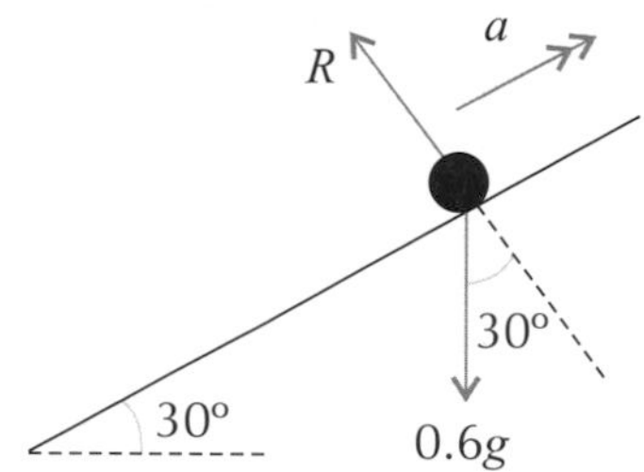

A particle of mass 600 g is propelled up the line of greatest slope of a smooth plane inclined at 30° to the horizontal. Immediately after the propelling force has stopped, the particle has speed 3 ms^{-1}. Find:

a) the distance the particle travels before coming instantaneously to rest,

- First, resolve parallel to the plane (↗) to find a:

$$F_{net} = ma$$
$$-0.6g\sin 30° = 0.6a$$
$$a = -4.9 \text{ ms}^{-2}$$

- Next, use one of the constant acceleration equations:

$$v^2 = u^2 + 2as$$
$$0 = 3^2 + 2(-4.9)s$$
$$s = 0.918 \text{ m (3 s.f.)}$$

b) the magnitude of the normal reaction from the plane.

- Now resolve perpendicular to the plane (↖):

$$F_{net} = ma$$
$$R - 0.6g\cos 30° = 0.6 \times 0$$
$$R = 5.09 \text{ N (3 s.f.)}$$

Tip: Remember — the normal reaction force is always perpendicular to the surface.

Tip: The particle is slowing down, so its acceleration is negative (i.e. it's decelerating).

Tip: The particle is moving parallel to the plane, so the acceleration perpendicular to the plane is zero.

Frictional forces

- You've already covered friction in Chapter 4, but back then you were only concerned with objects which were being held in **equilibrium**.
- When a **moving** object is acted on by a frictional force, friction is **limiting**, and the frictional force (F) is at its maximum value: $F = \mu R$. (Where μ is the coefficient of friction and R is the normal reaction between the object and the surface.)
- Friction **opposes** motion, so it will always act in the **opposite direction** to the direction an object is moving in.
- You'll need to use Newton's laws and $F = \mu R$ to solve problems involving objects which are accelerating and being acted on by friction.

Example 1

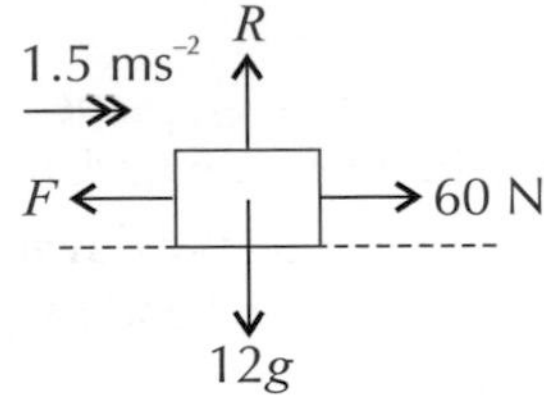

A block of mass 12 kg is being accelerated across a rough, horizontal plane by a force of magnitude 60 N, as shown above.
Given that the magnitude of the acceleration is 1.5 ms^{-2}, find the coefficient of friction between the block and the plane.

- First, resolve forces horizontally (→), to find the frictional force, F:

$$F_{net} = ma$$
$$60 - F = 12 \times 1.5$$
$$F = 42 \text{ N}$$

- Next, resolve forces vertically (↑) to find the normal reaction, R:

$$F_{net} = ma$$
$$R - 12g = 12 \times 0$$
$$R = 12g$$
$$= 117.6 \text{ N}$$

- The block is moving, so F takes its maximum possible value:

$$F = \mu R$$
$$42 = \mu \times 117.6$$
$$\mu = 0.36 \text{ (2 d.p.)}$$

Tip: Don't get confused between F and F_{net}. F is the frictional force and F_{net} is the overall resultant force.

Example 2

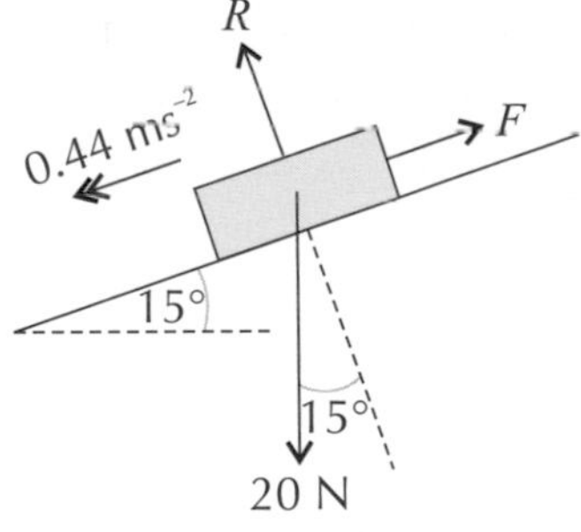

A small body of weight 20 N is released from rest on a rough plane angled at 15° to the horizontal. Given that the body accelerates down the plane at a rate of 0.44 ms^{-2}, find the coefficient of friction between the body and the plane.

- Resolve parallel to the plane (↙):

$$F_{net} = ma$$
$$20\sin 15° - F = \frac{20}{g} \times 0.44$$
$$F = 4.278... \text{ N}$$

Tip: The body is accelerating down the plane, so the frictional force acts up the slope.

- Resolve perpendicular to the plane (↖):

$$F_{net} = ma$$

$$R - 20\cos 15° = \frac{20}{g} \times 0$$

$$R = 20\cos 15° = 19.318... \text{ N}$$

- It's sliding, so:

$$F = \mu R$$

$$4.278... = \mu \times 19.318...$$

$$\mu = 0.22 \text{ (to 2 d.p.)}$$

Example 3

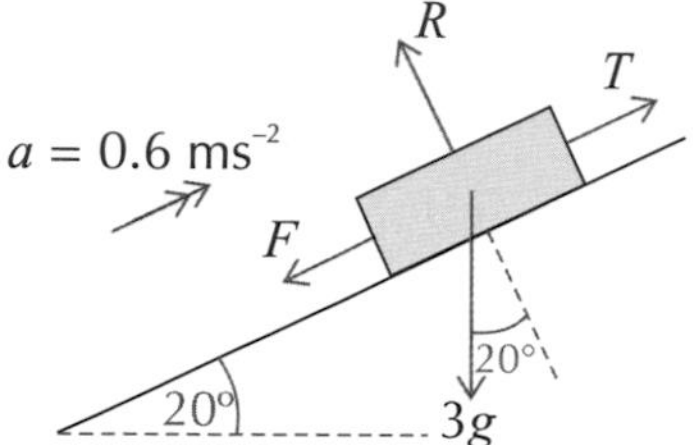

A mass of 3 kg is being pulled up a plane inclined at 20° to the horizontal by a rope parallel to the surface. Given that the mass is accelerating at 0.6 ms^{-2} and the coefficient of friction between the block and the plane is 0.4, find *T*, the tension in the rope.

- Resolve perpendicular to the plane (↖):

$$F_{net} = ma$$

$$R - 3g\cos 20° = 3 \times 0$$

$$R = 3g\cos 20°$$

$$= 27.626... \text{ N}$$

- The mass is sliding, so $F = \mu R$:

$$F = 0.4 \times 27.626...$$

$$= 11.050... \text{ N}$$

- Resolve parallel to the plane (↗):

$$F_{net} = ma$$

$$T - F - 3g\sin 20° = 3 \times 0.6$$

$$T = 1.8 + 11.050... + 3g\sin 20°$$

$$= 22.9 \text{ N (3 s.f.)}$$

Example 4

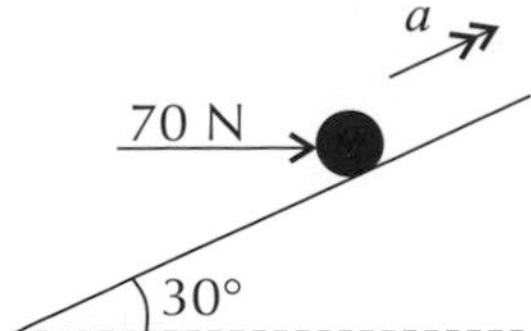

A particle of mass 5 kg is being accelerated up the line of greatest slope of a rough plane by a force of magnitude 70 N which acts horizontally.

The plane is inclined to the horizontal at an angle of 30°, as shown. The coefficient of friction between the particle and the plane is 0.4.

a) Draw a diagram showing all the forces acting on the particle.

- The frictional force, F, always acts to oppose motion, so it will act down the plane.
- The weight of the particle acts vertically downwards.
- The normal reaction force, R, acts perpendicular to the plane.

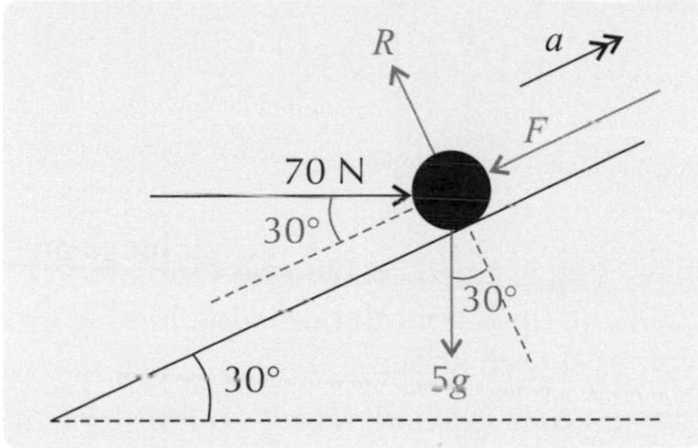

b) Find the magnitude of the particle's acceleration.

- Resolve perpendicular to the plane (↖):

$$R - 5g\cos30° - 70\sin30° = 5 \times 0$$

$$R = 5g\cos30° + 70\sin30°$$

$$= 77.435... \text{ N}$$

- The particle is moving, so:

$$F = \mu R$$

$$F = 0.4 \times 77.435...$$

$$= 30.974... \text{ N}$$

- Resolve parallel to the plane (↗):

$$F_{net} = ma$$

$$70\cos30° - 5g\sin30° - F = 5a$$

$$70\cos30° - 2.5g - 30.974... = 5a$$

$$5a = 5.147...$$

$$a = 1.03 \text{ ms}^{-2} \text{ (3 s.f.)}$$

Tip: The 70 N force acts horizontally, so you need to find the components parallel and perpendicular to the plane.

Exercise 1.2

Q1

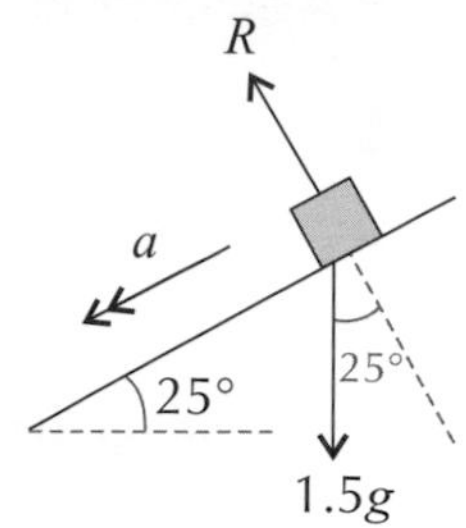

Q1 Hint: If a surface is smooth, it means there's no frictional force.

A wooden block of mass 1.5 kg is placed on a smooth plane which is inclined at 25° to the horizontal, as shown above. The block is released from rest and begins to accelerate down the slope.

a) What is the magnitude of the block's acceleration?

b) Assuming that the block's acceleration is constant, find the speed of the block 3 seconds after it is released.

Q2

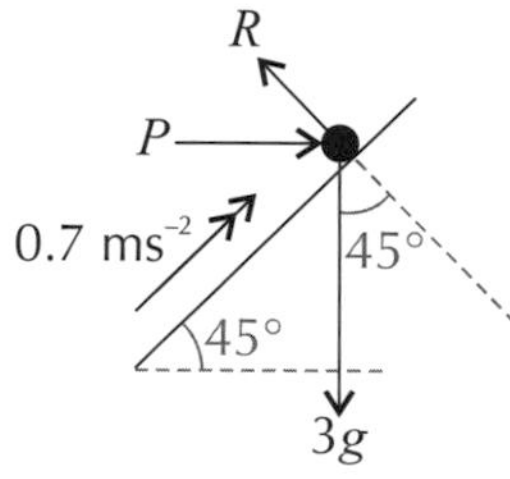

A particle of mass 3 kg is acted on by a horizontal force, P, which causes it to accelerate up a smooth plane inclined at an angle of 45° to the horizontal, as shown above.

a) Given that the particle is accelerating up the slope at a rate of 0.7 ms^{-2}, find the magnitude of the force P.

b) When the particle is travelling at a speed of 2 ms^{-1}, force P is removed. Find the time taken for the particle to come to rest.

Q2 b) Hint: When force P is removed, the particle will stop accelerating and begin to decelerate.

Q3 A horizontal force of magnitude 26 N is acting on a box of mass 4 kg, causing the box to accelerate across a rough, horizontal plane at a rate of 1.2 ms^{-2}.

a) Draw a labelled diagram to show the forces acting on the box.

b) Calculate the normal reaction, R, of the plane on the box.

c) Use Newton's second law to find the magnitude of the frictional force acting on the box.

d) Given that the box is accelerating, what can you say about the frictional force acting on the box?

e) Find the coefficient of friction, μ, between the box and the plane.

Q4 A box of mass 7 kg is accelerated across a rough horizontal plane by a horizontal force, P. The coefficient of friction, μ, between the box and the plane is 0.2 and the box accelerates at a rate of 0.8 ms^{-2}.

a) Draw a labelled diagram to show the forces acting on the box.

b) Calculate the normal reaction, R, of the plane on the box.

c) Calculate the magnitude of P.

Q5 A taut rope is pulling a block up a rough inclined plane angled at 40° to the horizontal. The rope is parallel to the plane.
The coefficient of friction between the block and the surface is 0.35 and the tension in the rope is 70 N.

a) Draw a diagram to show the forces acting on the block.
b) Given that the block is accelerating at a rate of 3.2 ms^{-2}, find the mass of the block.

Q5 Hint: Taut means that the rope is tight and straight, and has tension in it.

Q6

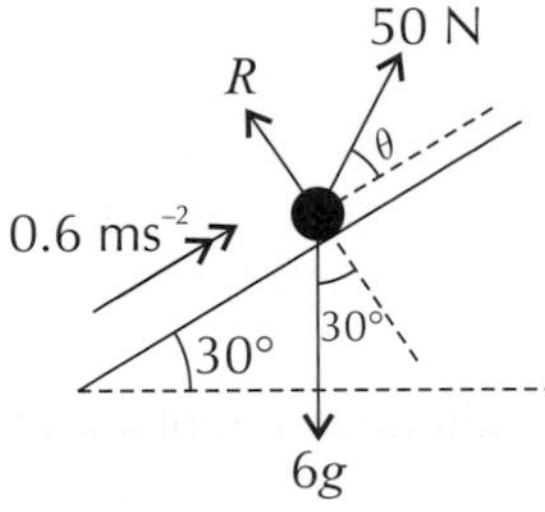

A particle of mass 6 kg is being pulled up a smooth plane inclined at an angle of 30° to the horizontal. The tension in the rope pulling the particle up the slope is 50 N and is at an angle θ above the plane, as shown above. Given that the particle is accelerating at a rate of 0.6 ms^{-2}, find θ.

Q7 A block of mass 1 kg is sliding down a rough plane of length 2 m, which is inclined at an angle of 50° to the horizontal.
The coefficient of friction between the block and the surface is 0.4.

a) Draw a diagram to show the forces acting on the block.
b) If the block is released from rest at the top of the plane, find how long it will take to reach the bottom of the plane.

Q8

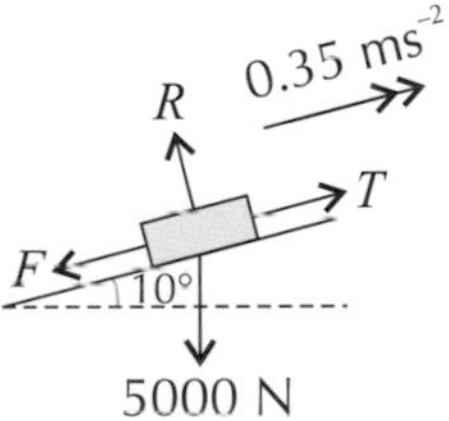

A rock weighing 5000 N is being pulled up a rough inclined plane which is at an angle of 10° to the horizontal, as shown.
The coefficient of friction between the rock and the plane is 0.1.
The rock is accelerating up the plane at a rate of 0.35 ms^{-2}.
Find T, the tension in the rope pulling the rock.

Q9 A package of mass 9 kg is moving up the line of greatest slope of a rough plane inclined at an angle of 22° to the horizontal.
The package is being pushed up the slope by a force of magnitude 110 N acting horizontally.

a) Draw a diagram showing all the forces acting on the package.
b) Given that the package is accelerating up the slope at a rate of 1.3 ms^{-2}, find μ, the coefficient of friction between the package and the plane.

Q9 Hint: Remember to split the horizontal force into components parallel and perpendicular to the slope.

2. Connected Particles

Learning Objectives:

- Be able to solve simple problems involving two connected particles moving in a straight line under a constant force.
- Be able to solve problems involving a smooth peg or pulley and two connected particles moving under gravity.
- Be able to solve connected particle problems where the forces involved change from one value to another (e.g. when the connection is severed).
- Be able to solve problems involving connected particles moving directly up or down a rough or smooth slope.

In this section you'll see how to apply Newton's laws to particles which are joined together and moving on a plane, or hanging either side of a pulley.

Connected particles

In situations where you have two (or more) particles **joined together**, you can still consider their motion **individually** and resolve the forces acting on each particle separately.

However, if the connection between the particles is **light**, **inextensible** and remains **taut**, and the particles are moving in the **same straight line**, they can also be considered to be moving as **one particle** with the **same acceleration**.

Example 1

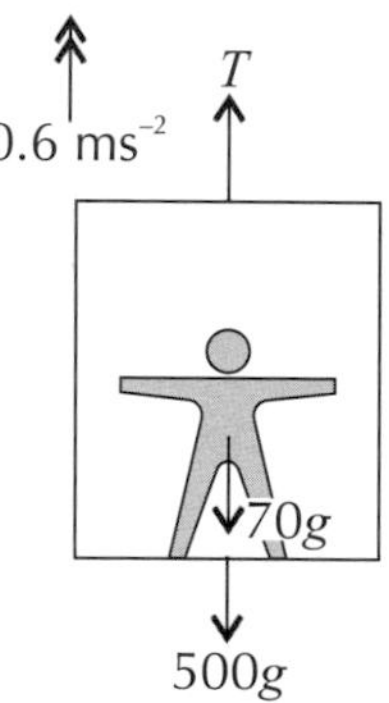

A person of mass 70 kg is standing in a lift of mass 500 kg. The lift is attached to a vertical light, inextensible cable, as shown. By modelling the person as a particle, and given that the lift is accelerating vertically upwards at a rate of 0.6 ms^{-2}, find:

a) T, the tension in the cable,

- Resolving vertically (↑) for the whole system:

$$F_{net} = ma$$
$$T - 570g = 570 \times 0.6$$
$$T = (570 \times 0.6) + (570 \times 9.8)$$
$$= 5928 \text{ N}$$

Tip: For part a), you can treat the whole system as one particle of mass (500 + 70) = 570 kg, because the whole system is accelerating together.

b) the force exerted on the person by the floor of the lift.

- Sketch a diagram showing the forces acting on the person:

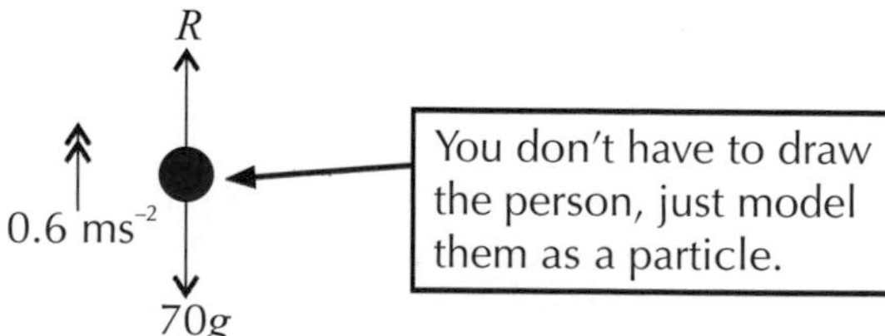

- Resolving vertically (↑) for the person in the lift:

$$F_{net} = ma$$
$$R - 70g = 70 \times 0.6$$
$$R = 42 + 70g$$
$$= 728 \text{ N}$$

Tip: In part b), you need to consider the person as a separate object.

Example 2

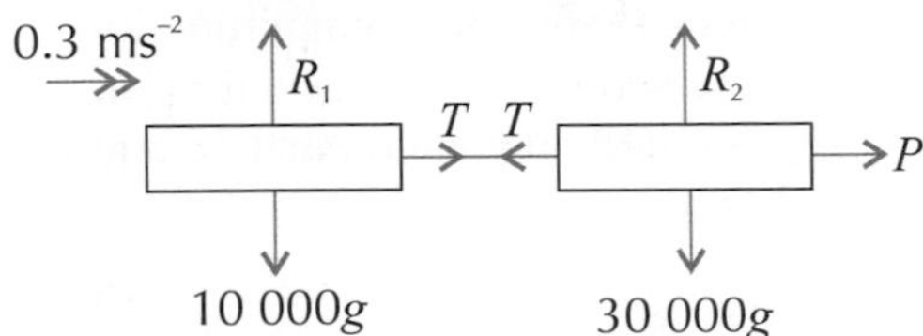

A 30 tonne locomotive engine is pulling a single 10 tonne carriage, as shown. They are accelerating at 0.3 ms^{-2} due to the force *P* generated by the engine. The coupling between the engine and the carriage can be modelled as light and inextensible. It's assumed that there are no forces resistant to motion.

a) **Find the magnitude of the driving force *P*.**

- Considering the engine and the carriage as a single particle, and resolving horizontally (→):

$F_{net} = ma$

$P = 40\ 000 \times 0.3$ ← This is the combined mass of the engine and the carriage.

$= 12\ 000$ N

b) **Find the magnitude of the tension in the coupling.**

- Resolving horizontally (→), considering only the forces acting on the carriage:

$F_{net} = ma$

$T = 10\ 000 \times 0.3$

$= 3000$ N

c) **When the engine and carriage are travelling at 15 ms^{-1}, the coupling breaks. Given that the driving force remains the same, find the distance travelled by the engine in the first 5 seconds after the coupling breaks.**

- Resolving horizontally (→), considering only the forces acting on the engine to find its new acceleration:

$F_{net} = ma$

$P = 30\ 000 \times a$

$a = 12\ 000 \div 30\ 000$

$= 0.4$ ms^{-2}

- Now use a constant acceleration equation to find the distance travelled:

$s = ut + \frac{1}{2}at^2$

$s = (15 \times 5) + (\frac{1}{2} \times 0.4 \times 5^2)$

$= 80$ m

Tip: T is the tension in the coupling. It is experienced by both the engine and the carriage with equal magnitude but in opposite directions.

Tip: 1 tonne = 1000 kg.

Tip: You don't need to know the value of the tension in part a) — you can just treat the whole system as one particle.

Tip: The coupling is modelled as being light and inextensible, so the tension will be constant throughout the coupling.

Tip: In part b), you could consider only the forces acting on the engine instead, but there are fewer acting on the carriage, so the calculation is easier.

Example 3

Two particles, A and B, of mass 6 kg and 8 kg respectively, are connected by a light, inextensible string. The particles are accelerating up a rough slope which is inclined at an angle of 20° to the horizontal.

The force causing the acceleration has magnitude 200 N and acts on A in a direction parallel to the slope.
The coefficient of friction between each particle and the slope is 0.6.

Find the acceleration of A.

Tip: The acceleration of A will be the same as the acceleration of the two particles combined.

- Treat the two particles as one combined particle with mass 6 kg + 8 kg = 14 kg, and resolve perpendicular to the plane (↖):

$$F_{net} = ma$$
$$R - 14g\cos 20° = 0$$
$$R = 14g\cos 20° \text{ N}$$

- The particles are moving, so the total frictional force acting on the two particles is:

$$F = \mu R$$
$$= 0.6 \times 14g\cos 20°$$
$$= 8.4g\cos 20°$$

Tip: The total frictional force acting on the two particles is the sum of the individual frictional forces: $F = F_A + F_B$

- Again, treat the two particles as one combined particle, but now resolve parallel to the plane (↗):

$$F_{net} = ma$$
$$200 - 14g\sin 20° - F = 14a$$
$$200 - 14g\sin 20° - 8.4g\cos 20° = 14a$$
$$a = 5.41 \text{ ms}^{-2} \text{ (3 s.f.)}$$

Exercise 2.1

Q1 A lift of mass 500 kg is carrying a load of weight 700 N.

a) Calculate the tension in the lift cable, given that the lift is accelerating vertically upwards at 0.2 ms^{-2} and that the cable is light, inextensible and vertical.

b) Find the reaction force between the floor of the lift and the load.

Q2 A lift is being tested for safety. The lift has a mass of 1000 kg and contains a load of mass 1400 kg. The lift is attached to a vertical light, inextensible cable.

a) Calculate the tension in the cable given that the lift is accelerating vertically downwards at a rate of 1.5 ms^{-2}.

b) Find the reaction force between the floor of the lift and the load.

c) The lift is raised to a height of 30 m above the ground. The cable is cut and the lift falls freely from rest to the ground. Find the speed of the lift as it hits the ground.

Q3

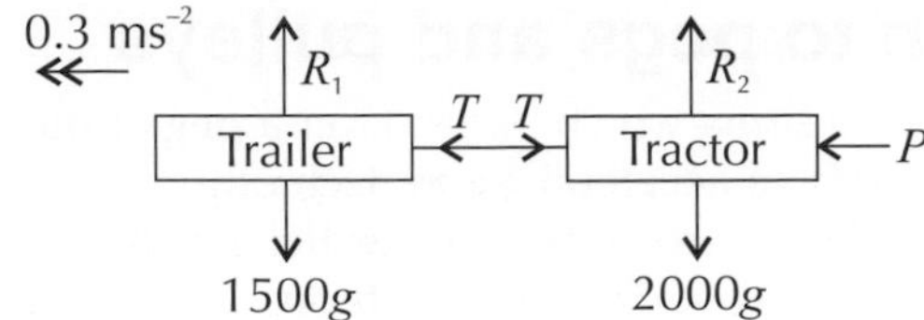

A tractor of mass 2 tonnes is pulling a trailer of mass 1.5 tonnes by means of a light, rigid coupling, as shown above. The tractor applies its brakes and both tractor and trailer decelerate at a rate of 0.3 ms^{-2}.

a) Calculate the braking force, P, generated by the tractor.

b) Find the magnitude of T, the thrust in the coupling between the tractor and the trailer.

c) State an assumption that has been made in this model of the motion of the tractor and trailer.

Q3 Hint: Remember — thrust is the force in a rigid rod. In this question, thrust acts just like tension would, but in the opposite directions.

Q3 Hint: Lots of assumptions have been made in this model — you only have to state one for part c). See Chapter 1 for more on modelling assumptions.

Q4 A car is towing a caravan along a level road. The car has mass 1200 kg and the caravan has mass 800 kg. Resistive forces of magnitude 600 N and 500 N act on the car and the caravan respectively. The acceleration of the car and caravan is 0.2 ms^{-2}.

a) Calculate the driving force of the car.

b) Find the tension in the tow bar.

c) The car and caravan are travelling at a speed of 20 ms^{-1} when the tow bar breaks. Given that the resistive forces remain constant, how long does the caravan take to come to rest?

Q4 Hint: In part a), add together the individual resistive forces to find the total resistance of the whole system.

Q5 A car of mass 900 kg is towing a trailer of mass 600 kg up a hill by means of a light, inextensible rope. The hill is angled at 12° to the horizontal. The resistive forces acting on the car and the trailer have magnitude 740 N and 200 N respectively. The driving force, P, exerted by the car has magnitude 7000 N.

a) Draw a diagram showing all the forces acting on the car and the trailer.

b) Calculate the acceleration of the car and trailer up the hill.

c) Calculate the tension in the rope.

d) Explain how you have used the modelling assumption that the rope is inextensible.

Q6

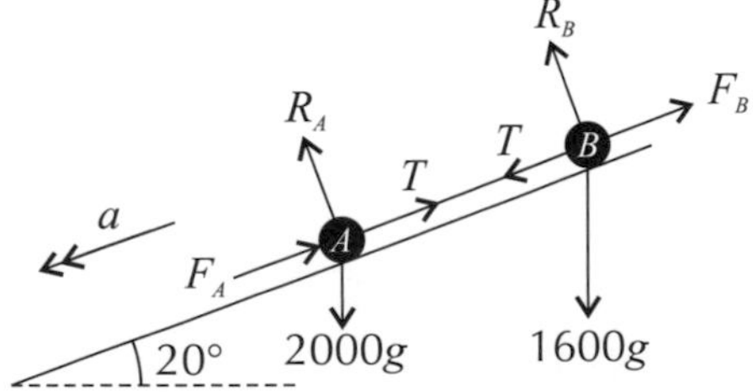

Two stone blocks coupled by a light, inextensible chain are sliding down a rough plane inclined at an angle of 20° to the horizontal, as shown above. Stone A has a mass of 2000 kg and stone B has a mass of 1600 kg. The coefficient of friction between stone A and the plane is 0.3 and between stone B and the plane is 0.4.

a) Find T, the tension in the chain.

b) Calculate the time taken for the stones to slide 25 m from rest.

Q6 Hint: In part a), resolve for each stone and form a pair of simultaneous equations.

Introduction to pegs and pulleys

Particles connected by a string which passes over a **peg** or **pulley** will move with the **same magnitude of acceleration** as each other (as long as the string is inextensible). However, the two connected particles **cannot** be treated as one because they will be moving in different directions.

If the peg or pulley is **smooth** (and it always will be in M1 questions), then the **magnitude** of the **tension** in the string connecting the particles will be the **same** either side of the peg or pulley.

Tip: In M1, all the pegs and pulleys will also be described as 'fixed' — this just means that the peg or pulley is held in place so that it won't move when the string passes over it.

Example 1

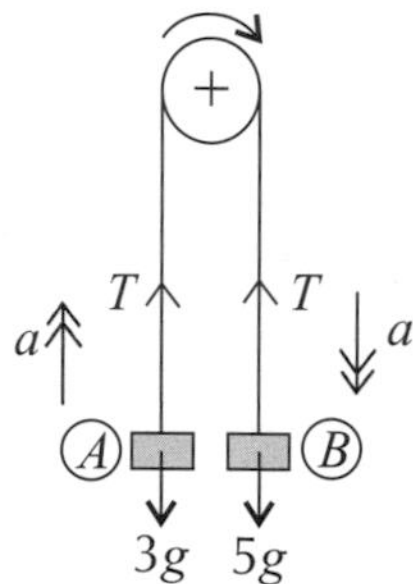

Masses of 3 kg and 5 kg are connected by a light, inextensible string and hang vertically either side of a smooth, fixed pulley. They are released from rest.

Tip: When the particles are released from rest, the heavier particle will move downwards, and the lighter particle will move upwards.

a) Find the magnitude of the acceleration of each mass.

- Resolving vertically (↑) for A: $F_{net} = ma$

  $T - 3g = 3a$ — call this equation ①

- Resolving vertically (↓) for B: $F_{net} = ma$

  $5g - T = 5a$

  $T = 5g - 5a$ — call this equation ②

- Substitute equation ② into equation ①:

  $(5g - 5a) - 3g = 3a$

  $2 \times 9.8 = 8a$

  $a = 2.45 \text{ ms}^{-2}$

Tip: The string is inextensible, so the acceleration of each particle will have the same magnitude, but opposite direction.

b) Find the time it takes for each mass to move 40 cm.

- Use an equation of constant acceleration:

  $s = ut + \frac{1}{2}at^2$

  $0.4 = (0 \times t) + (\frac{1}{2} \times 2.45 \times t^2)$

  So $t = \sqrt{\frac{0.8}{2.45}}$

  $= 0.571$ s (3 s.f.)

c) State any assumptions made in your model.

A does not hit the pulley and B does not hit the ground; there's no air resistance; the string is 'light' so the tension is the same for both A and B, and it doesn't break; the string is inextensible so the acceleration is the same for both masses; the pulley is fixed and smooth; acceleration due to gravity is constant ($g = 9.8 \text{ ms}^{-2}$).

Example 2

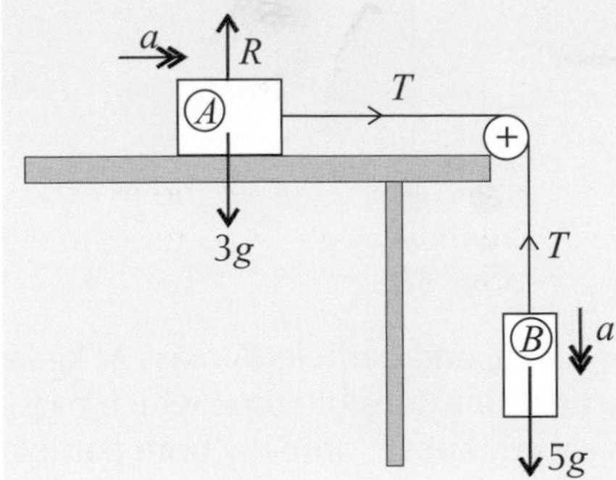

A particle of mass 3 kg is placed on a smooth, horizontal table. A light, inextensible string connects it over a smooth, fixed peg to a particle of mass 5 kg which hangs vertically, as shown. Find the tension in the string if the system is released from rest.

- Resolving horizontally (→) for A:

$$F_{net} = ma$$
$$T = 3a$$
$$a = \frac{T}{3} \quad \text{— call this equation ①}$$

- Resolving vertically (↓) for B:

$$F_{net} = ma$$
$$5g - T = 5a \quad \text{— call this equation ②}$$

- Substituting equation ① into equation ②:

$$5g - T = 5 \times \frac{T}{3}$$
$$\text{So } \frac{8}{3}T = 5g$$
$$T = 18.4 \text{ N (3 s.f.)}$$

Tip: Resolve for each particle in the direction of its acceleration.

Exercise 2.2

Q1 Two particles, A and B, of mass 3 kg and 2 kg respectively, are joined by a light inextensible string which passes over a fixed, smooth pulley. Initially, both particles are held at rest with particle A 60 cm higher than particle B. Both particles are then released from rest.

a) Draw a diagram showing the forces acting on the masses.

b) How long is it after the particles are released before they are level?

Q2

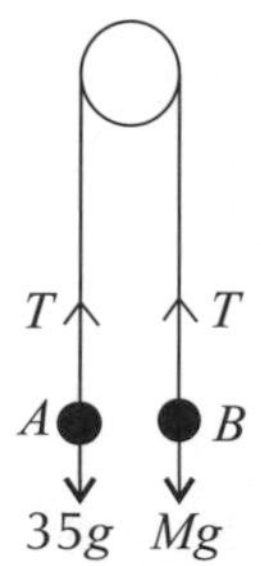

Q2 Hint: The mass of B is less than 35 kg, so when the system is released, A will accelerate downwards and B will accelerate upwards.

Particle A, mass 35 kg, and particle B, mass M kg ($M < 35$), are connected by a light, inextensible rope which passes over a fixed, smooth peg, as shown above. Initially both particles are level and they are released from rest.

a) Calculate T, the tension in the rope, given that the particles move 5 m vertically in the first 2 seconds after they are released.

b) Find M.

Q3

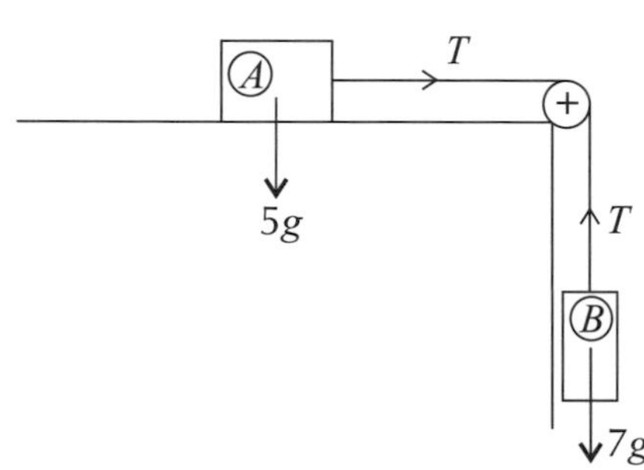

Particles A and B, of mass 5 kg and 7 kg respectively, are connected by a light, inextensible string which passes over a fixed, smooth pulley. Particle A is resting on a smooth horizontal surface and particle B is hanging vertically, as shown. The system is released from rest.

a) Find the magnitude of the acceleration of the particles.

b) Find the tension in the string.

c) What assumptions have you made in your model?

Q4 A bucket of stones with mass 50 kg is attached to one end of a light inextensible rope, the other end of which is attached to a counterweight of mass 10 kg. The rope passes over a smooth fixed pulley. The bucket is raised from rest on the ground to a height of 12 m in a time of 20 s by the addition of a constant force F acting vertically downwards on the counterweight.

a) Draw a diagram to show the forces acting on this system.

b) Calculate the tension in the rope.

c) Find the magnitude of F.

When the bucket is 12 m above the ground, the stones are removed and the force F stops acting on the counterweight.

d) Given that the bucket weighs 11 kg and the system is released from rest, find the speed of the bucket as it hits the ground.

Q5

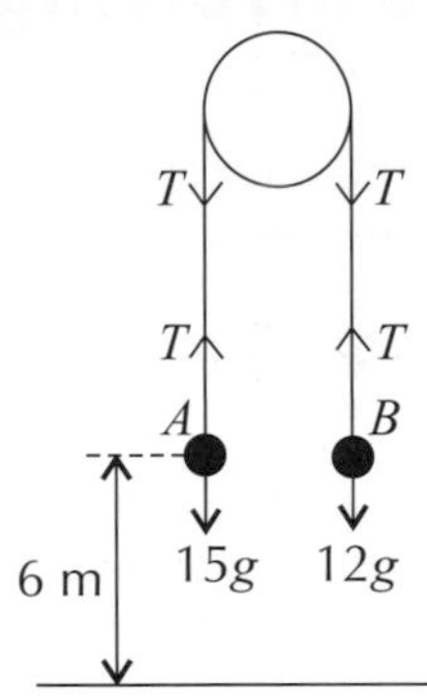

Two particles, A and B, of mass 15 kg and 12 kg respectively, are attached to the ends of a light inextensible string which passes over a fixed, smooth pulley. The particles are held at rest so that the string is taut and they are both 6 m above the horizontal ground, as shown above.

a) Find the acceleration of the particles immediately after they are released from rest.

b) Find the magnitude of the force which the string exerts on the pulley.

c) Particle A strikes the ground without rebounding. Particle B then moves freely under gravity without striking the pulley. Find the time between particle A hitting the ground and particle B coming to rest for the first time.

Q5 b) Hint: Consider the parts of the string either side of the pulley separately and remember that the tension is constant throughout the string.

Q5 c) Hint: The string is inextensible, so at the instant that A hits the ground, both A and B will be travelling with the same speed.

Q6

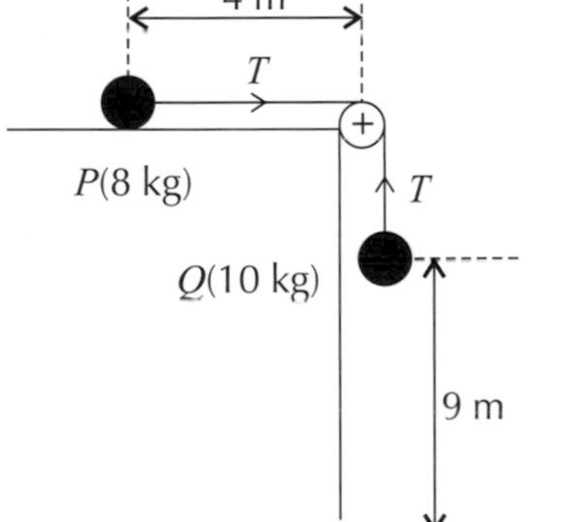

Two particles, P and Q, of mass 8 kg and 10 kg respectively, are attached to the ends of a light, inextensible string which passes over a fixed, smooth pulley. P is held at rest on a smooth horizontal surface, 4 m from the pulley, and Q hangs vertically, 9 m above the horizontal ground, as shown.

The system is released from rest and P begins to accelerate towards the pulley. At the instant P hits the pulley, the string breaks and Q then moves freely under gravity until it hits the ground.

Find the time between the instant the particles are released from rest and the instant when Q hits the ground.

Harder problems involving pegs and pulleys

These questions are just like those on the previous few pages, but they also include **frictional forces** and/or **sloped planes**. The method for answering them is exactly the same as for the problems on the previous pages: resolve the forces acting on **each particle** separately in the **direction of acceleration**.

Remember that as long as the string connecting the particles is **light** and **inextensible**, and the peg or pulley is **smooth**, the **tension** in the string will be **constant** and the two particles will have the same **magnitude** of **acceleration**.

Tip: Having well-drawn force diagrams is really important for these trickier problems.

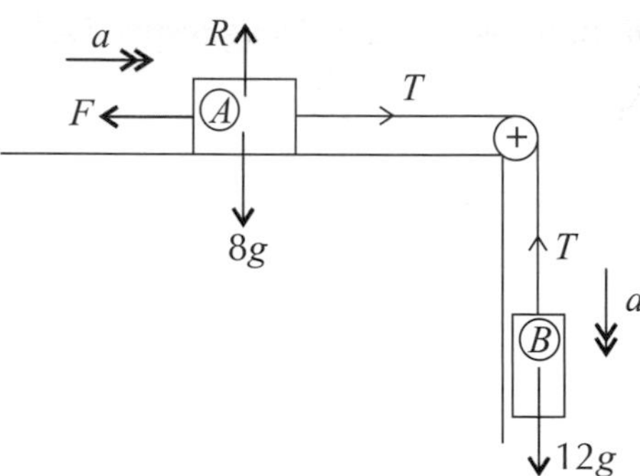

A block, A, of mass 8 kg, is placed on a rough horizontal table (μ = 0.5). A light inextensible string connects A to a second block, B, of mass 12 kg. The string passes over a fixed, smooth peg and B hangs vertically, as shown. The system is released from rest. Find the tension in the string.

- Resolve vertically for A (↑):

  $R - 8g = 0$

  $R = 8g$

- A is moving, so the frictional force takes its maximum value:

  $F = \mu R$

  $= 0.5 \times 8g$

  $= 39.2$ N

- Resolve horizontally for A (→):

  $F_{net} = ma$

  $T - F = 8a$

  $a = \frac{1}{8}(T - 39.2)$ — call this equation ①

- Resolve vertically for B (↓):

  $F_{net} = ma$

  $12g - T = 12a$ — call this equation ②

- Substitute equation ① into equation ② :

  $12g - T = 12 \times \frac{1}{8}(T - 39.2)$

  $2.5T = 117.6 + 58.8$

  $T = 70.6$ N (3 s.f.)

Example 2

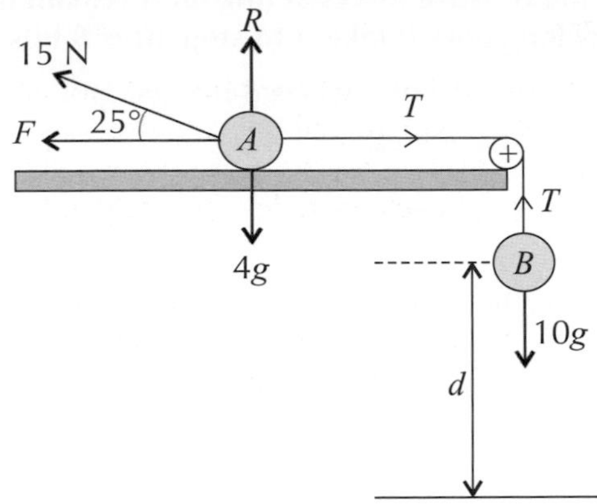

Particles A and B, of mass 4 kg and 10 kg respectively, are connected by a light inextensible string which passes over a fixed smooth pulley.
A force of 15 N acts on A at an angle of 25° to a rough horizontal plane, as shown. The coefficient of friction between A and the plane is 0.7.
B is released from rest and falls d m vertically to the ground in 2 seconds.

a) Find d.

- Resolve vertically for A (↑) to find the normal reaction, R:

$$R + 15\sin 25° - 4g = 0$$
$$R = 32.860... \text{ N}$$

- The particles are moving, so F takes its maximum value:

$$F = \mu R$$
$$= 0.7 \times 32.860...$$
$$= 23.002... \text{ N}$$

- Resolve horizontally for A (→):

$$T - 23.002... - 15\cos 25° = 4a$$
$$T = 4a + 36.597... \quad \text{— equation ①}$$

- Resolve vertically for B (↓):

$$10g - T = 10a$$
$$T = 98 - 10a \quad \text{— equation ②}$$

- Substitute equation ① into equation ②:

$$4a + 36.597... = 98 - 10a$$
$$a = 4.385... \text{ ms}^{-2}$$

- Using $s = ut + \frac{1}{2}at^2$: $s = d$, $u = 0$, $t = 2$, $a = 4.385...$

$$d = (0 \times 2) + \frac{1}{2}(4.385... \times 2^2)$$
$$= 8.77 \text{ m (3 s.f.)}$$

Tip: Try not to round the numbers in any of the intermediate steps of a calculation, otherwise your final answer might not be correct.

b) When B hits the ground, A carries on moving along the plane. Given that the resistive forces acting on A remain the same as in part a), how long does it take A to stop after B hits the ground?

- First, find the speed of A when B hits the ground:

$$v = u + at$$
$$v = 0 + (4.385... \times 2)$$
$$= 8.771... \text{ ms}^{-1}$$

- Next, resolve horizontally for A ($\rightarrow$) to find its deceleration:

$$-23.002... - 15\cos 25° = 4a$$
$$-36.597... = 4a$$
$$= -9.149... \text{ ms}^{-2}$$

- Now find the time taken for A to stop:

$$t = \frac{(v - u)}{a}$$
$$t = \frac{0 - 8.771...}{-9.149...}$$
$$= 0.959 \text{ s (to 3 s.f.)}$$

Tip: Remember that A and B will have the same acceleration up until the point when B hits the ground.

Tip: Once B has hit the ground, the string will go slack and there will be no tension force acting on A.

Example 3

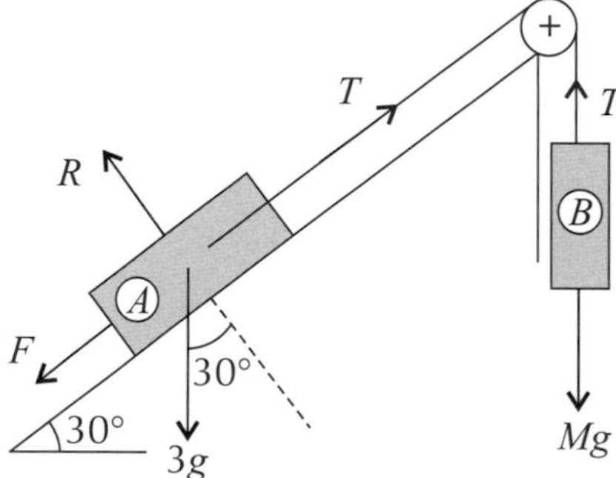

A block of mass 3 kg is held in equilibrium on a rough plane inclined at 30° to the horizontal. It is attached via a light, inextensible string to a mass of M kg hanging vertically beneath a fixed smooth pulley, as shown. The coefficient of friction between A and the plane is 0.4.

a) Find M, given that A is on the point of sliding up the plane.

- Resolve perpendicular to the plane ($\nwarrow$) for A:

$$R - 3g\cos 30° = 3 \times 0$$
$$R = 3g\cos 30°$$

- The friction is limiting, so:

$$F = \mu R$$
$$= 0.4 \times 3g\cos 30°$$
$$= 10.184... \text{ N}$$

Tip: A is "on the point of sliding" — this is another way of describing limiting equilibrium, which means that the frictional force takes its maximum possible value: $F = \mu R$. This is really a statics question — the particles aren't moving, so acceleration is zero in all directions.

- Resolve vertically (↓) for B:

$$Mg - T = M \times 0$$
$$T = Mg$$

- Resolve parallel to the plane (↗) for A:

$$T - F - 3g\sin 30° = 3 \times 0$$
$$Mg - 10.184... - 3g\sin 30° = 0$$
$$M = 2.54 \text{ kg (to 3 s.f.)}$$

b) What would M be if A were on the point of sliding down the plane?

- Resolve parallel to the plane (↗) for A:

$$T + F - 3g\sin 30° = 3 \times 0$$
$$Mg + 10.184... - 3g\sin 30° = 0$$
$$M = 0.461 \text{ kg (to 3 s.f.)}$$

Tip: You've already done all the hard work in part a), so in b), you only need to repeat the very last step and resolve parallel to the plane, with the frictional force acting in the opposite direction.

Example 4

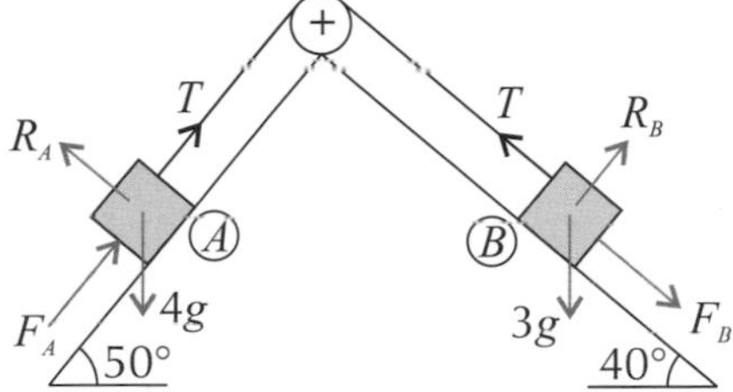

Two particles, A and B, of masses 4 kg and 3 kg respectively, are joined by a light inextensible string which passes over a smooth fixed pulley. The particles are positioned as shown in the diagram above. The system is released from rest and A begins to move down the slope and B begins to move up the slope. Given that the coefficient of friction between each particle and the surface is 0.2, find the magnitude of the acceleration of A.

- The particles are moving, so friction is limiting:

$$F_A = \mu R_A$$
$$= 0.2 \times 4g\cos 50° = 5.039... \text{ N}$$

$$F_B = \mu R_B$$
$$= 0.2 \times 3g\cos 40° = 4.504... \text{ N}$$

Tip: Find R_A and R_B by resolving perpendicular to each plane.

- Resolve parallel to the plane (↙) for A:

$$4g\sin 50° - F_A - T = 4a$$
$$24.989... - T = 4a \quad \text{— call this equation ①}$$

- Resolve parallel to the plane (↖) for B:

$$T - 3g\sin 40° - F_B = 3a$$
$$T - 23.402... = 3a$$
$$T = 3a + 23.402... \quad \text{— call this equation ②}$$

- Substitute equation ② into equation ①:

$$24.989... - 3a - 23.402... = 4a$$
$$a = 0.227 \text{ ms}^{-2} \text{ (3 s.f.)}$$

Exercise 2.3

Q1

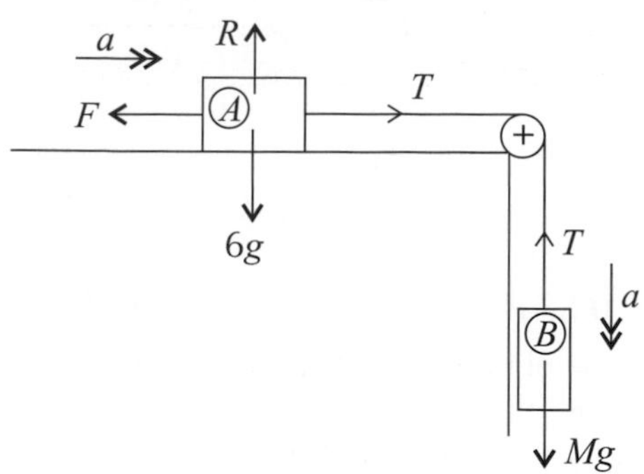

Two particles A and B, of mass 6 kg and M kg respectively, are joined by a light, inextensible string which passes over a fixed, smooth pulley. The particles are held at rest with A on a rough, horizontal surface and B hanging vertically, as shown above. Given that the coefficient of friction between A and the surface is 0.2 and that the tension in the string has magnitude 12 N, find:

a) the acceleration of A immediately after the particles are released,

b) the value of M.

Q2

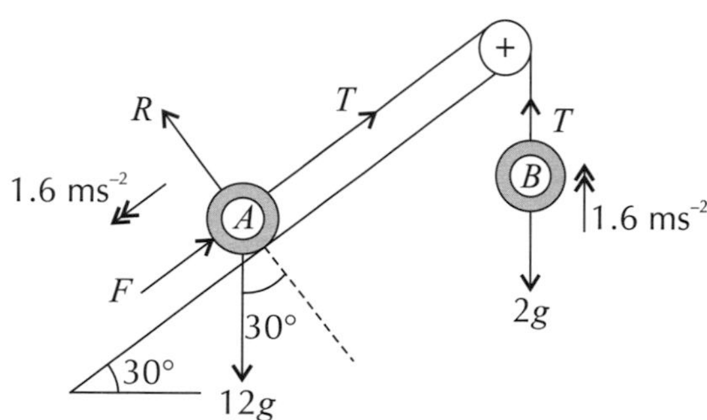

Particle A (mass 12 kg) is joined to particle B (mass 2 kg) by a light, inextensible string which passes over a smooth, fixed pulley, as shown above. The particles are released from rest and A begins to slide with acceleration 1.6 ms^{-2} down a rough plane which is inclined at an angle of 30° to the horizontal.

a) Find the magnitude of T, the tension in the string.

b) Find the coefficient of friction between A and the slope.

c) Find the distance travelled by each particle in the first 3 seconds after the particles are released.

d) State one assumption you have made in part c).

Q3

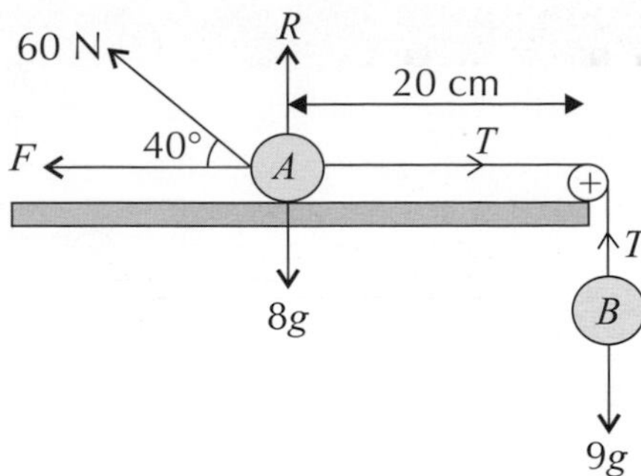

Particles A and B, of mass 8 kg and 9 kg respectively, are connected by a light, inextensible string which passes over a fixed, smooth pulley as shown. A force of 60 N acts on A at an angle of 40° to the rough, horizontal plane that A rests on. Particle A is held 20 cm from the pulley and when released from rest, accelerates towards the pulley at a rate of 0.4 ms^{-2}.

a) Find μ, the coefficient of friction between A and the plane.

b) Find the speed of A when it hits the pulley.

c) When A hits the pulley, the string breaks and B falls freely. Given that B was initially released from a position 60 cm above the horizontal ground, find the speed of B when it hits the ground.

Q3 Hint: Remember — while the particles are connected, they'll have the same speed.

Q4

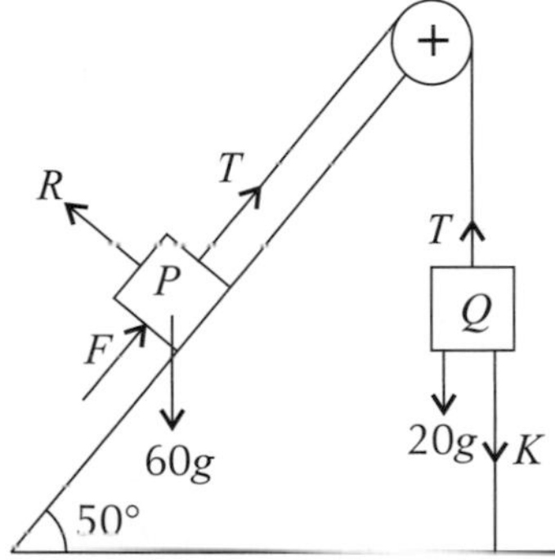

One end of a light inextensible string is attached to a block P, of mass 60 kg. The string passes over a fixed, smooth pulley and is attached at the other end to a block Q of mass 20 kg.

P lies on a rough plane ($\mu = 0.1$) inclined at an angle of 50° to the horizontal, and Q hangs vertically below the pulley, as shown above.

The system is held in limiting equilibrium with P on the point of sliding down the plane by a second light, inextensible string attached to Q at one end and the horizontal ground at the other. The tension in this second string has magnitude K N.

a) Find K.

b) The string fixing Q to the ground is cut. Find the speed of P 5 seconds after it has been released from rest. You may assume that Q does not hit the pulley in the first 5 seconds of its movement.

Q5

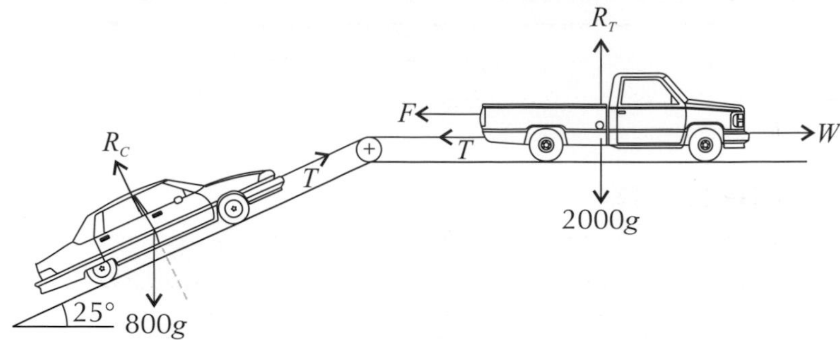

A truck of mass 2 tonnes is moving along a rough, horizontal plane ($\mu = 0.8$), and towing a car of mass 0.8 tonnes up a smooth plane, angled at 25° to the horizontal, as shown in the diagram above.

The chain between the truck and the car is modelled as a light, inextensible string passing over a fixed, smooth pulley.

The car is initially 25 m from the pulley and is towed 10 m towards the pulley in the first 30 seconds after starting from rest. The truck and the car move with constant acceleration.

You may assume that the frictional force between the truck and the horizontal plane takes its maximum value.

a) Find the tension in the chain.

b) Calculate W, the driving force of the truck.

c) The chain connecting the truck to the car snaps.
Assuming that all other forces remain constant, calculate the instantaneous acceleration of the truck.

Q6

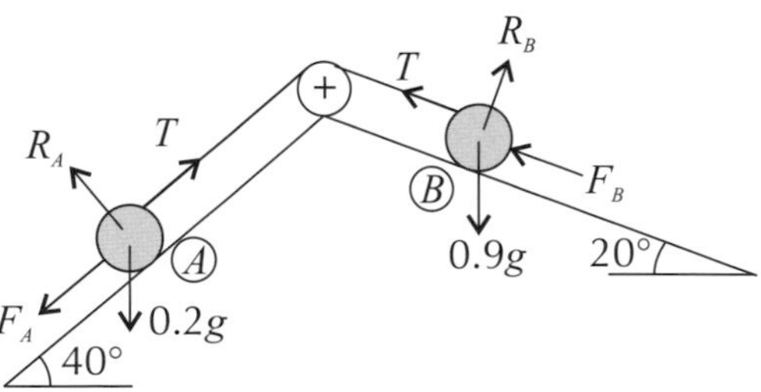

Particles A and B, of mass 0.2 kg and 0.9 kg respectively, are connected by a light inextensible string. The string passes over a smooth pulley fixed to the apex of a wedge.

A rests on a rough plane ($\mu_A = 0.7$) inclined at an angle of 40° to the horizontal and B rests on a different rough plane ($\mu_B = 0.05$) inclined at an angle of 20° to the horizontal, as shown above.

The particles are held at rest with A 35 cm from the pulley.

a) Given that A begins to accelerate up the slope when the particles are released from rest, find the tension in the string.

b) Find the speed of A when it reaches the pulley.

3. Momentum and Impulse

In this section you'll learn what momentum is, and how to calculate it for a moving particle. You'll also learn what happens to particles when they collide, and what is meant by impulse.

Learning Objectives:

- Be able to find the momentum of a moving object.
- Be able to apply the principle of conservation of momentum to problems involving the collision of two particles.
- Be able to find the impulse a force gives to an object.
- Be able to solve problems involving the collision of two particles or a particle colliding with a fixed surface using the impulse-momentum principle.

Momentum

- **Momentum** is a measure of how much "umph" a moving object has.
- It's found by **multiplying** an object's **mass** (m) by its **velocity** (v).

Momentum = Mass × Velocity　　　Momentum = mv

- For mass in kg and velocity in ms^{-1}, the unit of momentum is **$kgms^{-1}$** or **Ns**.
- Velocity is a **vector** quantity, so momentum is also a **vector quantity** (i.e. it has a **direction**). This means that the **sign** of the velocity and the momentum is important.

Examples

Find the momentum of the two particles below:

a) A particle with mass 6 kg, travelling in a straight line at 3 ms^{-1}.

Momentum = mv

= 6 × 3

= 18 $kgms^{-1}$

b) A particle with mass 2 kg, travelling in a straight line at –8 ms^{-1}.

Momentum = mv

= 2 × –8

= –16 Ns

Tip: You can give your answers in $kgms^{-1}$ or Ns.

Exercise 3.1

Q1 Calculate the momentum of the following particles with mass m and velocity v:

a) m = 3 kg, v = 6 ms^{-1}

b) m = 6.8 kg, v = 0.4 ms^{-1}

c) m = 1000 tonnes, v = 57 ms^{-1}

Q2 Find the mass in kg of each particle below with the given momentum and velocity v:

a) Momentum = 28 $kgms^{-1}$, v = 7 ms^{-1}

b) Momentum = 0.8 $kgms^{-1}$, v = 3.2 ms^{-1}

c) Momentum = 584 $kgms^{-1}$, v = 73 ms^{-1}

Q3 Find the velocity in ms^{-1} of the following particles with the given momentum and mass m:

a) m = 500 kg, momentum = 2000 Ns

b) m = 4 tonnes, momentum = 8000 Ns

c) m = 3.9 kg, momentum = 585 Ns

Conservation of momentum

A **collision** between two particles will cause the **velocity** of each particle to **change**. This **change in velocity** means that the **momentum** of each particle will also **change**.

However, the **total momentum** of the system remains **the same** before and after the collision.
This is the **principle of conservation of momentum**.

Total momentum before collision = Total momentum after collision

Tip: The total momentum of the system is just the momentum of A plus the momentum of B. Calculate this for A and B before and after the collision.

- So, for two colliding particles, A and B, of mass m_A and m_B respectively, the principle of conservation of momentum can be written as:

$$m_Au_A + m_Bu_B = m_Av_A + m_Bv_B$$

Where u_A and u_B are the velocities of A and B before the collision and v_A and v_B are the velocities after the collision:

Before Collision

A u_A ms^{-1} m_A kg B u_B ms^{-1} m_B kg

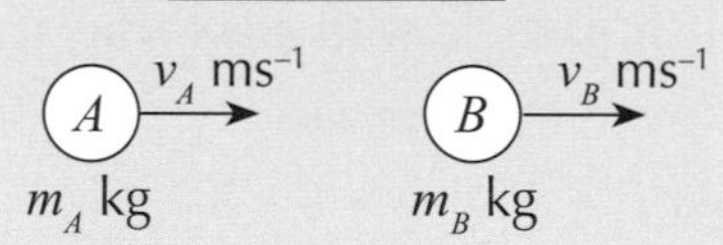

There are several possibilities for how the particles may move **after** a collision:

- The two particles move in **opposite directions** to each other.
- They both move in the **same direction** at **different speeds**.
- One or both of the particles **stops**.
- The two particles **coalesce** (stick together) and move as one object.

Example 1

Tip: It's a good idea to draw 'before' and 'after' diagrams to help you keep track of which direction each particle is moving in and with what speed.

Particle A, of mass 5 kg, and particle B, of mass 7 kg, move in a straight line in the same direction with velocities 6 ms^{-1} and 2 ms^{-1} respectively. After the collision, particle B continues in the same direction with velocity 4.2 ms^{-1}.

Find the velocity of A after the impact.

- First, draw a diagram showing the particles before the collision:

Before

A 6 ms^{-1} 5 kg B 2 ms^{-1} 7 kg

And write down the information you know:

$m_A = 5$ kg; $m_B = 7$ kg; $u_A = 6$ ms^{-1}; $u_B = 2$ ms^{-1}

- Next, draw a diagram showing the particles after the collision:

After

A → v_A, 5 kg; B → 4.2 ms^{-1}, 7 kg

And again, write down the information you know:

$m_A = 5$ kg; $m_B = 7$ kg; $v_A = ?$; $v_B = 4.2$ ms^{-1}

- Now you can use the principle of conservation of momentum, fill in the numbers you know, and rearrange to find v_A.

Total momentum before collision = Total momentum after collision

$$m_Au_A + m_Bu_B = m_Av_A + m_Bv_B$$
$$(5 \times 6) + (7 \times 2) = (5 \times v_A) + (7 \times 4.2)$$
$$44 = 5v_A + 29.4$$
$$v_A = 2.92 \text{ ms}^{-1}$$

Tip: v_A comes out as a positive value, which means A is moving in the same direction as before the collision (and this direction is assumed to be positive). If v_A was negative, it would mean A's direction of motion was reversed by the collision.

Example 2

Particle A, of mass 6 kg, and particle B, of mass 3 kg, are moving towards each other in a straight line at speeds of 2 ms^{-1} and 1 ms^{-1} respectively. Given that B rebounds with speed 3 ms^{-1} in the opposite direction to its initial velocity, find the velocity of A after the collision.

- Again, draw diagrams showing the particles before and after the collision and write down the values you are given in the question.

Before

A → 2 ms^{-1}, 6 kg; ← 1 ms^{-1} B, 3 kg

$m_A = 6$ kg; $m_B = 3$ kg;
$u_A = 2$ ms^{-1}; $u_B = -1$ ms^{-1}

After

A → v_A ms^{-1}, 6 kg; B → 3 ms^{-1}, 3 kg

$m_A = 6$ kg; $m_B = 3$ kg;
$v_A = ?$; $v_B = 3$ ms^{-1}

Tip: u_B is negative as particle B is moving in the opposite direction to particle A (and the left-to-right direction is assumed to be positive).

- Now use the principle of conservation of momentum:

Total momentum before collision = Total momentum after collision

$$m_Au_A + m_Bu_B = m_Av_A + m_Bv_B$$
$$(6 \times 2) + (3 \times -1) = (6 \times v_A) + (3 \times 3)$$
$$9 = 6v_A + 9$$
$$v_A = 0 \text{ ms}^{-1}$$

So, after the collision, particle A is stationary.

Tip: You don't know which direction A will travel in after the collision, so assume it will travel in the positive direction, and if the answer is negative, then it will be travelling in the opposite direction.

Example 3

A lump of ice of mass 0.1 kg is sliding across the smooth surface of a frozen lake with speed 4 ms⁻¹. It collides with a stationary stone of mass 0.3 kg. The lump of ice and the stone then move in opposite directions to each other at the same speed, v ms⁻¹. Find v.

- Call the lump of ice A and the stone B. Draw before and after diagrams and write down the information you know.

Before

4 ms⁻¹ 0 ms⁻¹
A B
0.1 kg 0.3 kg

After

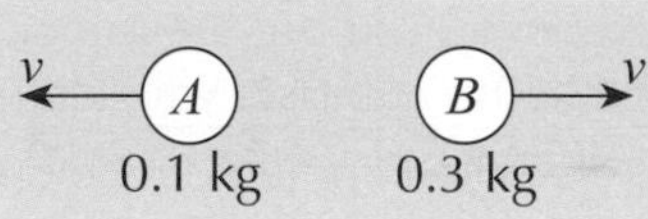

$m_A = 0.1$ kg; $m_B = 0.3$ kg; $u_A = 4$ ms⁻¹; $u_B = 0$ ms⁻¹; $v_A = -v$; $v_B = v$

> **Tip:** Although the speeds following the collision are the same, the two bodies are moving in different directions, so the velocities are different.

- Now use the principle of conservation of momentum:

Total momentum before collision = Total momentum after collision

$$m_A u_A + m_B u_B = m_A v_A + m_B v_B$$
$$(0.1 \times 4) + (0.3 \times 0) = (0.1 \times -v) + (0.3 \times v)$$
$$0.4 = 0.2v$$
$$v = 2 \text{ ms}^{-1}$$

Example 4

Two particles of mass 40 g and M kg move towards each other in a straight line with speeds of 6 ms⁻¹ and 3 ms⁻¹ respectively. The particles coalesce after impact and move with a speed of 2 ms⁻¹ in the same direction as that of the 40 g particle's initial velocity. Find M.

- Call the 40 g mass A and the M kg mass B. These two particles coalesce when they collide, to form a new particle. Call this particle C.

> **Tip:** Remember — when two particles coalesce, they will move together as one particle.

- Draw before and after diagrams and write down what you know.

Before

6 ms⁻¹ 3 ms⁻¹
A B
0.04 kg M kg

After

C 2 ms⁻¹
(M + 0.04) kg

$m_A = 0.04$ kg; $m_B = M$ kg; $m_C = m_A + m_B$

$u_A = 6$ ms⁻¹; $u_B = -3$ ms⁻¹; $v_C = 2$ ms⁻¹

- Now use the principle of conservation of momentum:

Total momentum before collision = Total momentum after collision

$$m_A u_A + m_B u_B = (m_A + m_B)v_B$$
$$(0.04 \times 6) + (M \times -3) = [(M + 0.04) \times 2]$$
$$0.24 - 3M = 2M + 0.08$$
$$5M = 0.16$$
$$M = 0.032 \text{ kg}$$

Exercise 3.2

Q1

Particles A and B, of mass 2 kg and 7 kg respectively, are moving in a straight line on a smooth horizontal surface. The particles collide and continue to move in the same straight line, as shown in the diagram above. Find the speed of A following the collision.

Q2 Particles A and B, of mass 3 kg and 8 kg respectively, are moving in the same direction along a smooth horizontal table when A collides directly with B. Immediately before the collision, A has speed 18 ms^{-1} and B has speed 5 ms^{-1}. Following the collision both particles continue to move in the same direction as before and B has speed 11 ms^{-1}.

a) Draw a diagram showing the particles before and after the collision.

b) Find the speed of A following the collision.

Q3 A particle P, of mass 6 kg, is moving with speed 2.5 ms^{-1} on a smooth horizontal surface when it collides with a stationary particle Q, of mass 4 kg. After the impact, particle Q moves with speed 6 ms^{-1} in the direction P had been moving in prior to the collision. Find the speed and direction of motion of P following the collision.

Q4 Two railway trucks, one of mass 8 tonnes and the other of mass 5 tonnes, are travelling in the same direction along the tracks with speeds 4 ms^{-1} and 3 ms^{-1} respectively. When the trucks collide they couple together (coalesce) and continue to move in the same direction. Find the speed of the coupled trucks, giving your answer in ms^{-1}, correct to 2 decimal places.

Q5 Two particles, of mass m kg and 2 kg, are moving towards each other on a smooth surface with speeds of 8 ms^{-1} and 3 ms^{-1} respectively. The two particles collide and are both brought to rest by the collision. Find the value of m.

Q6 A particle, P, of mass 4 kg moving with speed 3.5 ms^{-1} collides with another particle, Q, of mass 2 kg moving in the opposite direction with speed 1 ms^{-1}. Find the speed of each particle after the impact in each of the following possible outcomes:

a) the particles coalesce and move with speed v,

b) the particles both move in the same direction but Q moves at twice the speed of P,

c) the direction of motion of each particle is reversed, and the speed of Q is three times the speed of P.

Q7 Two particles, A and B, of mass m kg and $3m$ kg respectively, are moving in the same direction on a smooth horizontal plane. A has speed 5 ms^{-1} and B has speed u ms^{-1}. After impact, the direction of motion of A is reversed and the particles move in opposite directions with speeds of 1 ms^{-1} and 3 ms^{-1} respectively. Find the value of u.

Q8 A particle of mass 5 kg moving with speed u ms^{-1} collides with another particle of mass 4 kg moving in the same direction with speed 1.2 ms^{-1}. After the collision the particles coalesce and continue to move in the same direction with a speed of 1.5 ms^{-1}. Find the value of u.

Q9 Hint: If A comes to rest, and B continues moving, then the direction of motion of B must have been reversed as a result of the collision.

Q9 Two particles, A (mass 50 kg) and B (mass M kg), are moving in opposite directions with speeds 3 ms^{-1} and 2 ms^{-1} respectively. A and B collide, resulting in A coming to rest and B moving away at 4 ms^{-1}. Find the value of M.

Q10 Hint: To convert speeds in kmh^{-1} to ms^{-1}, first multiply by 1000 (to convert km to m) and then divide by 3600 (to convert 'per hour' to 'per second').

Q10 Two particles, P and Q, have mass 120 g and 90 g respectively. They are moving in opposite directions along the same straight line on a smooth horizontal surface. Immediately before they collide directly, P has speed 9 kmh^{-1} and Q has speed 11 kmh^{-1}. As a result of the collision, the direction of motion of Q is reversed and its speed immediately after the collision is 6 kmh^{-1}.

a) Find the speed of P immediately following the collision, in ms^{-1}.

b) State the direction of motion of P following the collision.

Q11 Two canal boats are moving along the same straight line in opposite directions towards each other. One has a mass of 2 tonnes and is moving at 4.5 ms^{-1}, the other has a mass of 2.5 tonnes and a speed of 3 ms^{-1}. The boats collide directly and as a result of the collision their directions are reversed. Given that the heavier boat moves off at twice the speed of the other, find the speed of each boat after the collision.

Q12 Two skaters of mass 60 kg and 40 kg are skating along the same straight line. They are moving in opposite directions with speeds of 3 ms^{-1} and 2 ms^{-1} respectively when they collide directly. The heavier skater holds the other skater and they continue to slide as one body along the same straight line at a constant speed. How far do the skaters travel in the first 6 seconds after colliding?

Q13 Two particles A and B, of mass $2m$ and $4m$ respectively, are moving on a smooth horizontal table when they collide directly. Immediately before the collision, A is moving with speed $4u$ and B is moving along the same straight line, but in the opposite direction with speed $6u$. As a result of the collision, the direction of motion of A is reversed and its speed is halved.

a) Find the velocity of B following the collision in terms of u.

b) Does the direction of motion of B change as a result of the collision? Explain your answer.

Q14 Three particles P, Q and R, of mass 1 kg, m kg and 4 kg respectively, are travelling in the same direction along the same straight line across a smooth horizontal surface with speeds 5 ms^{-1}, 3 ms^{-1} and 1.5 ms^{-1} respectively.

a) A collision occurs between P and Q, as a result of which P and Q move in opposite directions, each with speed 4 ms^{-1}. Find the value of m.

b) Q then goes on to collide with R. The collision causes the two particles to coalesce. Find the speed of the combined particle.

Q14 Hint: Just treat each collision between pairs of particles separately.

Q15 A particle A, of mass 5 kg, is moving in a straight line across a smooth horizontal surface with speed 2.8 ms^{-1}. It collides directly with a stationary particle B, of mass 2 kg. As a result of the collision, the direction of A is reversed and its speed is reduced to 1.2 ms^{-1}.

a) Find the speed and direction of motion of B following the collision.

b) B then collides with another stationary particle, C, of mass 7 kg. As a result of this collision, the direction of motion of B is reversed and C moves off in the opposite direction with speed 3.5 ms^{-1}. Is it possible for B to collide again with A?

Impulse

The **impulse** of a constant force applied to a body is defined as the **force multiplied** by the **time** over which the force acts:

$$\text{Impulse} = \text{Force} \times \text{Time}$$

For a force in newtons and time in seconds, the units of impulse are **Ns** or **kgms⁻¹**, just like momentum.

Tip: Force is a vector, so impulse is a vector quantity. You need to make sure the sign of the force is correct when working out an impulse.

Example 1

A body is at rest on a smooth horizontal plane.
A horizontal force of magnitude 12 N acts on the body for 4 seconds.
Find the magnitude of the impulse the force gives to the body.

$I = Ft$

$= 12 \times 4$

$= 48$ Ns

Tip: $I = Ft$ is just shorthand for Impulse = Force × Time

The impulse-momentum principle

- A **resultant** force acting on a body will cause the body to **accelerate** (this is Newton's second law). So, if a force F increases the velocity of a body of mass m from u to v:

$$F = ma$$
$$= m\left(\frac{v-u}{t}\right)$$
$$Ft = mv - mu$$

Tip: Rearrange $v = u + at$ to get $a = \frac{v-u}{t}$.

- However, remember that on the previous page, Ft was defined as the impulse of a force. So:

$$I = mv - mu$$

- This means that the **impulse of a force** can also be found by working out the **change in momentum** of whatever the force is acting on.
This is called the **impulse-momentum principle**:

Impulse = final momentum – initial momentum

Impulse = $mv - mu$

Tip: This is why impulse has the same units as momentum — Ns or kgms^{-1}.

Example 2

A body of mass 500 g is travelling in a straight line. Find the magnitude of the impulse needed to increase its speed from 2 ms^{-1} to 5 ms^{-1}.

Impulse = Change in momentum
$= mv - mu$
$= (0.5 \times 5) - (0.5 \times 2)$
$= 1.5$ Ns

Tip: Remember to change masses so that they are in kg.

Example 3

A 20 g ball is dropped 1 m onto horizontal ground.
The ball hits the ground at right angles and rebounds with speed 2 ms^{-1}.
Find the magnitude of the impulse given to the ball by the ground.

- First, work out the ball's speed immediately before it hits the ground:

$v^2 = u^2 + 2as$
$v^2 = 0^2 + (2 \times 9.8 \times 1)$
$v = 4.427...$ ms^{-1}

Tip: Choose a direction to be positive, and stick with it throughout your answer. Here, downwards is taken as the positive direction...

- Draw a diagram showing the ball before and after it collides with the floor:

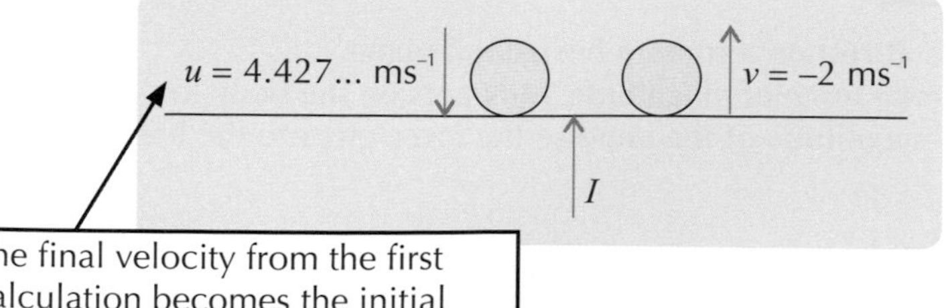

Tip: ...so the velocity of the ball after colliding with the floor is negative, as it's moving upwards.

- Now find the impulse given to the ball by the floor using the impulse-momentum principle:

Impulse = Change in momentum

$= mv - mu$

$= (0.02 \times -2) - (0.02 \times 4.427...)$

$= -0.1285...$

Magnitude of impulse = 0.129 Ns (3 s.f.)

Tip: The impulse is negative, because it acts vertically upwards, and downwards was chosen as the positive direction. But if the question asks for the magnitude of the impulse, make sure that's the answer you give.

Example 4

Two balls, *A* and *B*, have mass 0.6 kg and 0.9 kg respectively. The balls are initially at rest on a table. Ball *A* is given an impulse of magnitude 4.5 Ns towards ball *B*.

a) **Modelling the table as a smooth horizontal plane, find the speed of ball *A* before it collides with *B*.**

- Use the impulse-momentum principle to find the speed of *A* after the impulse has been applied:

Impulse $= mv - mu$

$4.5 = (0.6 \times v) - (0.6 \times 0)$

$4.5 = 0.6v$

$v = 7.5 \text{ ms}^{-1}$

b) **After the collision, both balls move in the same straight line, but in opposite directions. Given that the direction of motion of *A* is reversed and it moves with speed 1.5 ms^{-1}, find the speed of *B* immediately following the collision.**

- Now use the principle of conservation of momentum:

$$m_A u_A + m_B u_B = m_A v_A + m_B v_B$$

$$(0.6 \times 7.5) + (0.9 \times 0) = (0.6 \times -1.5) + (0.9 \times v)$$

$$4.5 = -0.9 + 0.9v$$

$$v = 6 \text{ ms}^{-1}$$

Tip: u_A in part b) will be v from part a).

Tip: You could do part b) by using the fact that the total momentum of the system is equal to the initial impulse given to *A*.

c) **Following the collision, *B* is brought to rest in 3 seconds as a result of a constant resistive force, *R*, applied in the direction directly opposite to its direction of motion. Find the magnitude of *R*.**

- First, use the impulse-momentum principle to find the impulse applied to *B* to bring it to rest:

$I = mv - mu$

$= (0.9 \times 0) - (0.9 \times 6)$

$= -5.4$

- Now use the definition of impulse to find *R*:

Impulse = Force × Time

$-5.4 = R \times 3$

$R = -1.8$ N so: magnitude of $R = 1.8$ N

Tip: Whenever you see an impulse/momentum question which talks about forces, you should be ready to use $I = Ft$ — although you could also answer this question by calculating the deceleration of *B* and using $F = ma$.

Tip: This is because of Newton's third law: ("For two bodies in contact with each other, the force each applies to the other is equal in magnitude but opposite in direction").

- During impact between **two particles** A and B, the impulse that A gives to B is the **same** as the impulse that B gives to A, but in the **opposite direction**.
- This fact is useful for working out the impulse a particle gives to a **fixed surface**, as you can't use the impulse-momentum principle (because the momentum of a fixed surface is assumed not to change).

Example 5

Before

2 ms^{-1}

A

2 kg

After

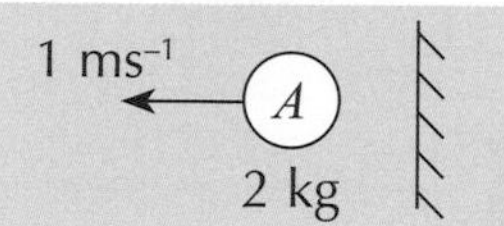

A particle, A, of mass 2 kg moving at 2 ms^{-1} collides at right angles with a fixed vertical surface. Given that the direction of motion of A is reversed by the collision and its speed is reduced to 1 ms^{-1}, find the impulse given to the wall by A during the collision.

- The wall is assumed not to experience a change in momentum, so find the change in momentum of A as a result of the collision. This will be equal in magnitude to the impulse given to A by the wall.

  Taking the initial direction of motion of A as positive:

  Impulse (on A) $= m_A v_A - m_A u_A$
  $= (2 \times -1) - (2 \times 2)$
  $= -6$ Ns

- The impulse given to the wall by A will be equal in magnitude, but in the opposite direction:

  So, impulse (on the wall) = 6 Ns

Exercise 3.3

Q1 A particle is acted on by a constant force of 7 N for 15 seconds. Find the magnitude of the impulse given to the particle.

Q2 A waterskier is towed for 9 seconds by a constant pulling force from a boat. If the waterskier receives an impulse of magnitude 2880 Ns, find the magnitude of the pulling force from the boat.

Q3 A body of mass 2 kg is travelling in a straight line. Find the magnitude of the impulse needed to increase its speed from 3 ms^{-1} to 5 ms^{-1}.

Q4 Hint: The question asks for the impulse, not just the magnitude of the impulse, so you need to give a direction as well as a magnitude.

Q4 A particle of mass 0.3 kg is moving at 4 ms^{-1}. Find the impulse needed to bring it to rest.

Q5 A particle of mass 0.08 kg is moving in a straight line when it receives an impulse of 0.6 Ns in the direction of its motion. Find the change in velocity of the particle.

Q6 A boy of mass 35 kg cycling along a straight path at 3.2 ms^{-1} is given an impulse of 21 Ns in the direction of his motion.
Find the boy's speed after the push.

Q7 A snooker ball of mass 0.15 kg at rest on a smooth horizontal table is given an impulse of 0.9 Ns by the cue which causes the ball to begin to move in a straight line. What is the speed of the ball immediately after it receives the impulse?

Q8 A hockey ball moving at 4.5 ms^{-1} is brought to rest by a player's stick. If the impulse given to the ball by the stick is 1.8 Ns in the direct opposite direction to the direction of motion of the ball, find the mass of the ball.

Q9 An empty dodgem car moving in a straight line at 1.2 ms^{-1} is given an impulse in the direction of motion which increases its speed to 2.1 ms^{-1}. Given that the impulse given by the push has magnitude 126 Ns, find the mass of the car.

Q10 A table tennis ball of mass 2.5 g is given an impulse of magnitude 0.03125 Ns by a bat. Given that the ball was moving at 5 ms^{-1} before receiving the impulse, and that as a result of the impulse, the ball's direction of motion is reversed, find the speed of the ball immediately after receiving the impulse.

Q10 Hint: Draw 'before' and 'after' diagrams if you need to.

Q11 A plane of mass 25 tonnes landing on a straight runway decelerates uniformly from a speed of 30 ms^{-1} to 1.8 ms^{-1} in 20 seconds.

a) Find the change in momentum of the plane.

b) Find the magnitude of the total resistive force acting on the plane.

Q12 An ice hockey puck of mass 180 g travelling in a straight line at 25 ms^{-1} across smooth ice strikes the back of a goal.
If the puck rebounds from the goal and moves back along the same straight line with a speed of 15 ms^{-1}, find:

a) the impulse exerted on the puck by the back of the goal,

b) the impulse exerted on the back of the goal by the puck.

Q13 A particle of mass 0.3 kg is dropped from a height of 10 m.

a) Find the speed of the particle when it hits the ground.

b) Given that the particle hits the ground at right angles and rebounds with a speed of 8 ms^{-1}, find the impulse exerted on the particle by the ground.

c) Find the maximum height reached by the particle after it rebounds.

Q13 Hint: Use the 'UVAST' equations here.

Q14 Two particles, A of mass 0.2 kg, and B, of mass 0.3 kg, are moving towards each other along the same straight line with speed 5 ms^{-1} and 8 ms^{-1} respectively. The bodies collide directly and B is brought to rest as a result of the collision. Find:

a) the magnitude of the impulse A gives to B,

b) the speed of A immediately after the impact.

Q14 Hint: Remember that the impulse A gives to B is equal in magnitude but opposite in direction to the impulse B gives to A.

Q15 A sled, P, of mass 1.2 tonnes moving across smooth ice at 7.2 kmh^{-1} slides into the back of another sled, Q, of mass 1.3 tonnes travelling in the same direction along the same straight line at 5.4 kmh^{-1}. Immediately following the collision, the 2 sleds continue to slide in the same straight line and in the same direction, and Q has speed 6.3 kmh^{-1}. Find:

a) the magnitude of the impulse given to Q by P,

b) the speed (in kmh^{-1}) of P immediately following the impact.

Q16 Hint: Consider only the change in momentum of A first.

Q16 A particle, A, of mass 4.8 kg moving at 2 ms^{-1} collides with another particle, B, of mass 2 kg travelling in the same straight line and in the same direction with a speed of u ms^{-1}.

If the impulse given to A by B has magnitude 2.4 Ns and the particles coalesce after impact and continue to move in the same direction with speed v ms^{-1}, find the values of u and v.

Q17 A red ball of mass 40 g is moving in a straight line with speed u ms^{-1} across a smooth plane. The red ball collides directly with a stationary blue ball of mass 60 g, as a result of which the red and blue balls have speed 0.8 ms^{-1} and 1.4 ms^{-1} respectively and the direction of motion of the red ball is reversed.

a) Find the value of u.

b) Find the magnitude of the impulse each ball receives in the collision.

Immediately following the collision, the blue ball is brought to rest by a constant resistive force of magnitude R N, acting directly opposite to its direction of motion. If the ball comes to rest exactly 3 seconds after the collision, find:

c) the value of R,

d) the distance the blue ball travels after the collision before coming to rest.

Q18 Hint: The particles are moving in opposite directions after the collision, so make sure you use the correct signs in your working.

Q18 Particles A and B, of mass M kg and $2M$ kg respectively, are moving across a smooth horizontal plane along the same straight line. The two particles collide directly, and following the collision, move in opposite directions, A with speed $\frac{U}{2}$ ms^{-1} and B with speed $\frac{U}{4}$ ms^{-1}. Given that the magnitude of the impulse each particle receives in the collision is $\frac{5MU}{2}$ Ns, describe the motion of the two particles immediately before the collision.

Review Exercise — Chapter 5

Q1 A horizontal force of 2 N acts on a 1.5 kg particle which is initially at rest on a smooth horizontal plane. Find the speed of the particle 3 seconds after it is released from rest.

Q2 Two forces act on a particle of mass 8 kg which is initially at rest on a smooth horizontal plane. The two forces are (24**i** + 18**j**) N and (6**i** + 22**j**) N (with **i** and **j** being perpendicular unit vectors in the plane). Find:

a) the magnitude and direction of the resulting acceleration of the particle,

b) the particle's distance from its starting point after 3 seconds.

Q3 A horizontal force P, acting on a 2 kg mass, generates an acceleration of 0.3 ms^{-2}.

a) Given that the mass is in contact with a rough horizontal plane which resists motion with a force of 1 N, find P.

b) Find the coefficient of friction, μ, to 2 d.p.

Q4 A brick of mass 1.2 kg is sliding down a rough plane which is inclined at 25° to the horizontal.

a) Given that the brick's acceleration is 0.3 ms^{-2}, find the coefficient of friction between the brick and the plane.

b) What assumptions have you made?

Q5

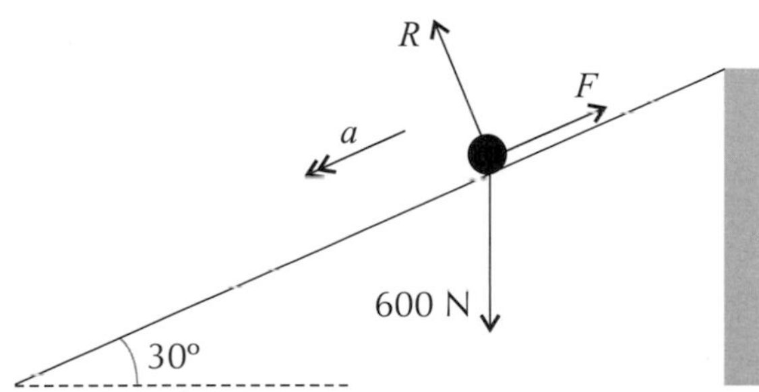

An army recruit of weight 600 N steps off a tower and accelerates down a "death slide" wire as shown. The recruit hangs from a light rope held between her hands and looped over the wire. The coefficient of friction between the rope and wire is 0.5. Given that the wire is 20 m long and makes an angle of 30° to the horizontal throughout its length, find how fast the recruit is travelling when she reaches the end of the wire.

Q6 A tractor of mass 2 tonnes experiences a resistance force of 1000 N whilst driving along a straight horizontal road. If the tractor engine provides a forward force of 1500 N and it's pulling a trailer of mass 1 tonne, and given that the tractor is accelerating at 0.05 ms^{-2}, find:

a) the resistance force acting on the trailer,

b) the tension in the coupling between the tractor and trailer.

Q7 Two particles are connected by a light, inextensible string and hang in a vertical plane either side of a fixed, smooth pulley. When released from rest the particles accelerate at 1.2 ms^{-2}. Given that the heavier particle has mass 4 kg, find the mass of the other particle.

Q8

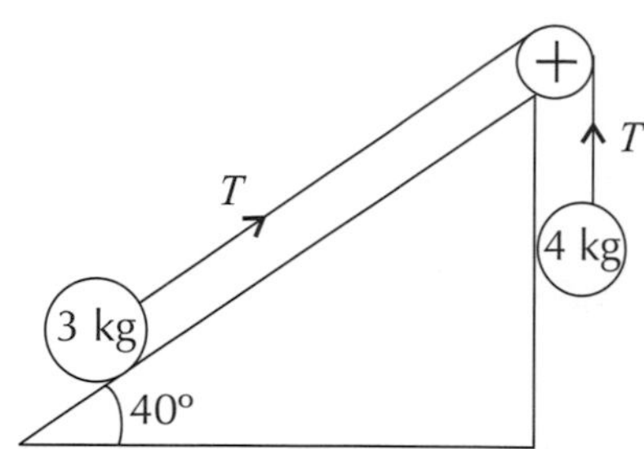

Two particles of mass 3 kg and 4 kg are connected by a light, inextensible string passing over a fixed, smooth pulley as shown. The 3 kg mass is on a smooth slope angled at 40° to the horizontal and the 4 kg mass hangs vertically below the pulley. Find:

a) the acceleration of the particles immediately after being released from rest,

b) the tension in the string,

c) the magnitude of force acting on the 3 kg mass in a direction parallel to the plane which would hold the particles in equilibrium.

Q9 Each diagram below represents the motion of two particles moving in the same straight line, before and after they collide. Find the missing mass or velocity in each case (masses are in kg and velocities are in ms^{-1}).

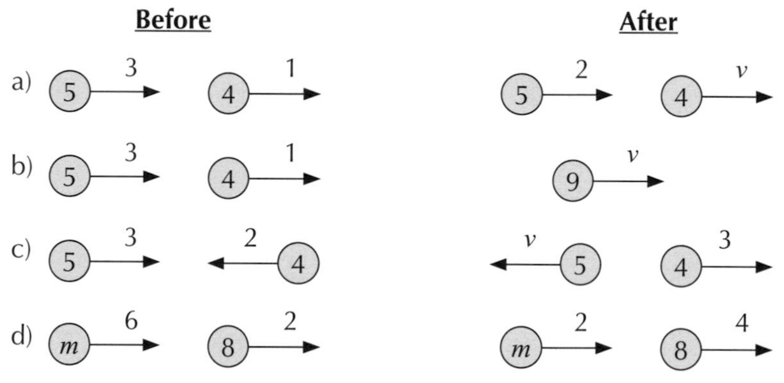

Q10 An impulse of 2 Ns acts on a ball of mass 300 g moving with velocity 5 ms^{-1}.
The impulse acts directly opposite to the direction of motion. Find the ball's new velocity.

Q11 A driving force of magnitude 8400 N acts on a train of mass 300 tonnes for 3 minutes.

a) Find the change in momentum of the train.

b) If the train starts from rest, find the final speed and the distance travelled.

Q12 A particle of mass 450 g is dropped from a height of 2 m onto a smooth, horizontal floor.
It rebounds to two thirds of its original height.
Find the impulse given to the particle by the ground.

Exam-Style Questions — Chapter 5

1

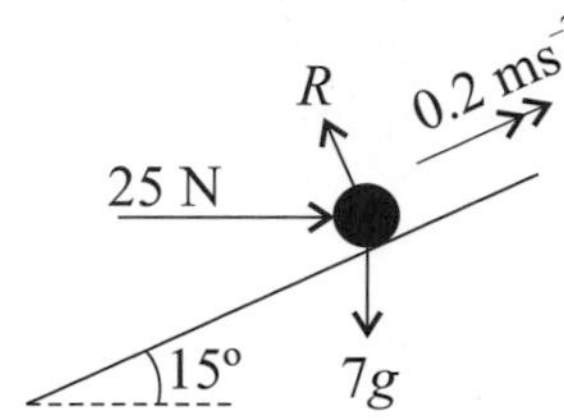

A horizontal force of 25 N causes a particle of mass 7 kg to accelerate up a rough plane inclined at 15° to the horizontal, with acceleration of magnitude 0.2 ms^{-2}, as shown.

a) Calculate the coefficient of friction between the mass and the plane to 2 d.p. *(5 marks)*

b) The 25 N force is now removed and the particle is released from rest. Find how long the particle takes to slide a distance of 3 m down the plane. *(7 marks)*

2 A car of mass 1500 kg is pulling a caravan of mass 500 kg. They experience resistive forces totalling 1000 N and 200 N respectively. The driving force generated by the car's engine is 2500 N. The coupling between the two does not break.

a) Find the acceleration of the car and caravan. *(3 marks)*

b) Find the tension in the coupling. *(2 marks)*

3 Two particles, P and Q, of mass 1 kg and m kg respectively, are linked by a light inextensible string passing over a smooth, fixed pulley, as shown below. P is on a rough slope inclined at 20° to the horizontal, where the coefficient of friction between P and the slope is 0.1, and Q hangs vertically below the pulley.

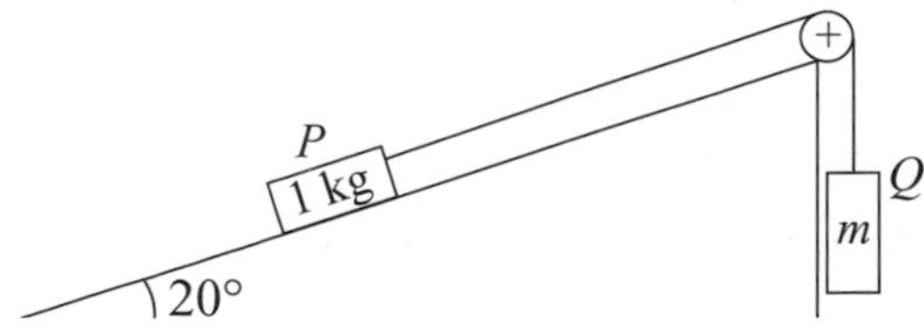

a) Given that P is on the point of sliding down the slope, find the mass of Q. *(5 marks)*

b) The mass of Q is changed to 1 kg and the particles are released from rest. Describe the motion of the system. *(5 marks)*

4 Two particles, A and B, of mass 0.8 kg and 1.2 kg respectively, are travelling in the same direction along the same straight line. A has speed 4 ms^{-1} and B has speed 2 ms^{-1}. A and B collide directly, as a result of which A continues moving in the same direction with speed 2.5 ms^{-1}.

Following the collision with A, B goes on to collide with a third particle, C, with mass m kg, travelling along the same straight line as B with speed 4 ms^{-1}, but in the opposite direction. Given that both B and C are brought to rest by this collision, find m.

(4 marks)

5 A coal wagon of mass 4 tonnes is rolling along a straight, smooth rail track with speed 2.5 ms^{-1}. It collides with a stationary wagon of mass 1 tonne. As a result of the collision, the wagons become coupled and move together along the track.

a) Find their speed after the collision. *(2 marks)*

b) Find the impulse given to the more massive wagon in the collision. *(2 marks)*

c) State two assumptions made in your model. *(2 marks)*

6 Two forces, $(x\mathbf{i} + y\mathbf{j})$ N and $(5\mathbf{i} + \mathbf{j})$ N, act on a particle, P, of mass 2.5 kg. The resultant of the two forces is $(8\mathbf{i} - 3\mathbf{j})$ N. Find:

a) the values of x and y, *(2 marks)*

b) the magnitude of the acceleration of P. *(3 marks)*

7 Two particles, A and B, are connected by a light, inextensible string which passes over a smooth, fixed pulley as shown below. A has a mass of 7 kg and B has a mass of 3 kg. The particles are released from rest with the string taut, and A falls until it strikes the ground at a speed of 5.9 ms^{-1}. Assume that A does not rebound after hitting the ground.

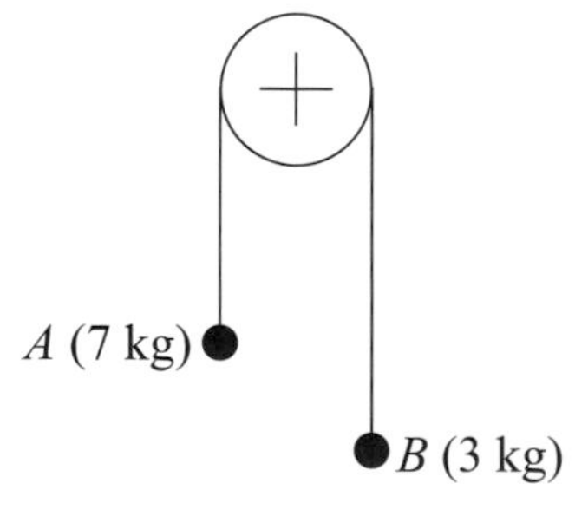

a) Find the time taken for A to hit the ground. *(4 marks)*

b) How far will B have travelled when A hits the ground? *(2 marks)*

c) Find the time (in s) from when A hits the ground until the string becomes taut again. *(4 marks)*

1. Moments

So far you've seen that a force applied to a particle can cause the particle to accelerate in a straight line in the direction of the force.

However, a force acting on a rigid body which is pivoted at a point along its length can cause the body to rotate about the pivot point.

Moments

- A **moment** is the **turning effect** a force has **around a point**.
- The **larger the magnitude** of the force, and the **greater the distance** between the force and the pivot, the **greater the moment**.
- Moments are either **clockwise** or **anticlockwise**.
- You can use the following formula to find the moment of a force about a point:

Moment = Magnitude of Force × Perpendicular Distance from the line of action of the force to the pivot

- Or, more concisely: **Moment =** Fd.
- If the force is measured in newtons and the distance is measured in metres, then the moment is measured in newton-metres, **Nm**.

Learning Objectives:

- Be able to find the moment of a force about a point.
- Be able to find the sum of moments about a point.
- Be able to find missing distances and forces in calculations involving rigid bodies in equilibrium.
- Be able to find the centre of mass of a non-uniform rod or beam.

Tip: The 'line of action' of the force is just the direction that the force acts in.

Example 1

A 2 m long plank is attached to a ship at one end, *O*. The plank is horizontal, and a bird lands on the other end, applying a downward force of magnitude 15 N, as shown. Model the plank as a light rod and find the turning effect of the bird on the plank.

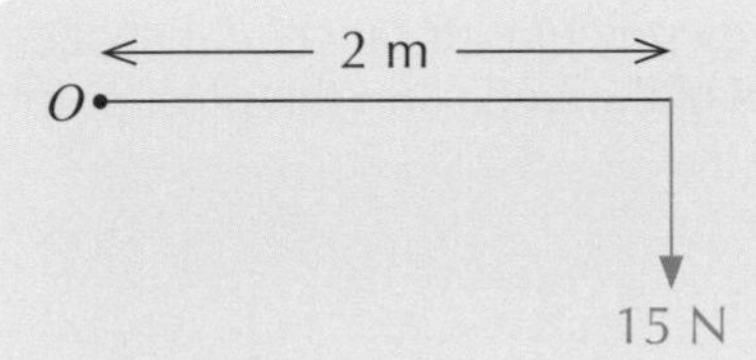

Use the formula:

Moment = Fd

= 15 × 2

= 30 Nm clockwise

Tip: Modelling the plank as a light rod means that you don't have to worry about its weight.

Tip: The point O is the pivot point.

Tip: Make sure you give a direction with your answer — i.e. which way the force will cause the rod to turn.

Example 2

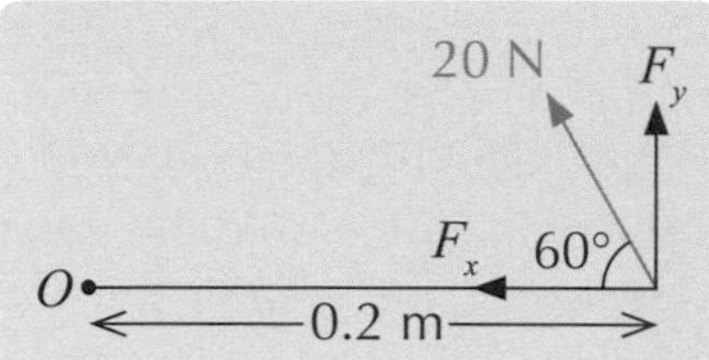

A spanner is attached to a bolt at a point, *O*. A force of 20 N is applied at an angle of 60° to the other end of the spanner, as shown.
Find the turning effect of the force upon the bolt.

- This time the force is acting at an angle — resolve the force to find its components acting parallel and perpendicular to the spanner:

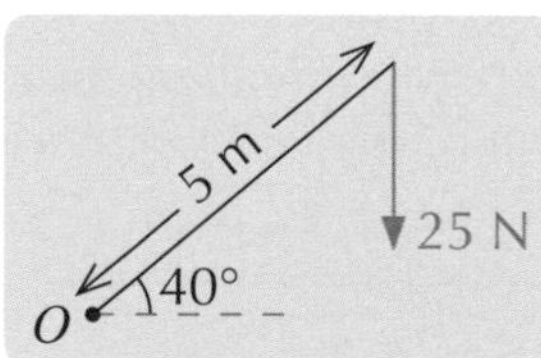

- F_x acts through O, so its moment is zero (it has no turning effect).
- Resolving perpendicular to the spanner, $F_y = 20\sin 60°$.
- F_y is a perpendicular distance of 0.2 m from O, so, using the formula:

  Moment = $20\sin 60° \times 0.2$
  = 3.46 Nm (3 s.f.) anticlockwise

Tip: 'Find the turning effect' means the same as 'find the moment'.

Tip: You can either find the component of the force acting perpendicular to the spanner (as done in the example), or you can find the perpendicular distance to the line of action of the force:

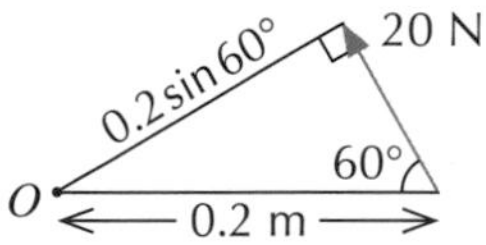

Moment = $20 \times 0.2\sin60°$

Example 3

A force of 25 N acts upon a point, *O*, via a light rod of length 5 m. The 25 N force acts vertically downwards, and the rod makes an angle of 40° with the horizontal, as shown.
What is the turning effect applied to *O*?

- You need the perpendicular distance, d, between the line of action of the force and the pivot point:

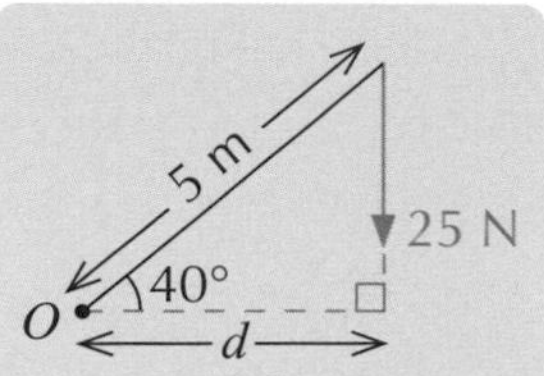

- $d = 5\cos 40°$, so:

  Moment = $25 \times 5\cos 40°$ = 95.8 Nm (3 s.f.) clockwise

Tip: You could've resolved the force to find the component acting perpendicular to the rod, as in Example 2:

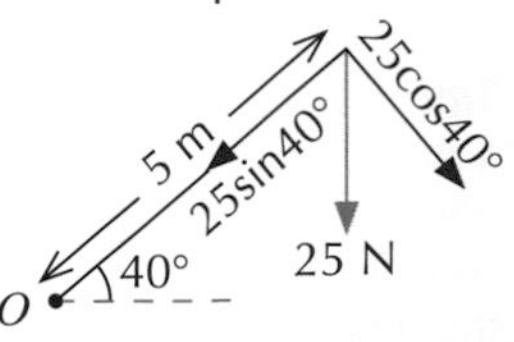

Moment = $25\cos40° \times 5$

Finding the sum of moments about a point

- If there are **two or more** forces acting on a rod or beam, then you can find the **sum of the moments** about a particular point.
- If the sum of the moments about a particular point is **zero**, then the rod is in **equilibrium** about **that point** (i.e. it **won't rotate** about that point).
- If the sum of the moments about a particular point is **not zero**, the rod will **turn** clockwise or anticlockwise about **that point**.
- The direction that the rod turns (i.e. clockwise or anticlockwise) is called the **sense** of rotation.

Example 4

The diagram shows the light rod AB. A force of magnitude 5 N acts vertically downwards at point C. A force of magnitude 4 N acts at point B, making an angle of 30° with the rod, as shown:

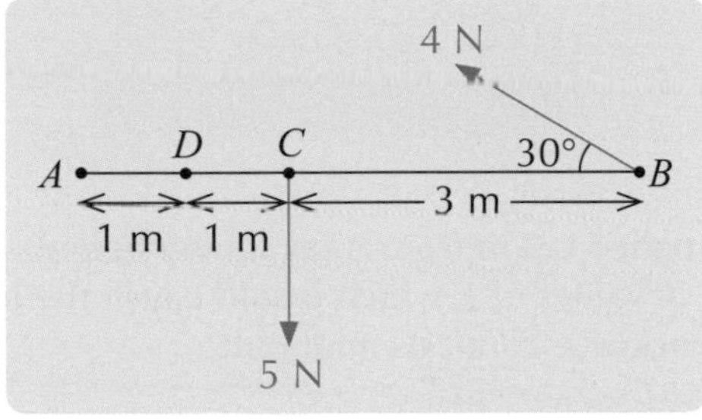

a) Show that the rod is in equilibrium about point A.

- Taking moments about A (with clockwise being the positive direction), and finding their sum:

  Sum of moments = (5 × 2) – (4 sin 30° × 5)
  = 10 – 10
  = 0 Nm

  This term is negative because the moment is anticlockwise.

- Total moment equals zero, so the rod is in equilibrium about A.

b) The rod is now pivoted at point D. Given that the forces acting on the rod are the same as in part a), will the rod rotate clockwise or anticlockwise about this point?

- Taking moments about D (with clockwise being the positive direction), and finding their sum:

  Sum of moments = (5 × 1) – (4 sin 30° × 4)
  = 5 – 8
  = –3 Nm

- The sum of moments is negative, so the rod will rotate anticlockwise.

Tip: When you're finding the sum of moments, you have to say which direction is positive — clockwise or anticlockwise.

Tip: Don't forget to resolve so that the line of action of the force and its distance from the pivot are perpendicular to each other.

Example 5

A light rod, AB, of length 4 m, is pivoted at its midpoint.
A 12 N force is applied to A, at an angle of 45° above the rod, and a 7 N force is applied to B, at an angle of 60° above the rod, as shown:

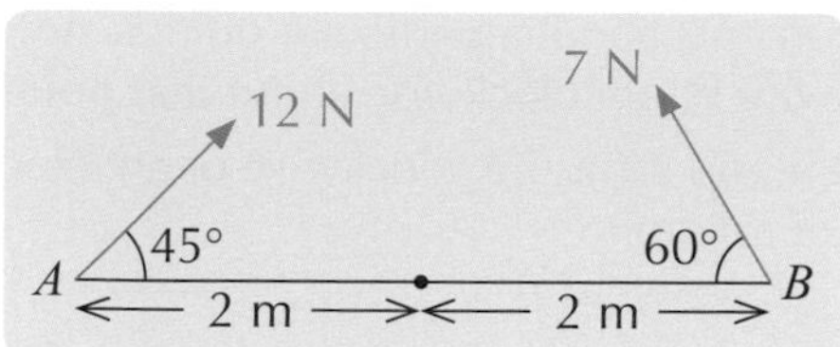

a) Find the sum of the moments about the midpoint.

- Taking moments about the midpoint (with clockwise positive), and finding their sum:

  Sum of moments $= (12\sin 45° \times 2) - (7\sin 60° \times 2)$

  $= (12\sqrt{2} - 7\sqrt{3})$ Nm

  $=$ **4.85 Nm (3 s.f.) clockwise**

Tip: The sense of rotation of the 12 N force is clockwise and the sense of rotation of the 7 N force is anticlockwise.

b) A force, F, is applied 0.5 m from A, as shown below. Find the range of values of F which would cause the beam to rotate anticlockwise about its midpoint.

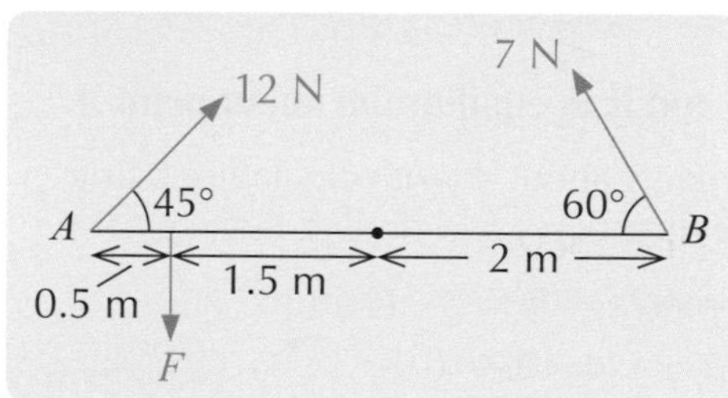

- Taking moments about the midpoint (with clockwise positive), and finding their sum:

  Sum of moments $= (12\sin 45° \times 2) - (7\sin 60° \times 2) - 1.5F$

  $= 12\sqrt{2} - 7\sqrt{3} - 1.5F$

- For the beam to rotate anticlockwise, the sum of moments must be negative:

  $12\sqrt{2} - 7\sqrt{3} - 1.5F < 0$

  $1.5F > 12\sqrt{2} - 7\sqrt{3}$

  $F > \left(8\sqrt{2} - \frac{14\sqrt{3}}{3}\right)$ N

  $\Rightarrow$ **$F > 3.23$ N (3 s.f.)**

Tip: The sum of moments must be negative for the beam to rotate anticlockwise, as clockwise was taken as the positive direction.

Example 6

***PQ* is a light rod of length 14 m inclined at an angle of 15° to the horizontal. A vertical force of magnitude 6 N acts at *P* and a horizontal force of magnitude 4 N acts at *Q*, as shown. The rod is pivoted at the point *X*.**

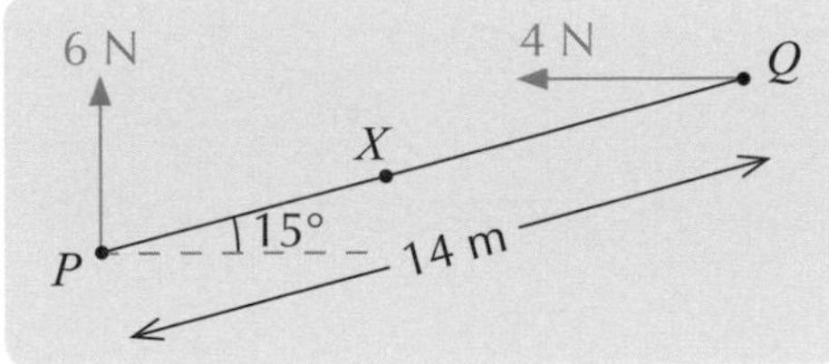

Given that the sum of the moments about *X* is 3 Nm anticlockwise, find the distance between *P* and *X*.

- Let d be the distance between P and X.
- First, find the perpendicular distances from X to the line of action of each force:

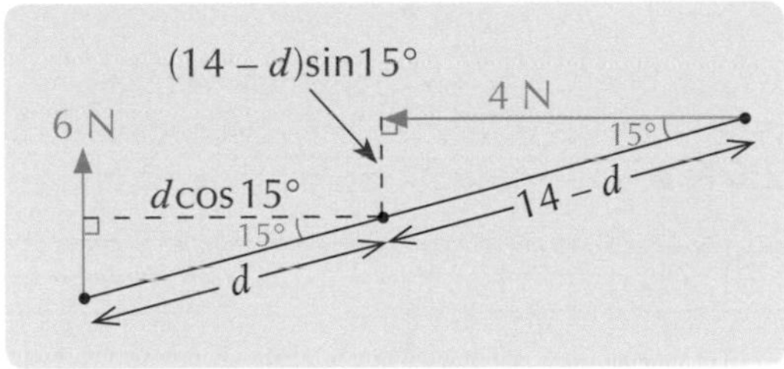

> **Tip:** Here, alternate angles are used to find the perpendicular distances — there are plenty of other ways you can do it.

- Now take moments about X (with <u>anticlockwise</u> positive), and find their sum:

  Sum of moments $= [4 \times (14 - d)\sin 15°] - (6 \times d\cos 15°)$
  $= 56\sin 15° - 4d\sin 15° - 6d\cos 15°$
  $= 56\sin 15° - d(4\sin 15° + 6\cos 15°)$

> **Tip:** You could take clockwise as positive if you wanted — the sum of the moments would then be –3 Nm.

- Sum of moments is 3 Nm, so:

  $3 = 56\sin 15° - d(4\sin 15° + 6\cos 15°)$

  $$\Rightarrow d = \frac{56\sin 15° - 3}{4\sin 15° + 6\cos 15°}$$

  $= 1.68$ m (3 s.f.)

Exercise 1.1

Q1 For each of the following light rods, find the moment of the force about A.

a) b) c)

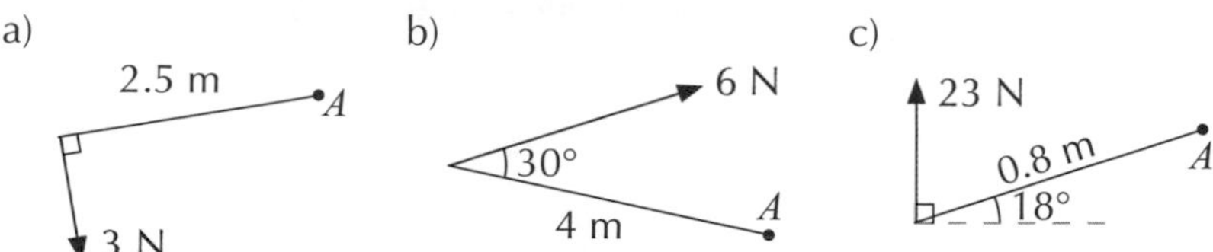

Q2 For each of the following light rods, find the sum of the moments about X.

a)

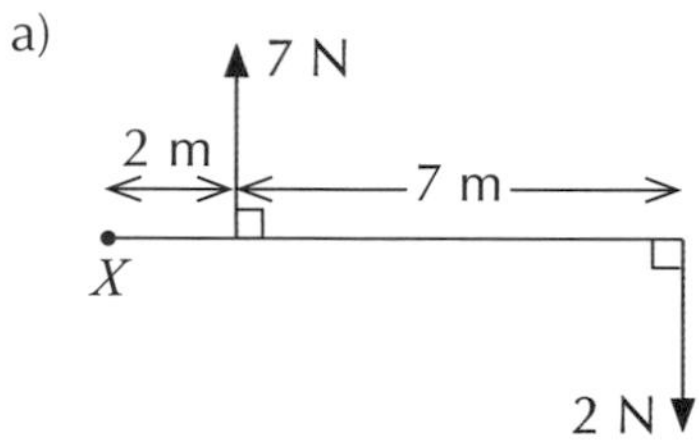

b)

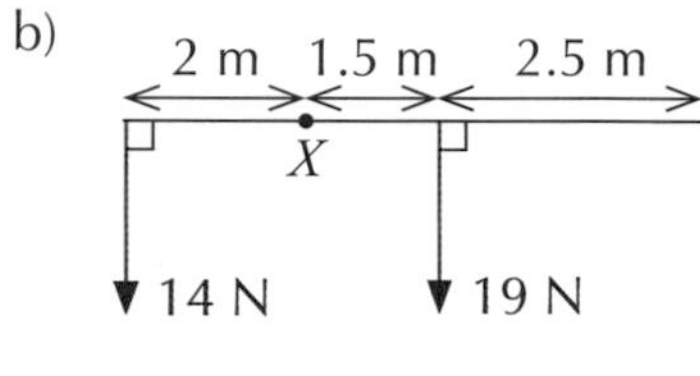

c)

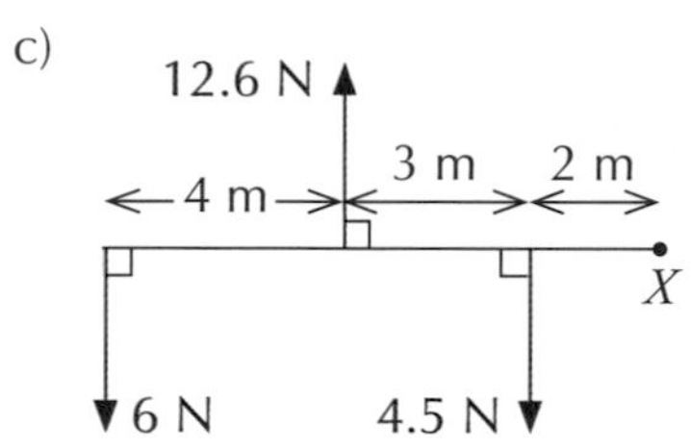

d)

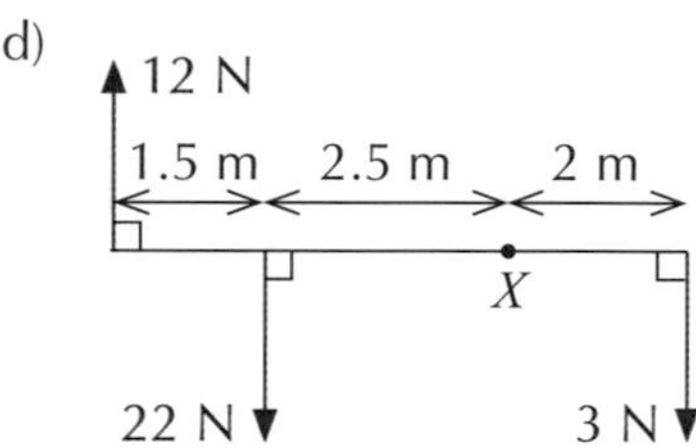

e)

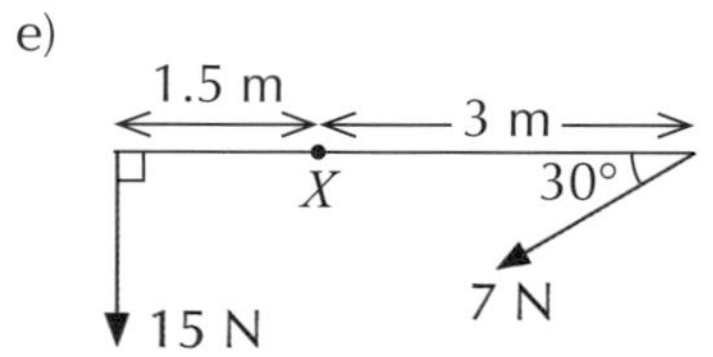

f)

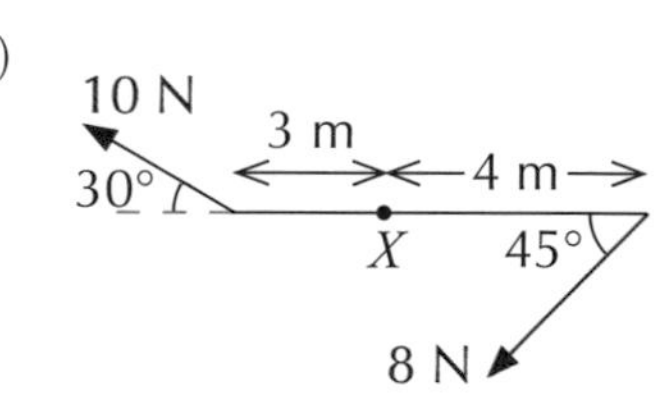

g)

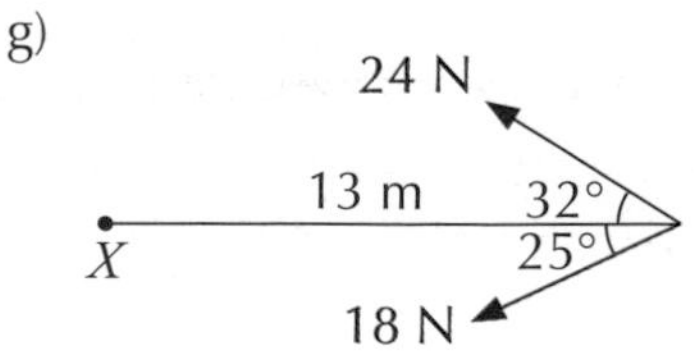

h)

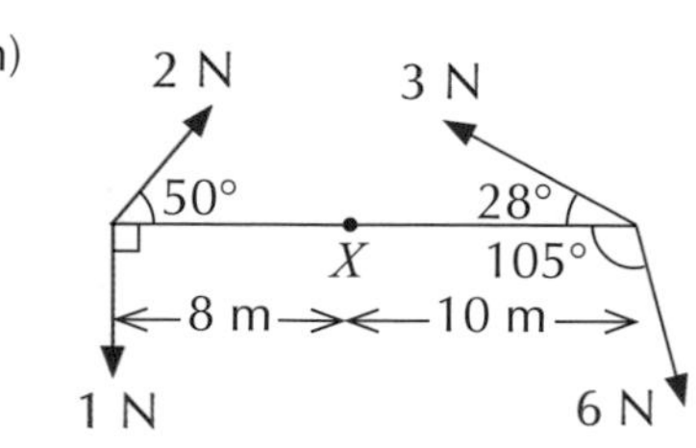

Q3

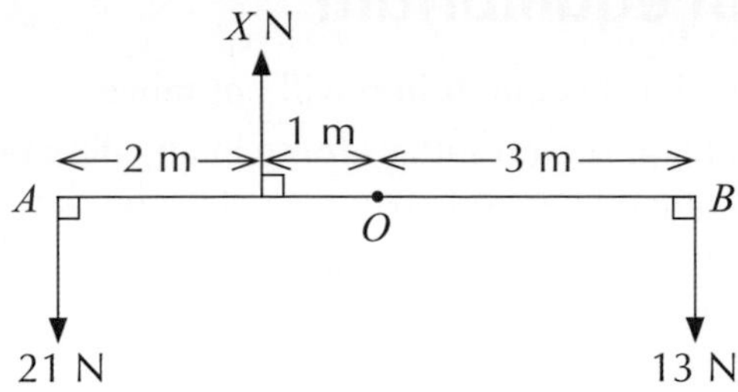

The diagram shows the light rod AB. Find the range of possible values for X, given that AB rotates clockwise about the point O.

Q4

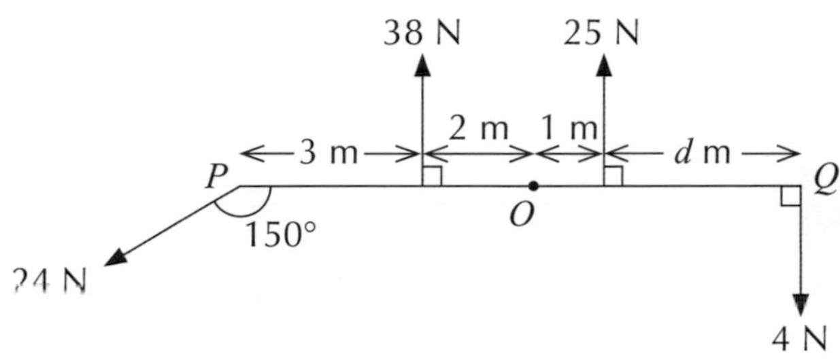

The diagram shows the light rod PQ. Find the range of possible values for d which will cause PQ to rotate anticlockwise about the point O.

Q5

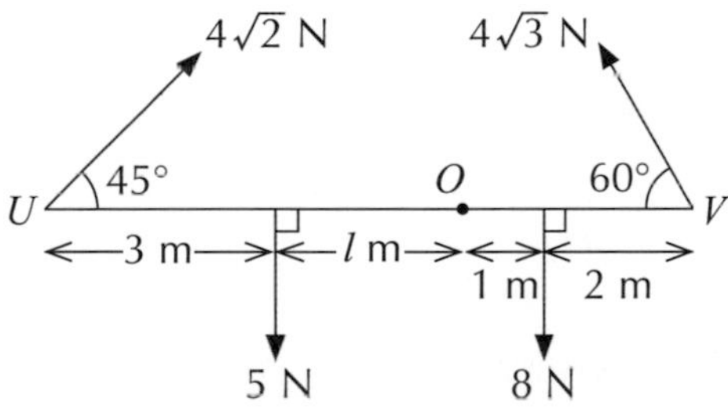

The diagram shows the light rod UV. The sum of the moments about O is 0.5 Nm anticlockwise. Find the value of l.

Q6

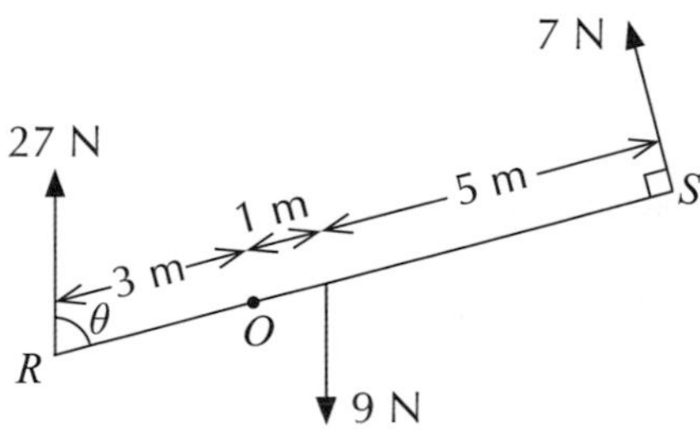

The diagram shows the light rod RS. The 27 N force and the 9 N force both act vertically. The 7 N force acts perpendicular to the rod. Find the value of θ given that the sum of the moments about O is 3 Nm clockwise.

Q6 Hint: You can either resolve forces perpendicular to the rod, or just calculate the perpendicular distances.

Moments in equilibrium

- A rigid body which is in **equilibrium** will **not move**.
- This means that there is **no resultant force** in **any direction** — any forces acting on the body will cancel each other out.
- It also means that the **sum of the moments** on the body **about any point** is **zero**.
- So, for a body in equilibrium:

Total Clockwise Moment	=	Total Anticlockwise Moment

- By **resolving forces** and **equating clockwise and anticlockwise moments**, you can solve problems involving bodies in equilibrium.

Example 1

Two weights of 30 N and 45 N are placed on a light 8 m beam. The 30 N weight is at one end of the beam, as shown, whilst the other weight is a distance *d* from the midpoint, *M*. The beam is held in equilibrium by a light, inextensible wire with tension *T* attached at *M*.

Find *T* and the distance *d*.

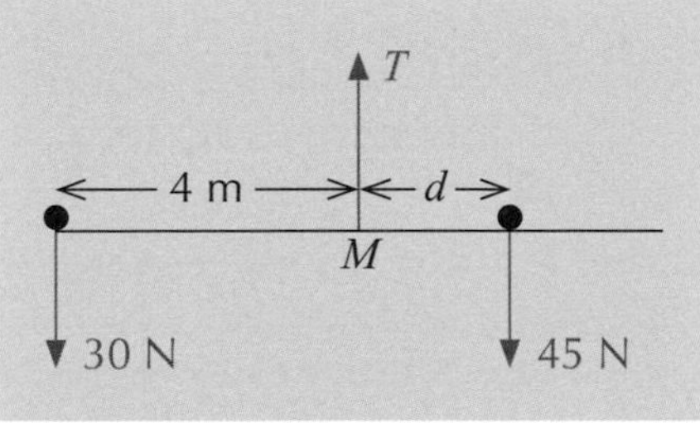

- First resolve forces vertically (forces 'up' = forces 'down'):

$T = 30 + 45$

$= 75 \text{ N}$

- Then take moments about M (moments clockwise = moments anticlockwise):

$45d = 30 \times 4$

$\Rightarrow d = 120 \div 45$

$= 2.67 \text{ m (3 s.f.)}$

Tip: The line of action of T passes through M, so the moment of T about M is zero.

Example 2

The diagram below shows a light rod AB, of length 10 m. Particles of mass M_A kg and M_B kg are placed at A and B respectively. The rod is supported in equilibrium by two vertical reaction forces of magnitude 145 N and 90 N, as shown below:

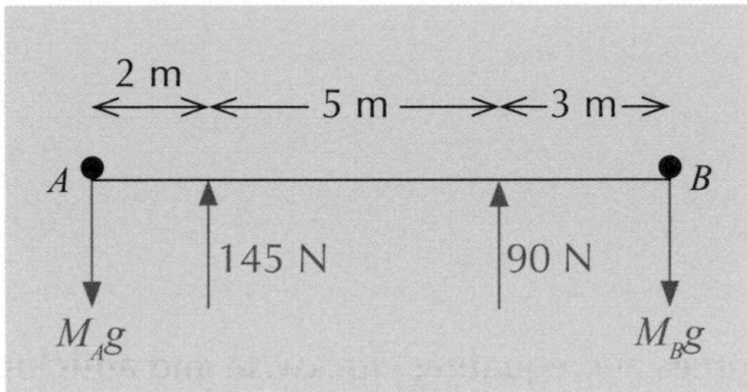

Find the values of M_A and M_B.

- As the rod is in equilibrium, you know that clockwise moments = anticlockwise moments. So, taking moments about A:

$$M_Bg \times 10 = (145 \times 2) + (90 \times 7)$$
$$\Rightarrow M_B = 920 \div 98$$
$$= 9.387... = 9.39 \text{ kg (3 s.f.)}$$

- You also know that there is no resultant force acting on the rod. So, resolving forces vertically ('forces up' = 'forces down'):

$$145 + 90 = M_Ag + M_Bg$$
$$\Rightarrow M_A + M_B = 235 \div 9.8 = 23.979...$$
$$\Rightarrow M_A = 23.979... - 9.387...$$
$$= 14.6 \text{ kg (3 s.f.)}$$

Tip: It's a good idea to take moments about a point where an unknown force is acting, as the moment of that force about the point will be zero, and it won't appear in the equation.

Centres of mass

- The **centre of mass** (**COM**) of an object is the point where the object's **weight** can be considered to act.
- The mass of a **uniform beam** is spread evenly along the length of the beam, and so the centre of mass is at its **midpoint**:

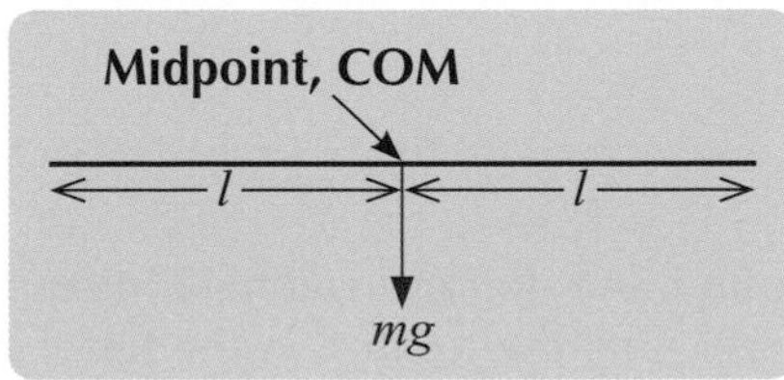

- The centre of mass of a **non-uniform beam** could be at **any point** along the beam.
- When you're **taking moments** and **resolving forces** for a heavy (i.e. not light) beam, you need to remember to include the **weight** of the beam in your calculations.

Tip: Up until now, all the beams have been light, so you haven't needed to worry about their weights.

Example 3

A 6 m long uniform beam AB of weight 40 N is supported at A by a vertical reaction R. AB is held horizontally by a vertical wire attached 1 m from the other end. A particle of weight of 30 N is placed 2 m from the support R.

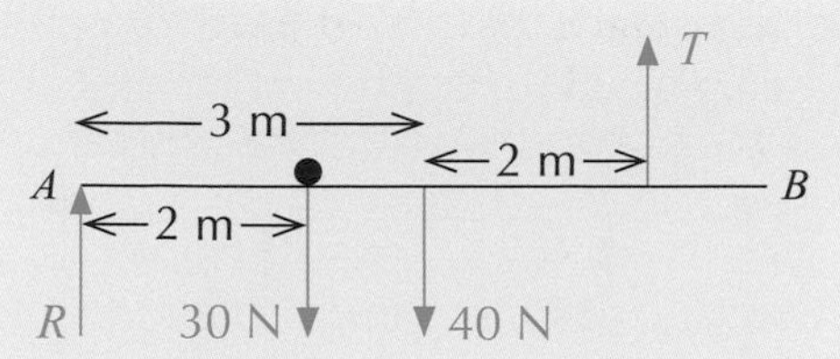

Find the tension T in the wire and the force R.

- Taking moments about A:

  Clockwise moments = Anticlockwise moments

  $(30 \times 2) + (40 \times 3) = 5T$

  This is the weight of the beam, acting at its centre.

  $\Rightarrow T = 180 \div 5 = 36 \text{ N}$

- Resolving vertically:

  $T + R = 30 + 40$

  $R = 70 - T = 70 - 36$

  $= 34 \text{ N}$

Example 4

A Christmas banner, AB, is attached to a ceiling by two pieces of tinsel. One piece of tinsel is attached to A, the other to the point C, where $BC = 0.6$ m. The banner has mass 8 kg and length 3.6 m and is held in equilibrium in a horizontal position.

a) Modelling the banner as a uniform rod held in equilibrium and the tinsel as light strings, find the tension in the tinsel at A and C.

- Taking moments about A:

  $(8g \times 1.8) = 3T_C$

  $\Rightarrow T_C = 141.2 \div 3 = 47.04 \text{ N}$

- Resolving vertically:

$T_A + T_C = 8g$

$\Rightarrow T_A = 8g - T_C = 78.4 - 47.04$

$= 31.36 \text{ N}$

b) The tinsel at A snaps and a downward force is applied at B to keep the banner horizontal and in equilibrium. Find the magnitude of the force applied at B and the new tension in the tinsel attached at C.

- Draw a diagram to show the new situation:

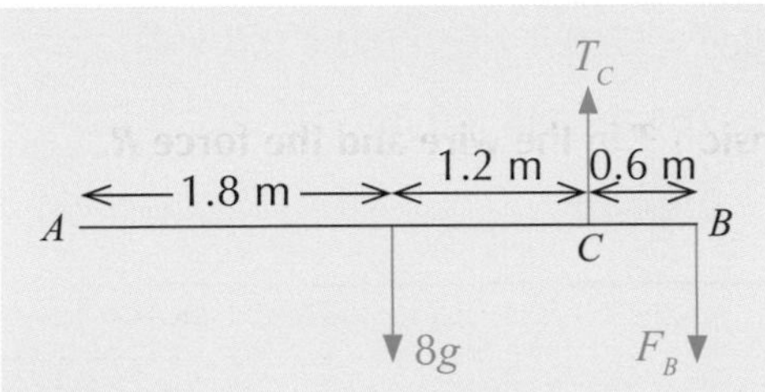

- Taking moments about C.

$8g \times 1.2 = F_B \times 0.6$

$\Rightarrow F_B = 94.08 \div 0.6$

$= 156.8 \text{ N}$

- Resolving vertically:

$T_C = 8g + F_B$

$= (8 \times 9.8) + 156.8$

$= 235.2 \text{ N}$

Example 5

A non-uniform beam of length 8 m and mass 48 kg is supported by legs attached at P and Q, 1 m from each end of the beam. A gymnast of mass 60 kg balances on the beam, 4 m from P. The reaction in the support at P has magnitude 539 N.

a) Draw a diagram showing the forces acting on the beam.

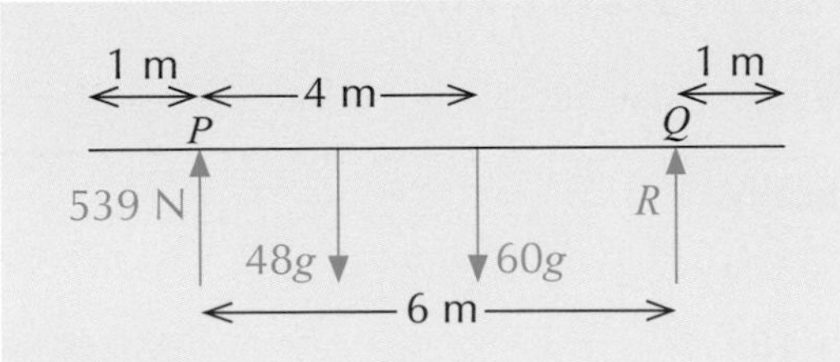

Tip: The beam is non-uniform, so you don't know exactly where its centre of mass is. Just draw the beam's weight acting *somewhere* on the beam.

b) Find the magnitude of the reaction at Q, and d, the distance of the centre of mass of the beam from P.

- Resolving vertically:

  $539 + R = 48g + 60g$

  $\Rightarrow R = 108g - 539$

  $= 519.4 \text{ N}$

- Taking moments about P:

  $(60g \times 4) + (48g \times d) = 519.4 \times 6$

  $\Rightarrow 48gd = (519.4 \times 6) - (60 \times 9.8 \times 4)$

  $\Rightarrow d = 764.4 \div (48 \times 9.8)$

  $= 1.625 \text{ m}$

The point of tilting

If a rod is '**about to tilt**' about a particular point of support, then any **normal reactions** acting at any other supports along the rod will be **zero**. The **tension** in any strings supporting the rod at any other point will also be **zero**.

Example 6

A non-uniform wooden plank of mass M kg rests horizontally on supports at A and B, as shown. When a bucket of water of mass 18 kg is placed at point C, the plank is in equilibrium, and is on the point of tilting about B.

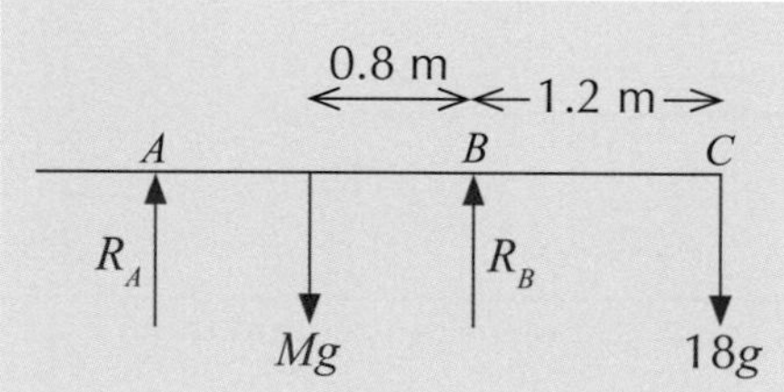

Find the value of M and the magnitude of the reaction at B.

Tip: The plank is on the point of tilting about B, so the reaction at A, R_A, is zero.

- Taking moments about B:

  $(18g \times 1.2) + 0 = Mg \times 0.8$

  $R_A = 0$, so the moment of the force is also zero.

  $\Rightarrow M = (18 \times 9.8 \times 1.2) \div (9.8 \times 0.8)$

  $= 27 \text{ kg}$

- Resolving vertically:

  $R_A + R_B = Mg + 18g$

  $0 + R_B = 27g + 18g$

  $\Rightarrow R_B = 441 \text{ N}$

Exercise 1.2

Q1

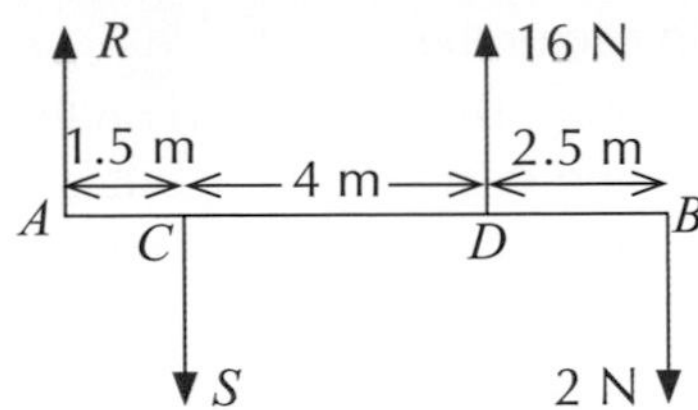

The diagram shows a light rod held horizontally in equilibrium by two vertical strings. Find the magnitudes of the forces R and S.

Q2

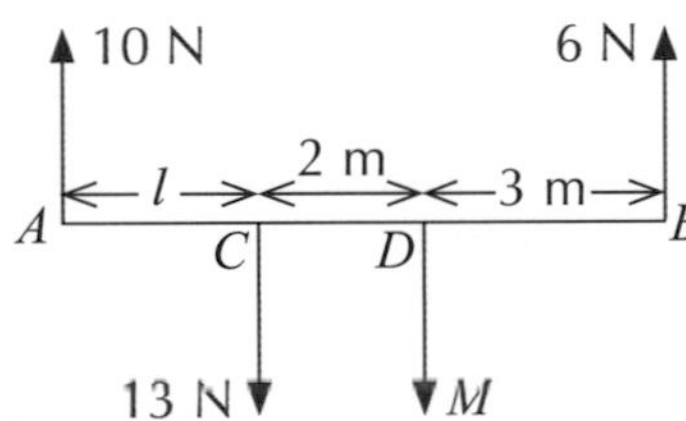

The diagram shows a light rod held horizontally in equilibrium by two vertical strings. Find the magnitude of the force M, and the distance l.

Q3

1.5 m
2 m
A
C
D
B
49 N
Mg
R_D

A uniform rod, AB, of length 5 m, rests horizontally in equilibrium on supports at C and D, as shown. If the magnitude of the normal reaction at C is 49 N, find:

a) the magnitude of the normal reaction at D,

b) the mass of the rod.

Q3 Hint: The rod is uniform, so its weight acts halfway along its length.

Q4

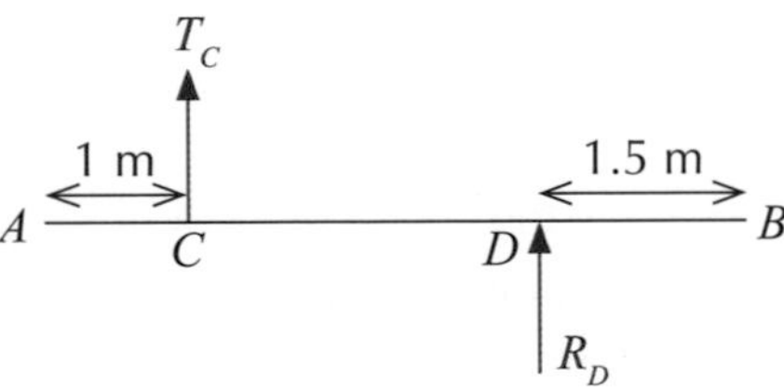

A uniform rod, AB, of mass 9 kg, is held in equilibrium by a vertical wire at C and a support at D, as shown. When an object of mass 3 kg is placed at B, the rod is still horizontal and in equilibrium, but is on the point of tilting about D.
Find the length of the rod.

Q4 Hint: When the rod is on the point of tilting about D, the tension in the wire at C will be zero.

Q5 A uniform beam, AB, has length 5 m and mass 8 kg. It is held horizontally in equilibrium by vertical ropes at B and the point C, 1 m from A.

a) Find the tension in each rope.

b) When a particle of mass 16 kg is placed on the beam, the beam remains horizontal and in equilibrium, but is on the point of tilting about C. Find the distance of the particle from A.

Q6

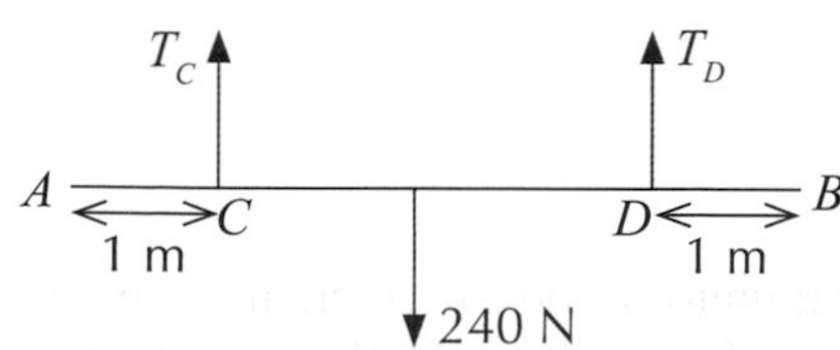

A 9 m long non-uniform beam, AB, of weight 240 N, is suspended between two trees to make a walkway. It is held in equilibrium by vertical wires at C and D, as shown. The magnitude of the tension in the wire at C is twice the magnitude of the tension in the wire at D.

a) Find the tension in each wire.

b) Find the distance of the centre of mass of the beam from A.

Q7 A non-uniform plank, AB, of length 6 m, is laid across a stream to form a bridge. A and B rest on horizontal ground, and the midpoint of the plank rests on a rock protruding from the water. A child of mass 36 kg stands on the bridge 1 m from A and a child of mass 25 kg stands on the bridge 1.5 m from B. The centre of mass of the plank is at point X, 2.5 m from B. The reaction at B is twice the reaction at A, and the reaction of the rock at the midpoint is four times the reaction at A.

a) Draw a diagram to show the forces acting on the plank.

b) Given that the plank is in equilibrium, find its mass.

c) State any modelling assumptions you have made.

Q8 A painter of mass 80 kg stands on a horizontal non-uniform 4 m plank, AB, of mass 20 kg. The plank rests on supports 1 m from each end, at C and D. The painter places paint pots, of mass 2.5 kg, 0.2 m from each end of the plank.

a) He stands at the centre of mass of the plank and finds that the reaction forces at C and D are in the ratio 4 : 1. Find the distance of the centre of mass of the plank from A.

b) He uses up all the paint in the pot near A, and discards the pot. He then stands on the plank at a point between D and B, and the plank is on the point of tilting about D. How far is he from B?

Q8 Hint: The reaction forces at C and D are in the ratio 4 : 1, so $R_C = 4R_D$.

Review Exercise — Chapter 6

Q1 For each of the following light rods, find the moment of the force about A.

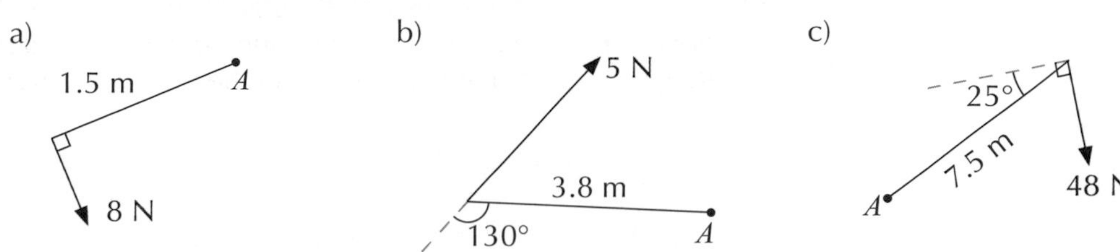

Q2 A horizontal uniform rod AB of length 12 m and mass 1.6 kg is acted on by an upward vertical force of magnitude 23 N at B. Find the sum of the moments about A.

Q3

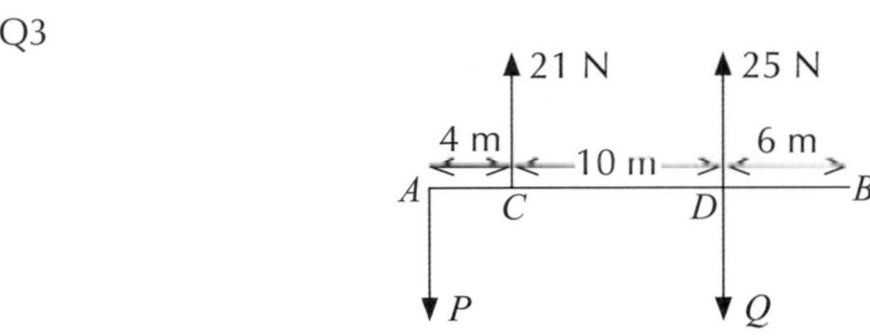

The diagram shows a light rod held horizontally in equilibrium by two vertical strings. Find the magnitudes of the forces P and Q.

Q4

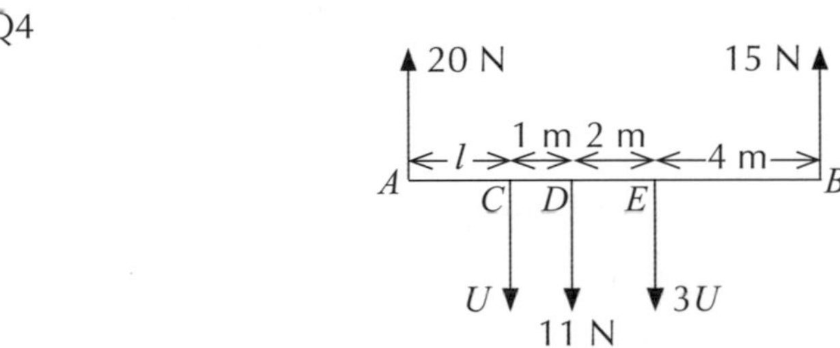

The diagram shows a light rod held horizontally in equilibrium by two vertical strings. Find U and l, giving your answers in N and m respectively.

Q5

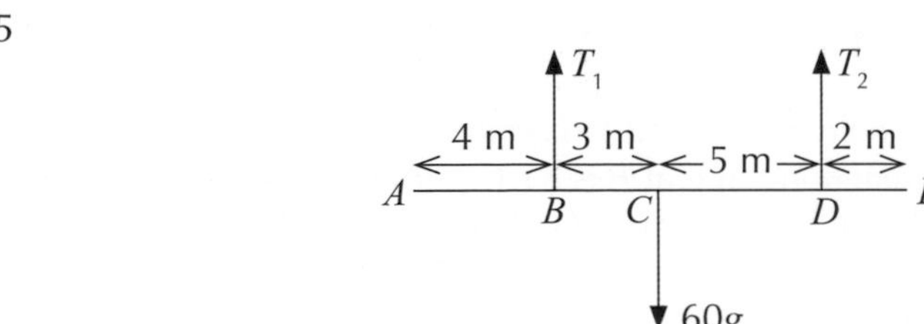

A 60 kg uniform beam, AE, of length 14 m, is horizontal and in equilibrium, supported by two vertical ropes attached to B and D, as shown. Find the tension in the two ropes.

Q6 A uniform rod of mass 3.5 kg is pivoted about one of its ends. When the rod is horizontal, there is a moment of 205.8 Nm about the pivot. Assuming that the only forces acting on the rod are its weight and the reaction at the pivot, find the rod's length.

Q7

←2.5 m→
A M B C
R_A $1.5g$ 44 N F N

A non-uniform rod of mass 1.5 kg rests horizontally in equilibrium on supports at A and B, as shown. When a downwards force of magnitude F N is applied to the rod at C, the rod remains horizontal and in equilibrium, but is on the point of tilting about B, where the normal reaction has magnitude 44 N.
Given that the distance between B and the centre of mass of the rod is 2.5 m, find:

a) the value of F,

b) the distance between the points B and C.

Q8

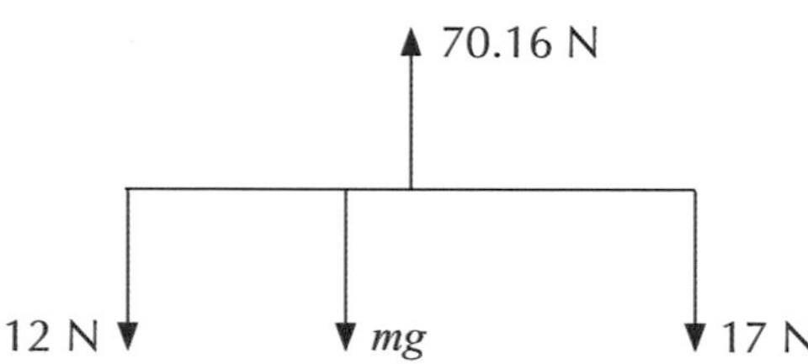

A non-uniform beam of length 13 m is suspended from a vertical wire attached to its midpoint. Downward vertical forces of magnitude 12 N and 17 N are applied to the ends of the beam, as shown. The tension in the wire is 70.16 N, and the beam is horizontal and in equilibrium. Find:

a) the mass of the beam,

b) the distance of the centre of mass of the beam from its midpoint.

Q9

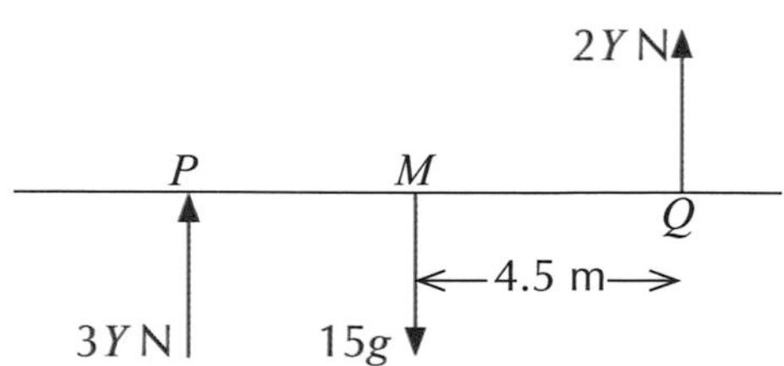

A non-uniform beam of mass 15 kg is held horizontally in equilibrium by a support at P and a vertical string at Q, as shown. The reaction force at P is $3Y$ N and the tension in the string is $2Y$ N. The centre of mass, M, of the beam is 4.5 m from Q. Find:

a) the value of Y,

b) the distance between the points P and M.

Exam-Style Questions — Chapter 6

1

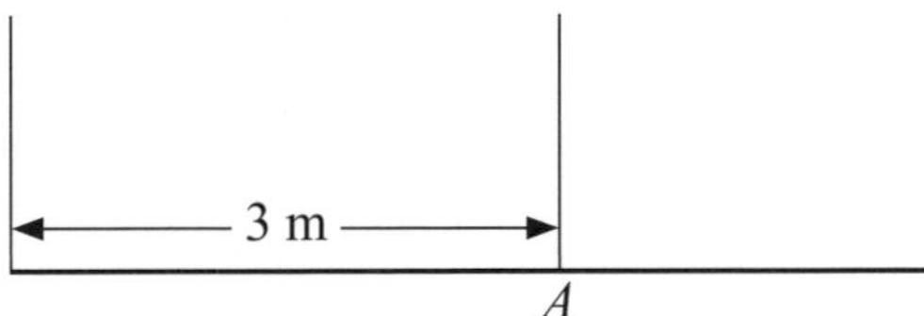

A horizontal uniform beam of length x and weight 18 N is held in equilibrium by two strings. One string is attached to one end of the beam and the other at point A, 3 m from the first string, as shown. The tension in the string at point A is 12 N.

Show that $x = 4$ m.

(2 marks)

2 A horizontal uniform beam, AB, of weight 16 N and length 10 m, is acted on by a set of forces. A downward vertical force of magnitude 31 N acts at B, an upward vertical force of magnitude $5X$ N acts 1 m from B, and a downward vertical force of magnitude X N acts at A. The point O is 2 m from A.

a) Draw a diagram to show the forces acting on the beam. *(2 marks)*

b) The rod is pivoted at O. Find the range of possible values for X for which the beam will rotate in such a way that A moves downwards and B moves upwards. *(4 marks)*

3 A 6 m long uniform beam of mass 20 kg is in equilibrium. One end is resting on a vertical pole, and the other end is held up by a vertical wire attached to that end so that the beam rests horizontally. There are two 10 kg weights attached to the beam, situated 2 m from either end.

a) Draw a diagram of the beam including all the forces acting on it. *(2 marks)*

Find, in terms of g:

b) T, the tension in the wire, *(3 marks)*

c) R, the normal reaction at the pole. *(2 marks)*

4 A non-uniform plank of wood, AB, is used to make a swing. The plank has mass 16 kg and length l m, and is held horizontal by vertical ropes attached at A and B.

a) When a boy of mass 12 kg sits at the centre of the plank, the tensions in the ropes at A and B are in the ratio 4 : 3 respectively. Find an expression, in terms of l, for the distance of the centre of mass of the plank from A. *(4 marks)*

b) The boy moves so that he is sat on the plank 1 m from B. The tensions in the ropes at A and B are now equal. Find the length of the plank. *(4 marks)*

c) State any modelling assumptions you have made. *(2 marks)*

5 A uniform beam AB of weight w N and length 7 m is pivoted at its midpoint. A body of mass 30 kg is placed on the beam, 1 m from A, and a body of mass m kg is placed on the beam, 1.5 m from B.

a) Draw a diagram to show the forces acting on the beam. *(2 marks)*

b) Given that the beam is initially horizontal, find the range of values of m for which the beam will rotate in such a way that A moves upwards and B moves downwards. *(4 marks)*

c) The body of mass m kg is replaced by a body of mass 12 kg. Find the distance that the body of mass 30 kg must be moved along the beam towards the pivot for the rod to be horizontal and in equilibrium. *(3 marks)*

6 A uniform log XY rests horizontally on two rocks P and Q, where $XP = l$ m, $0.5 < l < 0.9$, and $PQ = 0.4$ m. The log has weight 80 N and length 1.8 m, and the reaction at Q is 50 N.

a) Draw a diagram to show the forces acting on the log. *(2 marks)*

b) Find the value of l. *(3 marks)*

A large bird lands gently on the end of the log at Y, causing it to almost tip over about Q.

c) List three assumptions you would make when modelling the log, the rocks and the bird. *(3 marks)*

d) Find the mass of the bird. *(4 marks)*

e) Find the magnitude of the normal reaction at Q. *(2 marks)*

Answers

Chapter 1: Mathematical Models

1. Modelling

Exercise 1.1 — Modelling

Q1

W

Assumptions:
The apple is modelled as a particle.
The apple is initially at rest.
Air resistance can be ignored.
There are no other external forces acting.
The effect of gravity (g) is constant.

Q2

T

W

Assumptions:
The conker is modelled as a bead.
The shoelace is a light, inextensible string.
There are no other external forces acting.

Q3

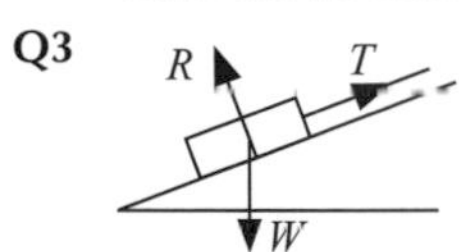

Assumptions:
The sledge is modelled as a particle.
The surface of the slope is smooth (it's icy).
The rope is a light, inextensible string.
The rope is parallel to the slope.
There are no other external forces acting.

Q4 a)

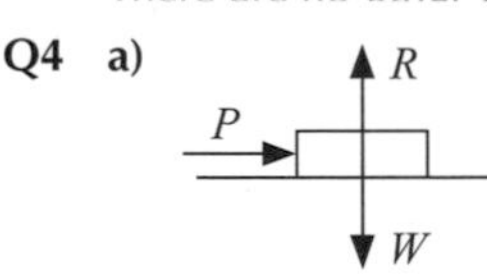

Assumptions:
The box is modelled as a particle.
The floor is smooth (it's polished).
There are no other external forces acting.

b)

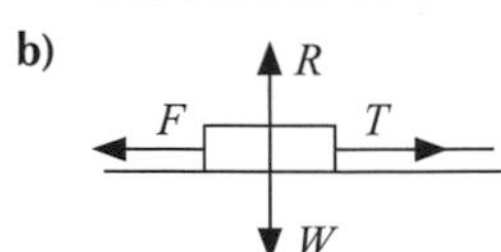

Assumptions:
The crate is modelled as a particle.
The rope is light and inextensible.
The floor is rough.
There are no other external forces acting.

Q5

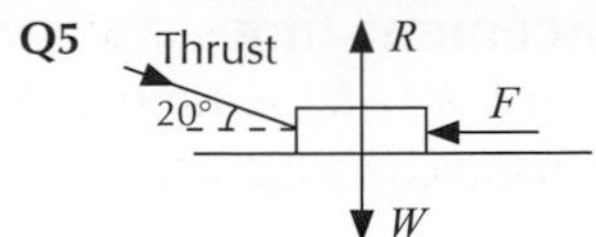

Assumptions:
The package is modelled as a particle.
The stick is light and rigid.
The ground is rough.
There are no other external forces acting.

Q6 a)

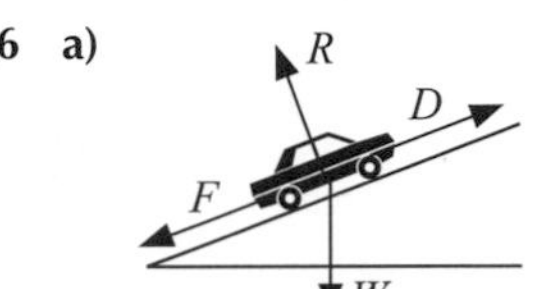

Assumptions:
The car is modelled as a particle.
The angle of the slope is constant.
The surface is rough.
There are no other external forces acting.

b)

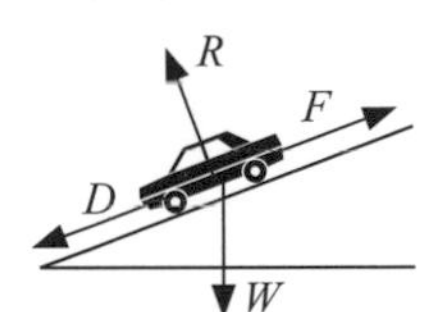

Assumptions:
The car is modelled as a particle.
The angle of the slope is constant.
The surface is rough.
There are no other external forces acting.

Q7

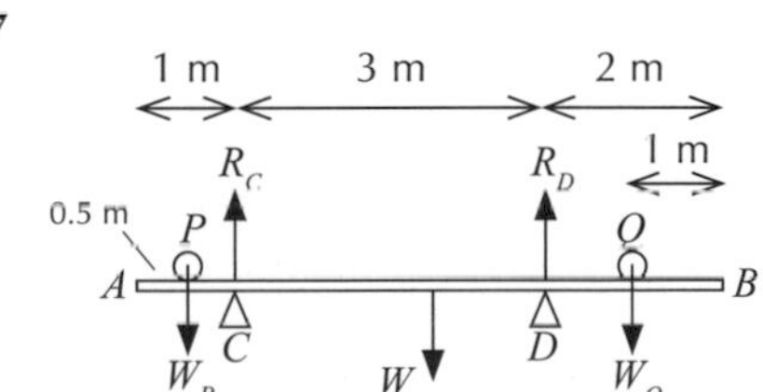

Assumptions:
The plank is modelled as a static, uniform, rigid beam.
The plank is horizontal.
P and Q are modelled as particles.
Each support acts at a single point.
There are no other external forces acting.

Chapter 2: Kinematics

1. Motion Graphs

Exercise 1.1 — Displacement-time graphs

Q1 The velocity is given by the gradient of the graph.
First stage:

$v = \text{gradient} = \frac{(40 - 0)\text{ km}}{(0.5 - 0)\text{ h}} = 80 \text{ kmh}^{-1}$

Second stage:

$v = \frac{(60 - 40)\text{ km}}{(1.5 - 0.5)\text{ h}} = 20 \text{ kmh}^{-1}$

Third stage:

$v = \frac{(0 - 60)\text{ km}}{(2 - 1.5)\text{ h}} = -120 \text{ kmh}^{-1}$

Q2 *A*: Starts from rest.

B: Travels 4 m in 20 s. Calculate the gradient to find the velocity during this stage:
$v = \frac{4\text{ m}}{20\text{ s}} = 0.2 \text{ ms}^{-1}$

C: Travels –2 m in 10 s.
$v = \frac{-2\text{ m}}{10\text{ s}} = -0.2 \text{ ms}^{-1}$

D: Stationary for 10 s.

E: Travels 4 m in 30 s.
$v = \frac{4\text{ m}}{30\text{ s}} = 0.133 \text{ ms}^{-1}$ (3 s.f.)

F: Stationary for 10 s.

G: Travels –6 m in 25 s.
$v = \frac{-6\text{ m}}{25\text{ s}} = -0.24 \text{ ms}^{-1}$

Q3 a) You need to calculate the time taken to travel between *B* and *C*. The coach travels 60 km at 40 kmh^{-1}, so the time taken is:
60 km ÷ 40 kmh^{-1} = 1.5 hours.

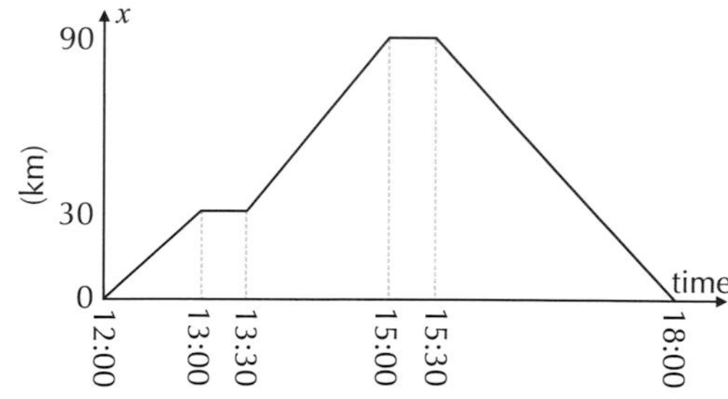

b) $v = -\frac{90\text{ km}}{2.5\text{ h}} = -36 \text{ kmh}^{-1}$

c) Total distance travelled =
30 km + 60 km + 90 km = 180 km

$\text{speed} = \frac{\text{distance}}{\text{time}} = \frac{180\text{ km}}{6\text{ h}} = 30 \text{ kmh}^{-1}$

Q4 The man travels 5 mph ÷ 1 h = 5 miles from 13:00 to 14:00, then 3 mph ÷ 1 h = 3 miles from 14:00 to 15:00.

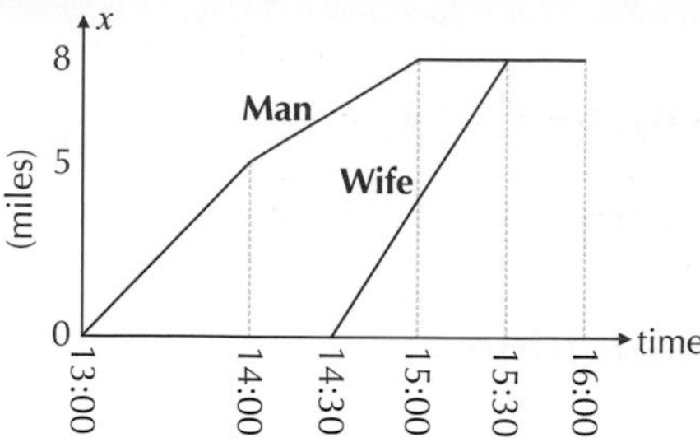

Q5 a) 500 m – 700 m + 600 m = 400 m
(The 700 m is subtracted because his velocity for that part of the journey is negative, so he is walking in the opposite direction.)

b)

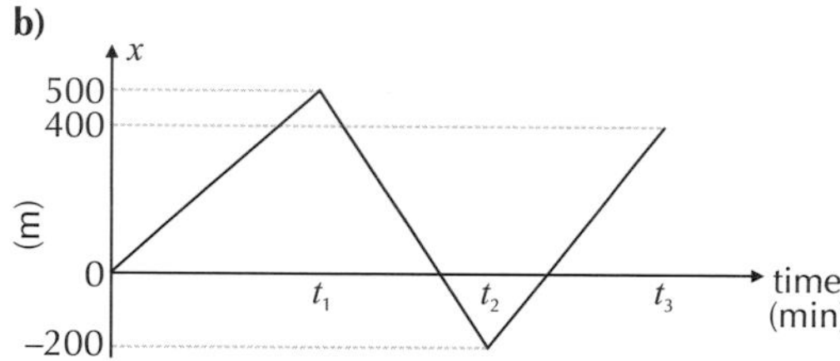

c) The gradient of each part of the graph is equal to the velocity during that stage. You already know the velocities, and the distances, for each stage, so you can use them to find the times:

$u = \frac{500}{t_1} \Rightarrow t_1 = \frac{500}{u}$

$-2u = \frac{-700}{t_2} \Rightarrow t_2 = \frac{350}{u}$

$1.5u = \frac{600}{t_3} \Rightarrow t_3 = \frac{400}{u}$

Total time = $t_1 + t_2 + t_3$

$= \frac{500}{u} + \frac{350}{u} + \frac{400}{u} = \frac{1250}{u}$ seconds

d) $\text{speed} = \frac{\text{distance}}{\text{time}} = (500 + 700 + 600) \div \frac{1250}{u}$
$= \frac{36u}{25} \text{ ms}^{-1}$

Q6 a)

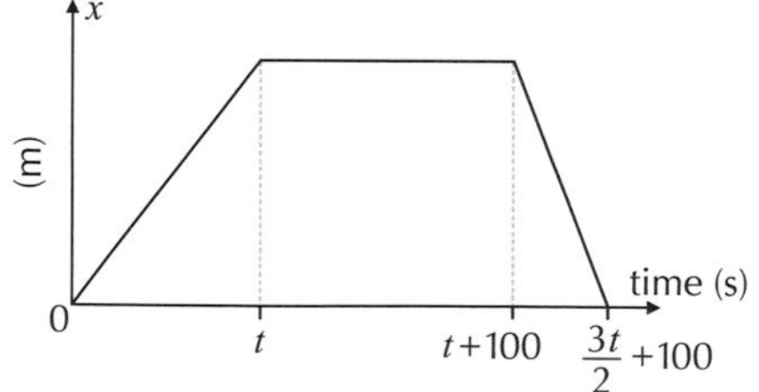

The $\frac{3}{2}t + 100$ comes from the fact that the car returns home at twice the speed that it travelled away from home, so must take half as long (i.e. $\frac{t}{2}$ seconds).
So the total time is:
$t + 100 + \frac{t}{2} = \frac{3}{2}t + 100$

b) Distance = speed × time
So distance covered in first part of journey = ut m
Car travels same distance in return journey, so total distance travelled = $2ut$ m.

c) Speed $= \frac{\text{distance}}{\text{time}} = \frac{2ut}{\frac{3}{2}t + 100} = \frac{4ut}{3t + 200}$ ms^{-1}

Exercise 1.2 — Speed-time and velocity-time graphs

Q1 The bus accelerates uniformly from rest to a velocity of 20 kmh^{-1} in 2 minutes. It then travels at this speed for 18 minutes, before decelerating uniformly to 10 kmh^{-1} in 5 minutes. Finally, it decelerates uniformly to rest in 10 minutes.

Q2

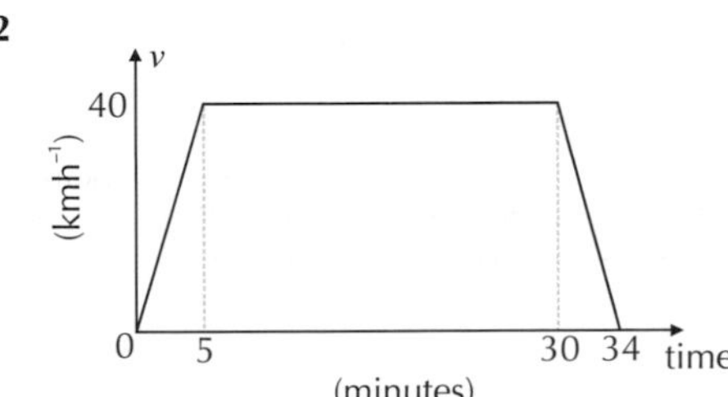

Q3 **a)** Acceleration is given by the gradient of the graph.
$a = \text{gradient} = \frac{15\text{ ms}^{-1}}{5\text{ s}} = 3\text{ ms}^{-2}$

b) $a = -\frac{15\text{ ms}^{-1}}{10\text{ s}} = -1.5\text{ ms}^{-2}$
So the particle decelerates at a rate of 1.5 ms^{-2}

Q4 **a)** Find the area under the graph by splitting it up into a rectangle and a triangle:
Area $= (V \times 20) + \frac{V \times 5}{2} = 22.5V$
This is equal to the distance travelled:
$22.5V = 900$
$V = 900 \div 22.5 = 40$ ms^{-1}

b) The car brakes for 5 seconds. The area under the graph between $t = 20$ s and $t = 25$ s is:
$\frac{V \times 5}{2} = \frac{40 \times 5}{2} = 100$ m

Q5 **a)**

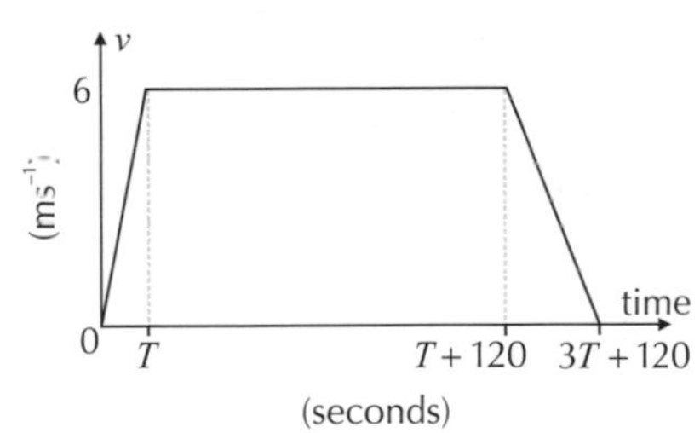

b) Find the area under the graph by splitting it up into a rectangle and two triangles:
Area $= \frac{6 \times T}{2} + (6 \times 120) + \frac{6 \times 2T}{2}$
$= 9T + 720$
This is equal to the distance travelled:
$9T + 720 = 765$
$9T = 45$
$T = 5$ s

c) $a = \text{gradient} = \frac{6\text{ ms}^{-1}}{5\text{ s}} = 1.2\text{ ms}^{-2}$

Q6 **a)**

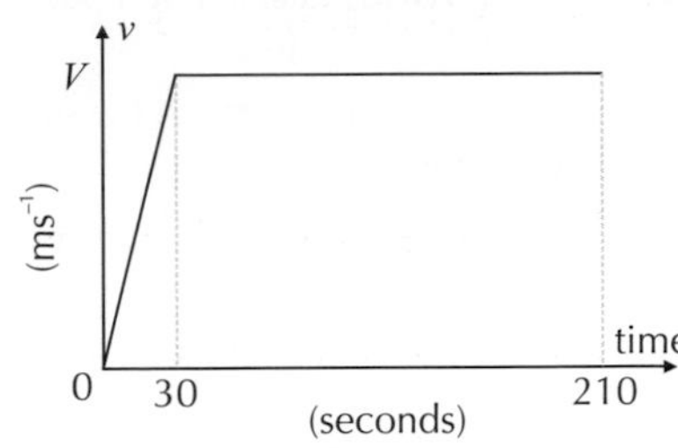

b) The gradient gives the acceleration, so:
$A = \frac{V}{30}$, or $V = 30A$

c) Area under graph $= \frac{30V}{2} + 180V = 195V$
This is equal to the distance travelled:
$195V = 2000$
Now, using the expression from b):
$195 \times 30A = 2000$
$\Rightarrow A = 0.342$ ms^{-2} (3 s.f.)

Q7 **a)**

v
50
(ms^{-1})
10
0
T
time
(seconds)

b) Split the area up into a rectangle and a triangle:
Area $= 10T + \frac{(50 - 10) \times T}{2} = 30T$

c) The gradient gives the acceleration, so considering the time the particle is accelerating:
$4 = \frac{(50 - 10)}{t_1} \Rightarrow t_1 = 10$
Now considering the time it is decelerating:
$-10 = \frac{(10 - 50)}{t_2} \Rightarrow t_2 = 4$
x is the area under the graph while the particle is accelerating:
$x = 10t_1 + \frac{(50 - 10) \times t_1}{2} = (10 \times 10) + \frac{40 \times 10}{2}$
$= 300$ m
y is the area under the graph while the particle is decelerating:
$y = 10t_2 + \frac{(50 - 10) \times t_2}{2} = (10 \times 4) + \frac{40 \times 4}{2}$
$= 120$ m
T is just the sum of t_1 and t_2:
$T = 10 + 4 = 14$ s

Q8 a) The gradient gives the acceleration, so:
$a = 0.375 = \frac{15}{t} \Rightarrow t = 40$ s
So it takes the train 40 s to reach the signal box.

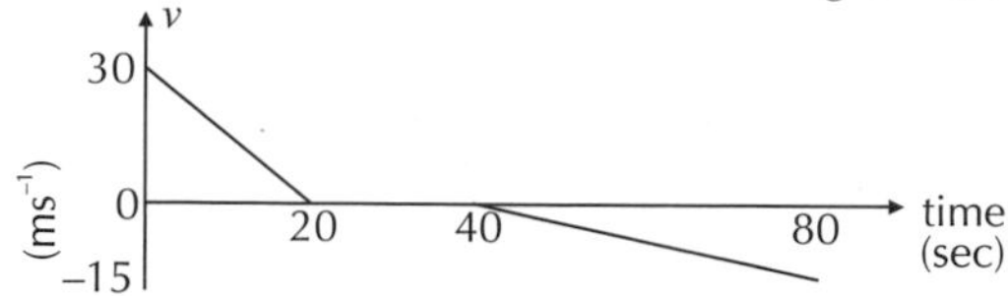

b) Gradient $= -\frac{30}{20} = -1.5$
So the train decelerates at a rate of 1.5 ms^{-2}

c) The distance is given by the area under the graph from $t = 0$ s to $t = 20$ s:
distance $= \frac{30 \times 20}{2} = 300$ m
You could also have found the area under the graph from t = 40 s to t = 80 s — the distance is the same.

Q9 a) Taking upwards as positive:

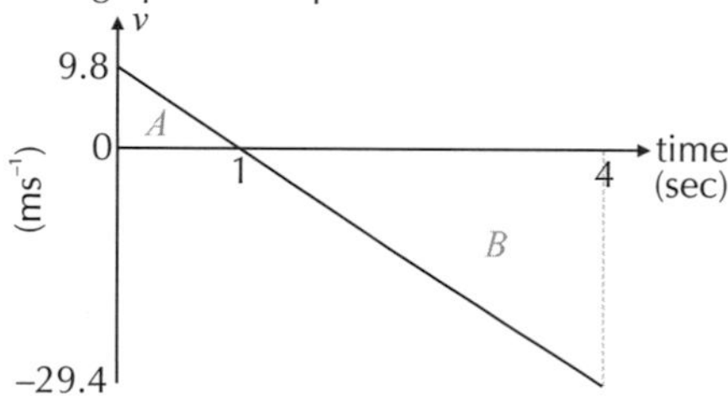

If you took downwards as positive, your graph should be the same as this, but flipped vertically. i.e. sloping upwards from –9.8 ms^{-1} to 29.4 ms^{-1}.

b) (i) As the stone travels upwards, it will slow down until it reaches its highest point, where it will have velocity $v = 0$ ms^{-1}. The distance the stone travels from the cliff edge to its highest point is equal to its displacement during this time. This is given by the area marked A on the graph.
Area $A = \frac{1 \times 9.8}{2} = 4.9$
So distance from cliff to highest point is 4.9 m.

(ii) As the stone falls from its highest point to the sea, its speed will increase from $v = 0$ ms^{-1} to $v = 29.4$ ms^{-1}. The distance the stone travels from its highest point to the sea is equal to the magnitude of its displacement during this time. This is given by the area marked B on the graph.
Area $B = \frac{3 \times -29.4}{2} = -44.1$ m
So the stone travels 44.1 m downwards from its highest point to the sea.

(iii) The height of the cliff is equal to the magnitude of the stone's final displacement from its starting point. Find this by adding the areas of A and B:
$4.9 + (-44.1) = -39.2$ m
So the height of the cliff is 39.2 m
You can also think of the height of the cliff as being the difference between your answers to a) and b): 44.1 – 4.9 = 39.2 m.

Exercise 1.3 — Acceleration-time graphs

Q1 a) The cyclist accelerates at a rate of 2 ms^{-2} for 10 s, then travels with constant velocity for 40 s. Finally, the cyclist decelerates at a rate of 1 ms^{-2} for 20 s.

b) The area under the acceleration-time graph while the cyclist is accelerating is:
$2\ ms^{-2} \times 10\ s = 20\ ms^{-1}$
The area under the graph while the cyclist is decelerating is:
$-1\ ms^{-2} \times 20\ s = -20\ ms^{-1}$
So the cyclist accelerates from rest to 20 ms^{-1}, then travels with constant velocity, then decelerates to rest.

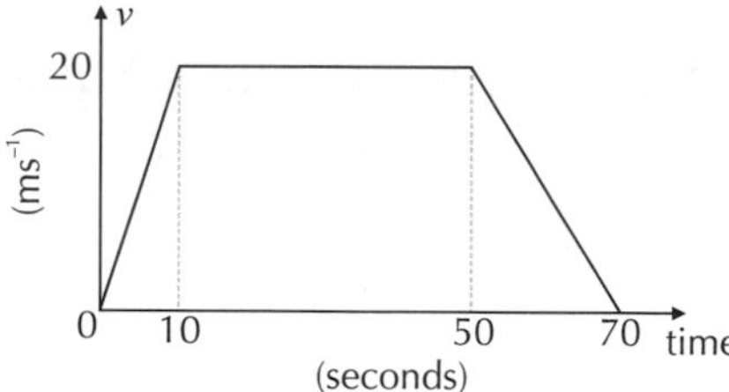

Q2 Find the gradient of the velocity-time graph.
For $t = 0$ s to $t = 5$ s:
$a = \frac{(15 - 10)\ ms^{-1}}{5\ s} = 1\ ms^{-2}$
For $t = 5$ s to $t = 15$ s:
$a = \frac{(5 - 15)\ ms^{-1}}{(15 - 5)\ s} = -1\ ms^{-2}$
For $t = 15$ s to $t = 20$ s:
$a = 0\ ms^{-2}$

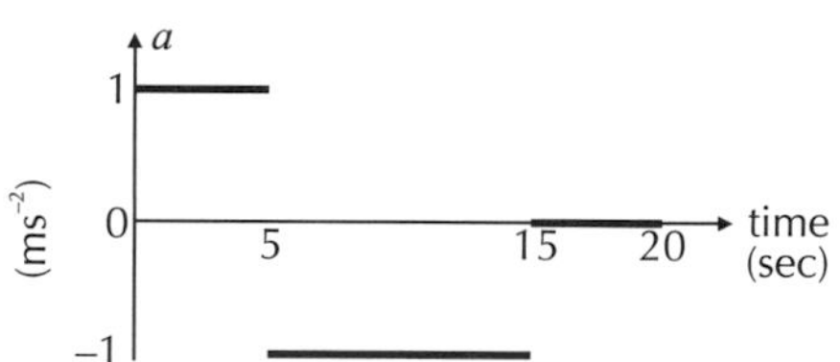

Q3 a) Taking downwards as positive:

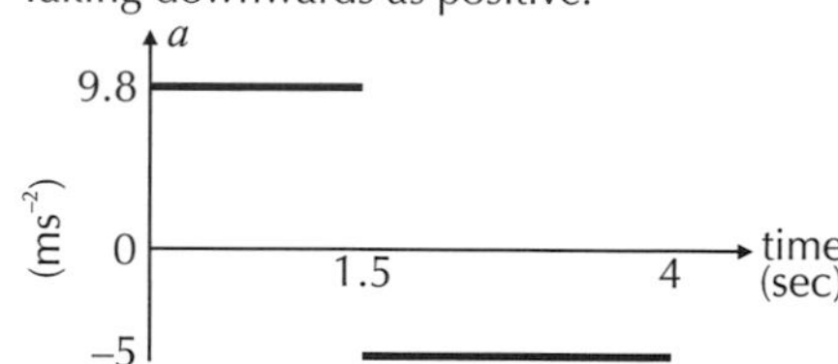

b) Velocity is area under graph from $t = 0$ s to $t = 1.5$ s:
$9.8\ ms^{-2} \times 1.5\ s = 14.7\ ms^{-1}$

c) Velocity is area under graph from $t = 0$ s to $t = 1.5$ s plus area under graph from $t = 1.5$ s to $t = 4$ s:
$14.7\ ms^{-1} + (-5\ ms^{-2} \times 2.5\ s) = 2.2\ ms^{-1}$

d)

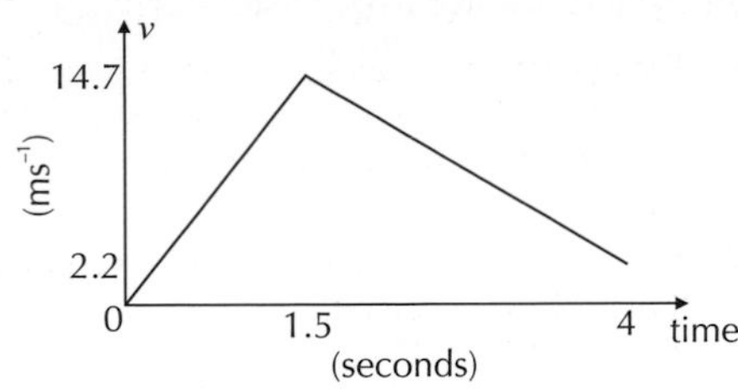

e) You need to find the area under the graph from $t = 1.5$ s to $t = 4$ s:
Area = $\frac{12.5 \times 2.5}{2} + (2.2 \times 2.5) = 21.125$
So depth of lake is 21.125 m.

2. Constant Acceleration Equations

Exercise 2.1 — Constant acceleration equations

Q1 a) $u = 0,\ v = 12,\ t = 5,\ a = a$
$v = u + at$
$12 = 0 + 5a$
$a = 12 \div 5 = 2.4 \text{ ms}^{-2}$

b) $u = 0,\ v = 12,\ t = 5,\ s = s$
$s = \left(\frac{u + v}{2}\right)t$
$s = \left(\frac{0 + 12}{2}\right) \times 5$
$s = 30$ m

Q2 a) $18 \times 1000 \div 60^2 = 5 \text{ ms}^{-1}$

b) $u = 5,\ v = 0,\ s = 50,\ t = t$
$s = \left(\frac{u + v}{2}\right)t$
$50 = \left(\frac{5 + 0}{2}\right)t$
$t = 50 \div 2.5 = 20$ s

c) $u = 5,\ v = 0,\ s = 50,\ a = a$
$v^2 = u^2 + 2as$
$0 = 5^2 + 2a \times 50$
$2a = -5^2 \div 50$
$a = -0.25$
So the cyclist decelerates at a rate of 0.25 ms^{-2}

Q3 a) $s = 30,\ v = 12,\ t = 3,\ u = u$
$s = \left(\frac{u + v}{2}\right)t$
$30 = \left(\frac{u + 12}{2}\right) \times 3$
$20 = u + 12$
$u = 8 \text{ ms}^{-1}$

b) $s = 30,\ v = 12,\ t = 3,\ a = a$
$s = vt - \frac{1}{2}at^2$
$30 = (12 \times 3) - \frac{1}{2}a \times 3^2$
$4.5a = 6$
$a = 1.33 \text{ ms}^{-2}$ (3 s.f.)

Q4 $u = 20,\ v = 0,\ t = 2.5 \times 60 = 150,\ s = s$
$s = \left(\frac{u + v}{2}\right)t$
$s = \left(\frac{20 + 0}{2}\right) \times 150 = 1500$ m

Q5 a) $u = 5,\ v = 25,\ s = 60,\ a = a$
$v^2 = u^2 + 2as$
$25^2 = 5^2 + (2a \times 60)$
$625 = 25 + 120a$
$a = 600 \times 120 = 5 \text{ ms}^{-2}$

b) Acceleration is constant.
The skier is modelled as a particle.

Q6 a) $a = -1,\ s = 50,\ v = 4,\ u = u$
$v^2 = u^2 + 2as$
$4^2 = u^2 + (2 \times -1 \times 50)$
$u^2 = 116$
$u = 10.8 \text{ ms}^{-1}$ (3 s.f.)

b) $a = -1,\ s = 50,\ v = 4,\ t = t$
$s = vt - \frac{1}{2}at^2$
$50 = 4t - \frac{1}{2}(-1)t^2$
$t^2 + 8t - 100 = 0$
Solve using the quadratic formula or by completing the square:
$(t + 4)^2 - 116 = 0$
$t + 4 = \pm\sqrt{116}$
$t = -4 \pm \sqrt{116}$
$t = -14.77...$ or $t = 6.77...$
You can ignore the negative solution, as t must be positive. So $t = 6.77$ s (3 s.f.)

Q7 a) From the first post to the second post:
$s = 30,\ t = 2$
$s = ut + \frac{1}{2}at^2$
$30 = 2u + \frac{1}{2}a \times 2^2$
$30 = 2u + 2a$
$15 = u + a$
$\Rightarrow u = 15 - a$ **eqn1**
From the first post to the third post:
$s = 60,\ t = 3$
$s = ut + \frac{1}{2}at^2$
$60 = 3u + \frac{1}{2}a \times 3^2$
$60 = 3u + 4.5a$
$\Rightarrow 20 = u + 1.5a$ **eqn2**
Substituting **eqn1** into **eqn2**:
$20 = (15 - a) + 1.5a$
$5 = 0.5a$
$a = 10 \text{ ms}^{-2}$

b) Use expression for u from part a):
$u = 15 - a = 15 - 10 = 5 \text{ ms}^{-1}$

Q8 a) While the bus is in the tunnel,
$u = 20,\ t = 25,\ a = 0.$
$s = ut + \frac{1}{2}at^2$
$s = (20 \times 25) + 0$
$s = 500$ m

b) Before the tunnel:
$u = U,\ v = 20,\ t = 15$
$s = \left(\frac{u+v}{2}\right)t$
$s = \left(\frac{U+20}{2}\right) \times 15$
After tunnel:
$u = 20,\ v = U,\ t = 30$
$s = \left(\frac{u+v}{2}\right)t$
$s = \left(\frac{20+U}{2}\right) \times 30$
Total distance travelled:
$1580 = 15\left(\frac{U+20}{2}\right) + 500 + 30\left(\frac{20+U}{2}\right)$
$1080 = 45\left(\frac{U+20}{2}\right)$
$48 = U + 20$
$U = 28$ ms^{-1}

Exercise 2.2 — Gravity

Q1 $u = 0,\ a = 9.8,\ t = 3,\ s = s$
$s = ut + \frac{1}{2}at^2$
$s = 0 + \frac{1}{2} \times 9.8 \times 3^2$
$s = 44.1$ m

Q2 a) $u = 0,\ a = 9.8,\ s = 5,\ t = t$
$s = ut + \frac{1}{2}at^2$
$5 = 0 + \frac{1}{2} \times 9.8 \times t^2$
$t^2 = 1.02...$
$t = 1.01$ s (3 s.f.)

b) $u = 0,\ a = 9.8,\ s = 5,\ v = v$
$v^2 = u^2 + 2as$
$v^2 = 0 + 2 \times 9.8 \times 5$
$v^2 = 98$
$v = 9.90$ ms^{-1} (3 s.f.)

Q3 a) Taking upwards as positive:
$u = 30,\ a = -9.8,\ v = 0,\ s = s$
$v^2 = u^2 + 2as$
$0 = 30^2 + (2 \times -9.8 \times s)$
$s = 900 \div 19.6 = 45.918...$
$s = 45.9$ m (3 s.f.)

b) $u = 30,\ a = -9.8,\ s = 0,\ t = t$
$s = ut + \frac{1}{2}at^2$
$0 = 30t + \frac{1}{2} \times -9.8t^2$
$0 = 30t - 4.9t^2$
$0 = t(30 - 4.9t)$
$t = 0$ or $(30 - 4.9t) = 0$
$30 = 4.9t$
$t = 30 \div 4.9 = 6.122...$
So $t = 6.12$ s (3 s.f.)

c) $u = 30,\ a = -9.8,\ t = 2,\ v = v$
$v = u + at$
$v = 30 + (-9.8 \times 2) = 10.4$ ms^{-1}
v is positive, so the object is moving upwards.

Q4 a) Taking upwards as positive:
$u = u,\ t = 3,\ v = -20,\ a = -9.8$
$v = u + at$
$-20 = u - 9.8 \times 3$
$u = 9.4$ ms^{-1}

b) $t = 3,\ v = -20,\ a = -9.8,\ s = -d$
$s = vt - \frac{1}{2}at^2$
$-d = (-20 \times 3) + (4.9 \times 9)$
$d = 15.9$ m

Q5 a) Taking upwards as positive:
$u = 8,\ a = -9.8,\ v = 0,\ s = s$
$v^2 = u^2 + 2as$
$0 = 8^2 + (2 \times -9.8s)$
$s = 64 \div 19.6 = 3.265...$
Thrown from 5 m above ground, so max height = 3.265... + 5 = 8.27 m (3 s.f.)

b) $s = 8 - 5 = 3,\ u = 8,\ a = -9.8,\ t = t$
$s = ut + \frac{1}{2}at^2$
$3 = 8t + \frac{1}{2} \times -9.8t^2$
$4.9t^2 - 8t + 3 = 0$
Solve using the quadratic formula:
$t = \frac{8 \pm \sqrt{8^2 - (4 \times 4.9 \times 3)}}{9.8}$
$t = 0.583...$ or $t = 1.049...$
So required time is given by 1.049... – 0.583... = 0.465 s (3 s.f.)

Q6 a) Taking upwards as positive:
$u = 12,\ v = 0,\ a = -9.8,\ s = s$
$v^2 = u^2 + 2as$
$0 = 12^2 - 2 \times 9.8s$
$s = 144 \div 19.6$
$s = 7.3469... = 7.35$ m (3 s.f.)

b) $u = 12,\ v = 0,\ a = -9.8,\ t = t$
$v = u + at$
$0 = 12 - 9.8t$
$t = 12 \div 9.8$
$t = 1.2244... = 1.22$ s (3 s.f.)

c) Distance between 5th and 8th floors = 7.3469...
So distance between each floor = 7.3469... ÷ 3
Distance between ground and 5th floor = 5(7.3469... ÷ 3) = 12.244...
So $u = 12,\ a = -9.8,\ s = -12.244...,\ v = v$
$v^2 = u^2 + 2as$
$v^2 = 12^2 + (2 \times -9.8 \times -12.244...)$
$v^2 = 384$
$v = 19.595... = 19.6$ ms^{-1} (3 s.f.)

Q7 a) Take upwards as positive.
p is the time that the object is at its highest point.
So $u = 24.5,\ v = 0,\ a = -9.8,\ t = p$
$v = u + at$
$0 = 24.5 - 9.8p$
$p = 24.5 \div 9.8 = 2.5$ s

b) q is the time that the object lands. From the graph, this is 29.4 m below the point of projection.
$u = 24.5$, $a = -9.8$, $s = -29.4$, $t = q$
$s = ut + \frac{1}{2}at^2$
$-29.4 = 24.5q - \frac{1}{2}(9.8)q^2$
Dividing each term by 4.9, and rearranging:
$q^2 - 5q - 6 = 0$
$(q - 6)(q + 1) = 0$
So $q = 6$ or $q = -1$
q is a time, and must be positive, so $q = 6$ s

c) r is the object's max height.
$u = 24.5$, $v = 0$, $a = -9.8$, $s = s$
$v^2 = u^2 + 2as$
$0 = 24.5^2 + (2 \times -9.8s)$
$s = 24.5^2 \div 19.6 = 30.625$
The object was projected from 29.4 m above the ground, so:
$r = 30.625 + 29.4 = 60.025$ m

Q8 a) Take upwards as positive. When the projectile is moving between the two targets:
$s = 120$, $t = 3$, $a = -9.8$, $u = u$
$s = ut + \frac{1}{2}at^2$
$120 = 3u + \frac{1}{2}(-9.8 \times 3^2)$
$3u = 164.1$
$u = 54.7$ ms^{-1} — this is the speed of the projectile as it passes the first target.
When the projectile is moving between the point of projection and the first target:
$s = 150$, $v = 54.7$, $a = -9.8$, $u = u$
$v^2 = u^2 + 2as$
$54.7^2 = u^2 + (2 \times -9.8 \times 150)$
$u^2 = 5932.09$
$u = 77.020...$
So the projectile is projected at 77.0 ms^{-1} (3 s.f.)

b) $u = 77.020...$, $v = 0$, $a = -9.8$, $s = s$
$v^2 = u^2 + 2as$
$0 = 77.020...^2 + (2 \times -9.8s)$
$s = 77.020...^2 \div 19.6 = 302.657...$
The projectile is projected from 50 m below ground, so the max height above ground is:
$302.657... - 50 = 252.657... = 253$ m (3 s.f.)

c) $v = 54.7$, $u = 77.020...$, $a = -9.8$, $t = t$
$v = u + at$
$54.7 = 77.020... - 9.8t$
$t = (77.020... - 54.7) \div 9.8 = 2.2775...$
$t = 2.28$ s (3 s.f.)

Exercise 2.3 — More complicated problems

Q1 a) $u = 2$, $v = 6$, $s = 28$, $t = t$
$s = \left(\frac{u+v}{2}\right)t$
$28 = \left(\frac{2+6}{2}\right)t$
$28 = 4t$
$t = 7$ s

b)

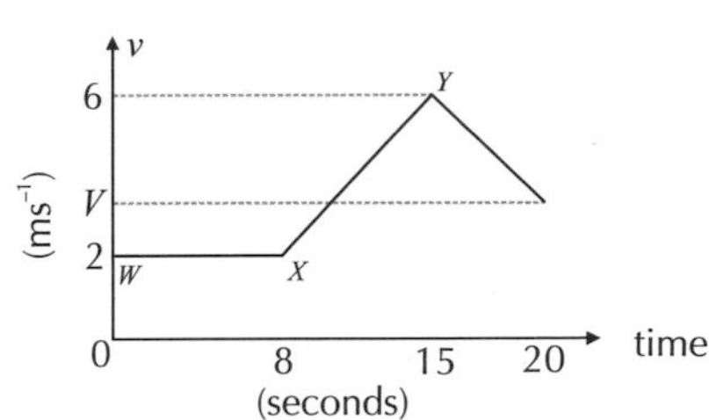

c) The area under the graph gives the total distance travelled.

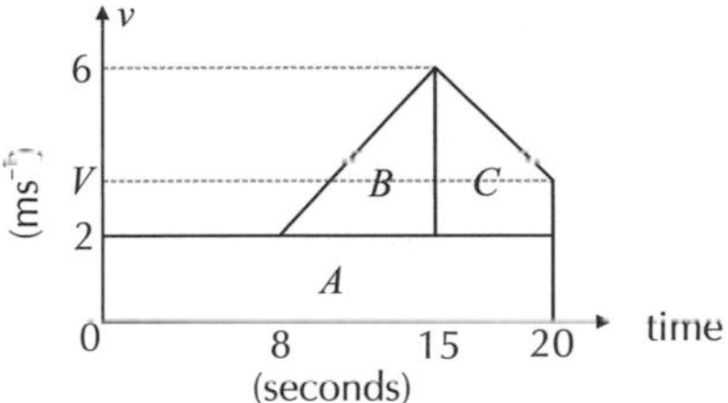

Area of $A = 20 \times 2 = 40$
Area of $B = \left(\frac{7 \times 4}{2}\right) = 14$
Area of $C = \left(\frac{4 + (V - 2)}{2}\right) \times 5 = 5 + 2.5V$
Total area $= 40 + 14 + 5 + 2.5V = 59 + 2.5V$
Total distance travelled is 67 m, so:
$59 + 2.5V = 67$
$2.5V = 8$
$V = 3.2$ ms^{-1}

Q2 a)

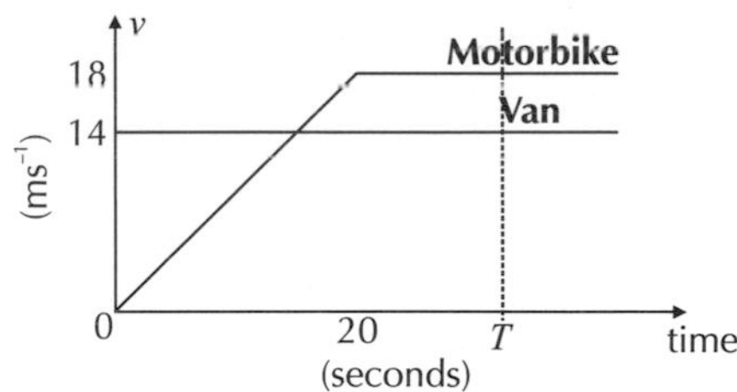

b) The motorbike overtakes the van T seconds after setting off. At this point, the two vehicles will have covered the same distance since $t = 0$, and so the areas under the graphs up to this point will be the same.
Van area $= 14 \times T$
Motorbike area $= \left(\frac{T + (T - 20)}{2}\right) \times 18$
$= 18T - 180$
Making the two areas equal to each other:
$14T = 18T - 180$
$4T = 180$
$T = 45$ seconds

Q3 a) Write down the *uvast* variables for X and Y, considering the movement of each car separately. In each case, take the direction that the car moves as being positive.

$u_X = 15,\ a_X = 1,\ t_X = t$
$u_Y = 20,\ a_Y = 2,\ t_Y = t$
Using $s = ut + \frac{1}{2}at^2$:
$s_X = 15t + \frac{1}{2}t^2$
$s_Y = 20t + t^2$
They collide when $s_X + s_Y = 30$:
$15t + \frac{1}{2}t^2 + 20t + t^2 = 30$
$35t + \frac{3}{2}t^2 = 30$
Multiplying throughout by 2 and rearranging:
$3t^2 + 70t - 60 = 0$
Solve using the quadratic formula:
$$t = \frac{-70 \pm \sqrt{70^2 - (4 \times 3 \times -60)}}{6}$$
$t = 0.8277...$ or $t = -24.161...$
So $t = 0.828$ s (3 s.f.)

b) Use $v = u + at$ on the two cars separately. Again, take the direction of motion as being positive for each car.
X: $v_X = 15 + 0.8277...$
$v_X = 15.8\ \text{ms}^{-1}$ (3 s.f.)
Y: $v_Y = 20 + 2(0.8277...)$
$v_Y = 21.7\ \text{ms}^{-1}$ (3 s.f.)

c) $s = ut + \frac{1}{2}at^2$
$s_X = (15 \times 0.8277...) + \frac{1}{2}(0.8277...)^2$
$s_X = 12.759... = 12.8$ m (3 s.f.)

Q4 a)

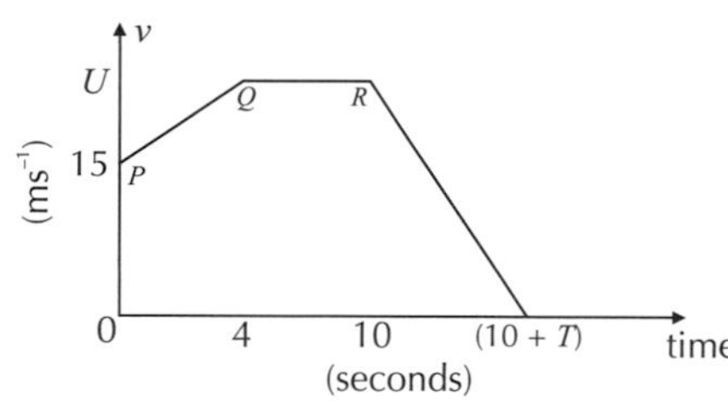

b) From P to Q:
$u = 15,\ v = U,\ a = 3,\ t = 4$
$v = u + at$
$U = 15 + (3 \times 4) = 27\ \text{ms}^{-1}$

c) The area under the graph from P to Q is:
$\frac{1}{2} \times (15 + 27) \times 4 = 84$
So the distance from P to Q is 84 m.
The area under the graph from Q to R is:
$27 \times 6 = 162$
So the distance from Q to R is 162 m.
The total distance travelled is 405 m, so the distance the particle travels in coming to rest is:
$405 - 162 - 84 = 159$ m
So, from R to rest:
$u = U = 27,\ v = 0,\ s = 159,\ t = T$
$s = \left(\frac{u+v}{2}\right)t$
$159 = \left(\frac{27}{2}\right)T$
$\Rightarrow T = 11.777... = 11.8$ s (3 s.f.)
So the particle comes to rest $10 + 11.8 = 21.8$ s (3 s.f.) after passing P.

d) Gradient of graph $= \frac{0 - U}{T} = \frac{-27}{11.777...}$
$= -2.292...$
So it decelerates at a rate of $2.29\ \text{ms}^{-2}$ (3 s.f.)

Q5 a) Write down the *uvast* variables for the two balls:
$u_1 = 5,\ a_1 = -0.5,\ t_1 = t$
$u_2 = 4,\ a_2 = 0,\ t_2 = t - 3$
Using $s = ut + \frac{1}{2}at^2$:
First ball: $s_1 = 5t + \frac{1}{2}(-0.5)t^2$
$s_1 = 5t - 0.25t^2$
Second ball: $s_2 = 4(t - 3) + 0$
$s_2 = 4t - 12$
They are level when $s_1 = s_2$:
$5t - 0.25t^2 = 4t - 12$
Multiplying throughout by 4 and rearranging:
$t^2 - 4t - 48 = 0$
Solve using the quadratic formula or by completing the square:
$(t - 2)^2 - 52 = 0$
$t - 2 = \pm\sqrt{52}$
$t = 2 \pm \sqrt{52}$
$t = 9.2111...$ or $t = -5.2111...$
So the second ball passes the first ball 9.21 s (3 s.f.) after the first ball is rolled.

b) Using $s_2 = 4t - 12$ from part a):
$s_2 = (4 \times 9.2111...) - 12$
$= 24.844... = 24.8$ m (3 s.f.)

c) Find the time that the first ball comes to rest using $v = u + at$ with $v = 0$:
$0 = 5 - 0.5t \Rightarrow t = 10$ s
Now find the distance the first ball travels in this time using $s = ut + \frac{1}{2}at^2$:
$s_1 = (5 \times 10) + \frac{1}{2}(-0.5 \times 10^2) = 25$ m
Find the distance the second ball travels in 15 s using $s = ut + \frac{1}{2}at^2$:
$s_2 = 4(15 - 3) + 0 = 48$ m
So the second ball is 48 m – 25 m = 23 m ahead.

Q6 a) Take upwards as the positive direction.
Find the time that B is at its highest point:
$u_B = 5,\ v_B = 0,\ a_B = -9.8,\ t_B = t$
Using $v = u + at$:
$0 = 5 - 9.8t$
$\Rightarrow t = 5 \div 9.8 = 0.5102...$
Now find the displacement of A at this time (remembering that A is released 1 s before B):
$u_A = 0,\ a_A = -9.8,\ t_A = 1 + 0.5102... = 1.5102...$
Using $s = ut + \frac{1}{2}at^2$:
$s = 0 + \frac{1}{2}(-9.8 \times 1.5102...^2) = -11.1755...$
So A has travelled 11.2 m (3 s.f.)

b) Using $s = ut + \frac{1}{2}at^2$:

A: $u_A = 0$, $a_A = -9.8$, $t_A = t$

$s = 0 + \frac{1}{2}(-9.8t^2)$

$s = -4.9t^2$

B: $u_B = 5$, $a_B = -9.8$, $t_B = t - 1$

$s = 5(t - 1) + \frac{1}{2} \times -9.8(t - 1)^2$

$s = 5t - 5 - 4.9(t^2 - 2t + 1)$

$s = 14.8t - 9.9 - 4.9t^2$

So A has moved $4.9t^2$ m down from a height of 40 m, and B has moved $(14.8t - 9.9 - 4.9t^2)$ m up from a height of 10 m.

A and B are at the same level when:

$40 - 4.9t^2 = 10 + 14.8t - 9.9 - 4.9t^2$

$\Rightarrow 39.9 = 14.8t$

$\Rightarrow t = 39.9 \div 14.8 = 2.6959...$

So they become level 2.70 seconds (3 s.f.) after A is dropped.

c) Using $s = -4.9t^2$ (from part b)) for particle A:

$s = -4.9 \times (2.6959...)^2 = -35.6138...$

$40 - 35.6138... = 4.3861...$

So they are 4.39 m (3 s.f.) above the ground.

Review Exercise — Chapter 2

Q1 a) Acceleration = gradient of graph:

$a = \frac{5 - 0}{3} = 1.67 \text{ ms}^{-2}$ (3 s.f.)

b) Acceleration = gradient of graph:

$a = \frac{0 - 5}{1} = -5 \text{ ms}^{-2}$

So deceleration is 5 ms^{-2}

c) Distance travelled = area under graph.

Split the area into a rectangle and a triangle:

Distance = $(2 \times 5) + \frac{1 \times 5}{2} = 12.5$ m

Q2 Velocity = gradient of graph:

A: $v = \frac{80 \text{ km}}{1 \text{ h}} = 80 \text{ kmh}^{-1}$

B: $v = \frac{(120 - 80) \text{ km}}{(2.5 - 1) \text{ h}} = 26.7 \text{ kmh}^{-1}$ (3 s.f.)

C: $v = 0 \text{ kmh}^{-1}$

D: $v = \frac{(200 - 120) \text{ km}}{(4 - 3) \text{ h}} = 80 \text{ kmh}^{-1}$

Q3

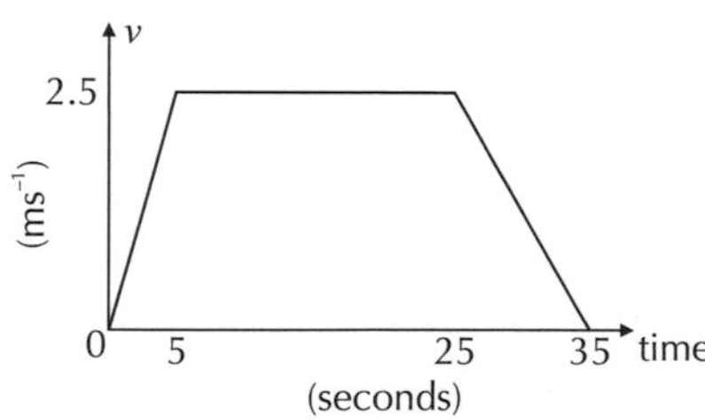

Distance = area under graph:

$(5 \times 2.5) \div 2 + (20 \times 2.5) + (10 \times 2.5) \div 2$

$= 68.75$ m

Q4 $u = 3$, $v = 9$, $s = s$, $t = 2$.

Using $s = \left(\frac{u + v}{2}\right)t$:

$s = \frac{1}{2}(3 + 9) \times 2$

$s = \frac{1}{2}(12) \times 2 = 12$ m

Q5 a) $a = 0.2$, $u = 6$, $t = 20$, $s = s$

$s = ut + \frac{1}{2}at^2$

$s = (6 \times 20) + \frac{1}{2}(0.2 \times 20^2)$

$s = 160$ m

b) $v = u + at$

$v = 6 + (0.2 \times 20)$

$v = 10 \text{ ms}^{-1}$

Q6 a) Taking upwards as positive:

$u = 35$, $v = 0$, $a = -9.8$, $s = s$

$v^2 = u^2 + 2as$

$0 = 35^2 + 2(-9.8s)$

$s = 35^2 \div 19.6$

$s = 62.5$ m

b) $u = 35$, $a = -9.8$, $s = 0$, $t = t$

$s = ut + \frac{1}{2}at^2$

$0 = 35t + \frac{1}{2}(-9.8t^2)$

$0 = 35t - 4.9t^2$

$0 = t(35 - 4.9t)$

So $t = 0$ or $(35 - 4.9t) = 0$

$35 = 4.9t \Rightarrow t = 35 \div 4.9 = 7.1428...$

$t = 7.14$ s (3 s.f.)

Q7 $u = 11$, $a = -3.8$, $v = 0$, $s = s$

$v^2 = u^2 + 2as$

$0 = 11^2 + (2 \times -3.8 \times s)$

$s = 121 \div 7.6 = 15.921...$ m

$15.921... < 25$, so the horse stops before it reaches the edge of the cliff.

Q8 a)

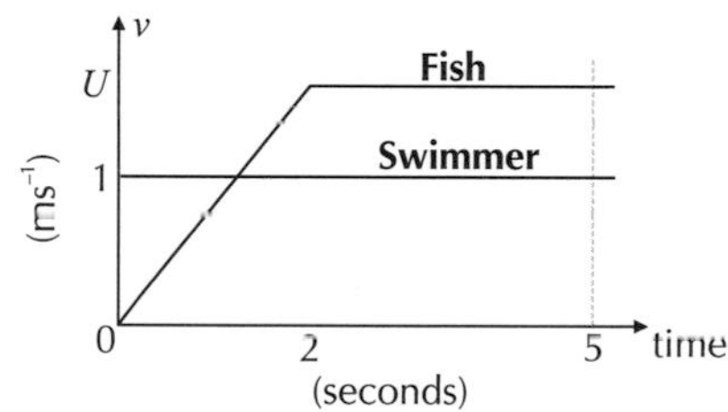

b) When the fish overtakes the swimmer, they have travelled the same distance.

The distance they have travelled is given by the area under the graph.

Distance travelled by swimmer = $1 \times 5 = 5$ m

Distance travelled by fish = $\frac{U \times 2}{2} + U(5 - 2)$

$= 4U$ m

So $5 = 4U \Rightarrow U = 5 \div 4 = 1.25 \text{ ms}^{-1}$

Exam-Style Questions — Chapter 2

1 a) Using $v = u + at$, taking down as positive:
$u = u$, $v = 17$, $a = 9.8$, $t = 1.2$
$17 = u + (9.8 \times 1.2)$
So $u = 5.24 \text{ ms}^{-1}$
[3 marks available in total]:
- ***1 mark for using appropriate equation***
- ***1 mark for correct workings***
- ***1 mark for correct value of u***

These kind of questions are trivial if you've memorised all those constant acceleration equations.

b) Using $s = ut + \frac{1}{2}at^2$, taking down as positive:
$u = 17$, $a = 9.8$, $s = s$, $t = 2.1$
$s = (17 \times 2.1) + \frac{1}{2}(9.8 \times 2.1^2)$
So $s = 57.309$
$h = \frac{s}{14} = 4.0935 \text{ m}$
[4 marks available in total]:
- ***1 mark for using appropriate equation***
- ***1 mark for correct value of s***
- ***1 mark for correct workings***
- ***1 mark for correct value of h***

2 a)

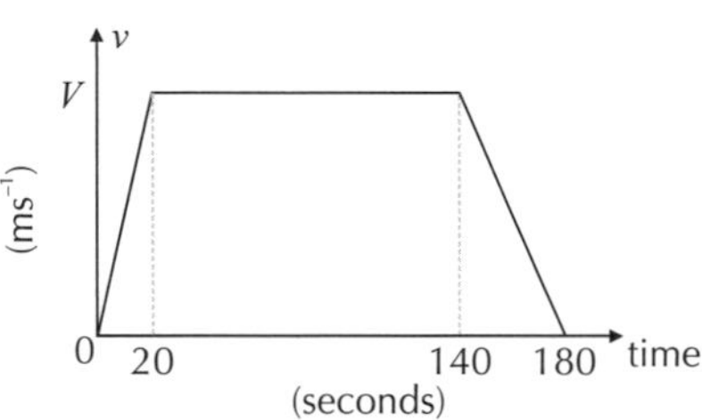

[3 marks available in total]:
- ***1 mark for the correct shape***
- ***1 mark for the correct times***
- ***1 mark for correctly marking V on vertical axis***

b) Area under graph (area of trapezium) = distance
$\frac{1}{2}(120 + 180)V = 2100$
$V = \frac{2100}{150} = 14 \text{ ms}^{-1}$
[3 marks available in total]:
- ***1 mark for using Area under graph = distance***
- ***1 mark for correct workings***
- ***1 mark for correct value of V***

The area could also be worked out in other ways, say, using two triangles and a rectangle. Best to use whatever's easiest for you.

c) Distance = area under graph
$= \frac{1}{2} \times 40 \times 14 = 280 \text{ m}$
[2 marks available in total]:
- ***1 mark for using Area under graph = distance***
- ***1 mark for correct value***

d) Using $a = \frac{v - u}{t}$:
Acceleration period:
$t = 20$, $v = 14$, $u = 0$
$a = (14 - 0) \div 20 = 0.7 \text{ ms}^{-2}$
Deceleration period:
$t = 40$, $v = 0$, $u = 14$
$a = (0 - 14) \div 40 = -0.35 \text{ ms}^{-2}$

[3 marks available in total]:
- ***1 mark for correct shape***
- ***1 mark for correct value of acceleration (0.7 ms^{-2})***
- ***1 mark for correct value of deceleration (0.35 ms^{-2})***

Yep, sometimes you're not given the values you need to label a graph and you have to work them out yourself. All good practice.

3 a)

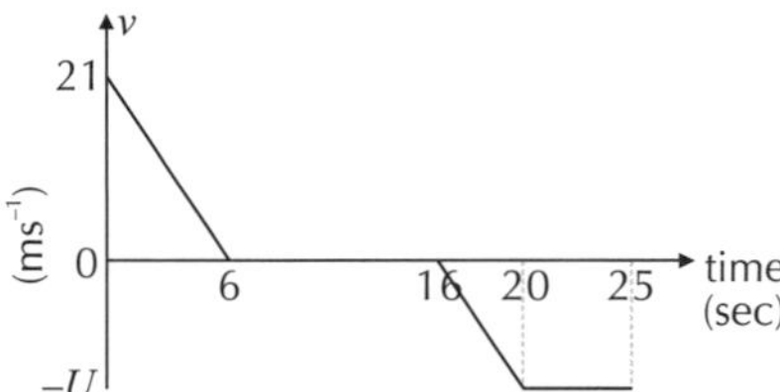

[3 marks available in total]:
- ***1 mark for the correct shape***
- ***1 mark for the correct times***
- ***1 mark for the correct velocities***

b) Gradient of graph while van is decelerating
$= -\frac{21}{6} = -3.5$
So the van decelerates at a rate of 3.5 ms^{-2}
[2 marks available in total]:
- ***1 mark for using gradient = acceleration***
- ***1 mark for correct value of deceleration***

You could also do this using $v = u + at$ with $v = 0$, $u = 21$ and $t = 6$.

c) Area under graph = distance
Area under graph =
$\frac{21 \times 6}{2} + \frac{U \times 4}{2} + (U \times 5) = 63 + 7U$
$63 + 7U = 161$
$\Rightarrow U = 98 \div 7 = 14 \text{ ms}^{-1}$
[3 marks available in total]:
- ***1 mark for using Area under graph = distance***
- ***1 mark for correct workings***
- ***1 mark for correct value of U***

d) Displacement =
(distance travelled in positive direction) – (distance travelled in negative direction)

Displacement = $\frac{21 \times 6}{2} - \left[\frac{U \times 4}{2} + (U \times 5)\right]$

$= 63 - 7U = 63 - 7(14)$

$= -35$ m

So the van is 35 m from his initial position, in the negative direction.

[2 marks available in total]:
- ***1 mark for correct workings***
- ***1 mark for correct value of displacement***

4 a) Taking up as positive:

$u = u$, $v = -20$, $a = -9.8$, $s = -8$

$v^2 = u^2 + 2as$

$(-20)^2 = u^2 + (2 \times -9.8 \times -8)$

$u = \sqrt{400 - 156.8}$

$\Rightarrow u = 15.594... = 15.6$ ms^{-1} (3 s.f.)

[3 marks available in total]:
- ***1 mark for using appropriate equation***
- ***1 mark for correct workings***
- ***1 mark for correct value of u***

b) Taking up as positive:

$u = 15.594...$, $v = -20$, $a = -9.8$, $t = t$

$v = u + at$

$-20 = 15.594... - 9.8t$

$9.8t = 35.594...$

$\Rightarrow t = 3.632... = 3.63$ s (3 s.f.)

[3 marks available in total]:
- ***1 mark for using appropriate equation***
- ***1 mark for correct workings***
- ***1 mark for correct value of t***

You could also have done this using $s = ut + \frac{1}{2}at^2$ or $s = vt - \frac{1}{2}at^2$. It's okay to use other equations as long as you get the right answer in the end.

5 a) (i) A is the point that the ball is at its maximum vertical height above the ground.
[1 mark]

(ii) $u = 5$, $v = 0$, $a = -9.8$, $t = t$

Using $v = u + at$:

$0 = 5 - 9.8t$

$\Rightarrow t = 5 \div 9.8 = 0.5102...$

$t = 0.510$ s (3 s.f.)

[3 marks available in total]:
- ***1 mark for using appropriate equation***
- ***1 mark for correct workings***
- ***1 mark for correct value of t***

b) (i) B is the point that the ball hits the ground (for the first time).
[1 mark]

(ii) $u = 5$, $a = -9.8$, $s = -2$, $v = v$

Using $v^2 = u^2 + 2as$:

$v^2 = 5^2 + 2(-9.8 \times -2) = 64.2$

$\Rightarrow v = -8.0124... = -8.01$ ms^{-1} (3 s.f.)

The velocity is negative at B as the ball is travelling in the negative direction (you can also see this from the graph).

[3 marks available in total]:
- ***1 mark for using appropriate equation***
- ***1 mark for correct workings***
- ***1 mark for correct value of v***

c) The ball bounces off the ground at C, so it changes direction, which means its velocity changes from negative to positive.
[1 mark]

6 a) Find the time that P reaches its max height:

$u_P = 17.64$, $v_P = 0$, $a_P = -9.8$, $t_P = t$

Using $v = u + at$:

$0 = 17.64 - 9.8t$

$\Rightarrow t = 17.64 \div 9.8 = 1.8$ s

[3 marks available in total]:
- ***1 mark for using appropriate equation***
- ***1 mark for correct workings***
- ***1 mark for correct value of t***

b) Write down the *uvast* variables for P and Q:

$u_P = 17.64$, $a_P = -9.8$, $t_P = t$

$u_Q = 25$, $a_Q = -9.8$, $t_Q = t - 1.8$

Using $s = ut + \frac{1}{2}at^2$:

P: $s_P = 17.64t + \frac{1}{2}(-9.8)t^2$

$s_P = 17.64t - 4.9t^2$

Q: $s_Q = 25(t - 1.8) + \frac{1}{2}(-9.8)(t - 1.8)^2$

$s_Q = 25t - 45 - 4.9(t^2 - 3.6t + 3.24)$

$s_Q = 42.64t - 4.9t^2 - 60.876$

They are level when $s_P = s_Q$:

$17.64t - 4.9t^2 = 42.64t - 4.9t^2 - 60.876$

$17.64t = 42.64t - 60.876$

$60.876 = 25t$

$\Rightarrow t = 60.876 \div 25 = 2.43504$

$t = 2.44$ s (3 s.f.)

[5 marks available in total]:
- ***1 mark for using appropriate equation***
- ***1 mark for correct equation for*** s_P
- ***1 mark for correct equation for*** s_Q
- ***1 mark for stating*** $s_P = s_Q$
- ***1 mark for correct value of t***

c) Using $s = ut + \frac{1}{2}at^2$ for particle P:

$s = (17.64 \times 2.43504) + \frac{1}{2}(-9.8 \times 2.43504^2)$

$s = 13.899... = 13.9$ m (3 s.f.)

[3 marks available in total]:
- ***1 mark for using appropriate equation***
- ***1 mark for correct workings***
- ***1 mark for correct value of s***

Chapter 3: Vectors

1. Vectors

Exercise 1.1 — Vectors — the basics

Q1 **a)** Scalar **b)** Vector **c)** Scalar
d) Scalar **e)** Vector **f)** Scalar

Q2

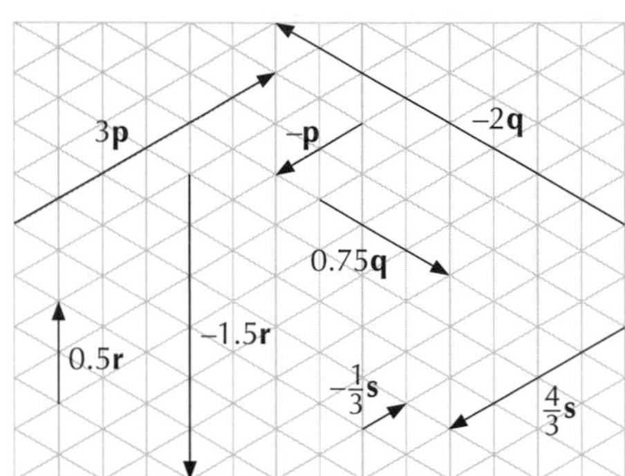

Q3 **a)** **a** and **d**, **b** and **h**, **c** and **i**, **e** and **g**, **f** and **j**
b) **d** = 2**a**, **b** = 4**h**, **c** = 3**i**, **e** = 0.75**g**, **f** = 2**j**

Q4 2**a** + 6**b** and 0.6**a** + 1.8**b**

Exercise 1.2 — Resultant vectors

Q1

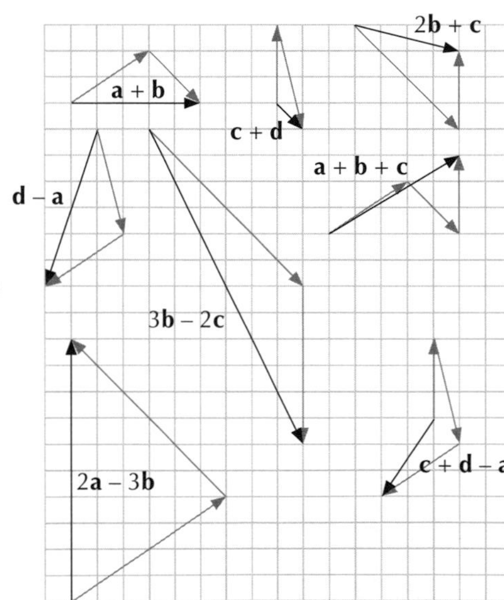

Q2

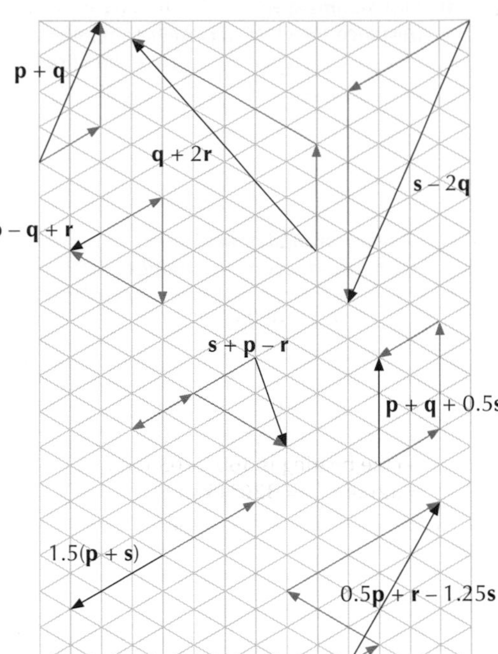

Q3 Draw a diagram of the journey:

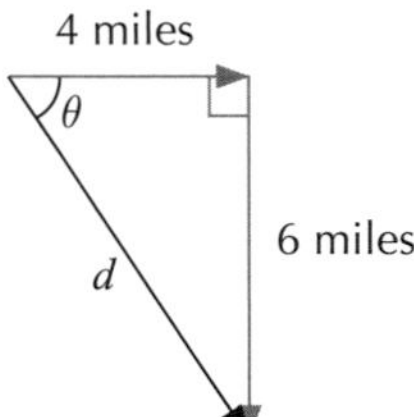

d is his distance from the car park.
Using Pythagoras' theorem:
$d = \sqrt{6^2 + 4^2} = \sqrt{52} = 7.21$ miles (3 s.f.)
Using trigonometry:
$\theta = \tan^{-1}\left(\frac{6}{4}\right) = 56.30...°$
So his bearing is 090° + 056.30...° = 146.30...°
= 146° (3 s.f.)

Q4 Draw a diagram:

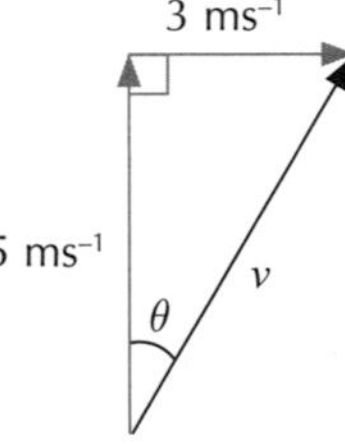

v is the resultant speed.
Using Pythagoras' theorem:
$v = \sqrt{5^2 + 3^2} = \sqrt{34} = 5.83$ ms^{-1} (3 s.f.)
Using trigonometry:
$\theta = \tan^{-1}\left(\frac{3}{5}\right) = 31.0°$ (3 s.f.)
So the direction is 31.0° (3 s.f.) from the initial direction of the boat towards the direction of the wind.

Q5 **a)** The plane travels 120 km in 2 hours, so its resultant speed is 120 km ÷ 2 h = 60 kmh^{-1}

b) Draw a diagram:

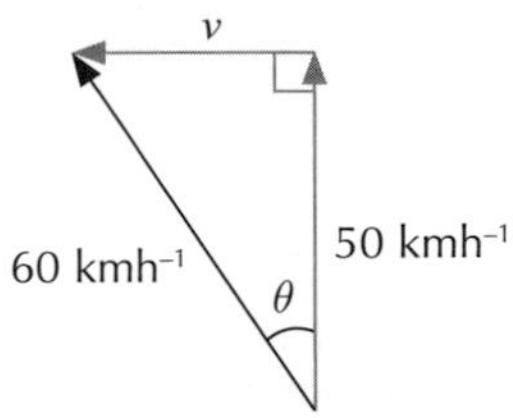

v is the speed of the wind.
Using Pythagoras' theorem:
$v = \sqrt{60^2 - 50^2} = \sqrt{1100} = 33.2$ kmh^{-1} (3 s.f.)

c) Using trigonometry:
$\theta = \cos^{-1}\left(\frac{50}{60}\right) = 33.55...°$ (3 s.f.)
So the bearing is 360° – 033.55...°
= 326.44...° = 326° (3 s.f.)

Q6 Draw a diagram using the information given:

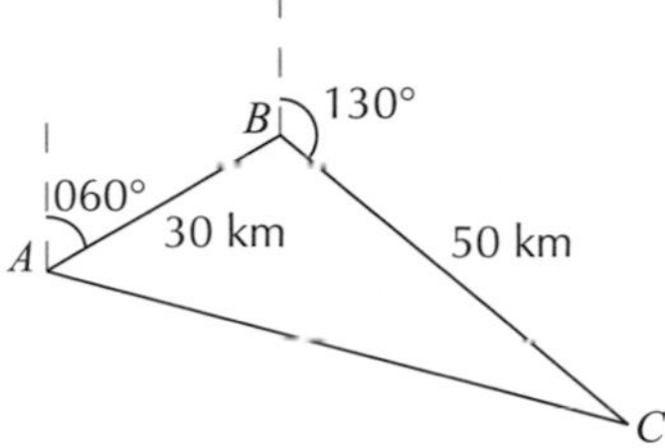

Fill in the missing angles around B — use supplementary angles to find 120° and angles around a point to find 110°.

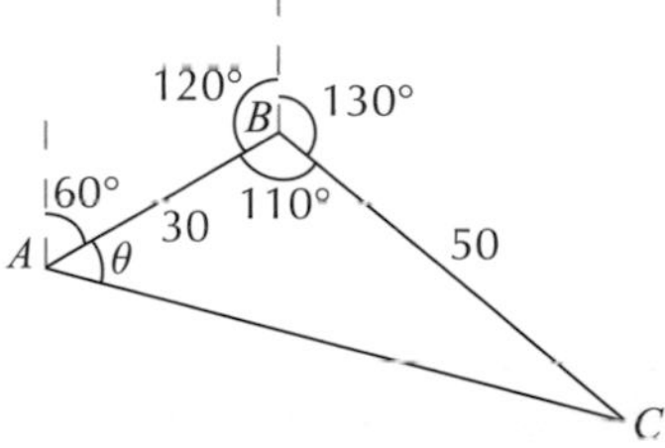

Now use the cosine rule to find the distance AC:
$AC^2 = 30^2 + 50^2 - (2 \times 30 \times 50)\cos 110°$
$AC^2 = 4426.06...$
$AC = 66.528... = 66.5$ km (3 s.f.)
Then use the sine rule to find the angle θ:
$\frac{\sin\theta}{50} = \frac{\sin 110°}{66.528...}$
$\Rightarrow \sin\theta = 0.706...$
$\Rightarrow \theta = 44.92...°$
So the bearing is 060° + 44.92...° = 104.92...°
= 105°
So he has to travel 66.5 km (3 s.f.) along a bearing of 105°.

Exercise 1.3 — Unit vectors

Q1 $\mathbf{q} = 4\mathbf{i} + 2\mathbf{j} = \begin{pmatrix}4\\2\end{pmatrix}$ $\quad \mathbf{r} = \mathbf{i} - 3\mathbf{j} = \begin{pmatrix}1\\-3\end{pmatrix}$

$\mathbf{s} = -4\mathbf{i} - 4\mathbf{j} = \begin{pmatrix}-4\\-4\end{pmatrix}$ $\quad \mathbf{t} = -3\mathbf{j} = \begin{pmatrix}0\\-3\end{pmatrix}$

$\mathbf{u} = 5\mathbf{i} = \begin{pmatrix}5\\0\end{pmatrix}$ $\quad \mathbf{v} = \mathbf{i} + 2\mathbf{j} = \begin{pmatrix}1\\2\end{pmatrix}$

$\mathbf{w} = 4\mathbf{j} = \begin{pmatrix}0\\4\end{pmatrix}$ $\quad \mathbf{x} = -2\mathbf{i} = \begin{pmatrix}-2\\0\end{pmatrix}$

$\mathbf{y} = -6\mathbf{i} + 4\mathbf{j} = \begin{pmatrix}-6\\4\end{pmatrix}$ $\quad \mathbf{z} = -2\mathbf{i} - 6\mathbf{j} = \begin{pmatrix}-2\\-6\end{pmatrix}$

Q2 The grid is divided into unit squares:

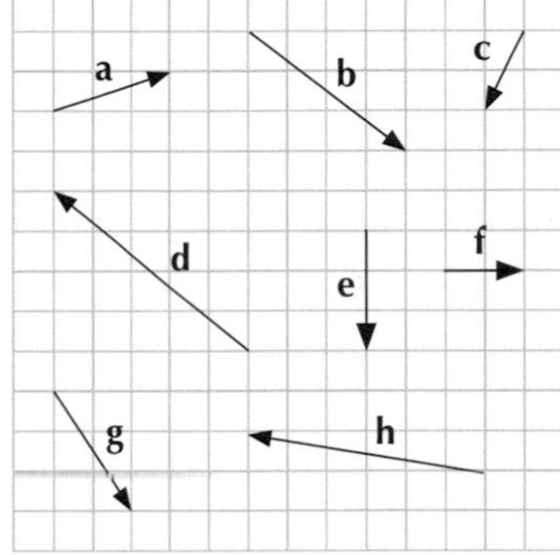

Q3 **a)** $\mathbf{p} + \mathbf{q} = (2 - 7)\mathbf{i} + (-6 + 11)\mathbf{j} = -5\mathbf{i} + 5\mathbf{j}$

b) $\mathbf{u} + \mathbf{v} = (-9 + 7)\mathbf{i} + (-13 - 8)\mathbf{j} = -2\mathbf{i} - 21\mathbf{j}$

c) $\mathbf{w} + \mathbf{z} = (-19 + -12)\mathbf{i} + (-14 - 20)\mathbf{j} = -31\mathbf{i} - 34\mathbf{j}$

Q4 **a)** $3\mathbf{b} = 3(\mathbf{i} - 3\mathbf{j}) = 3\mathbf{i} - 9\mathbf{j}$

b) $4\mathbf{e} = 4(-4\mathbf{i} + 2\mathbf{j}) = -16\mathbf{i} + 8\mathbf{j}$

c) $-2\mathbf{a} = -2(2\mathbf{i} + \mathbf{j}) = -4\mathbf{i} - 2\mathbf{j}$

d) $\mathbf{f} + \mathbf{c} = (-6\mathbf{i} - 5\mathbf{j}) + (5\mathbf{i} + 2\mathbf{j}) = -\mathbf{i} - 3\mathbf{j}$

e) $\mathbf{d} - \mathbf{a} = (-\mathbf{i} + \mathbf{j}) - (2\mathbf{i} + \mathbf{j}) = -3\mathbf{i}$

f) $\mathbf{b} - 2\mathbf{f} = (\mathbf{i} - 3\mathbf{j}) - 2(-6\mathbf{i} - 5\mathbf{j}) = (\mathbf{i} - 3\mathbf{j}) + (12\mathbf{i} + 10\mathbf{j})$
$= 13\mathbf{i} + 7\mathbf{j}$

g) $0.5\mathbf{c} = 0.5(5\mathbf{i} + 2\mathbf{j}) = 2.5\mathbf{i} + \mathbf{j}$

h) $0.5\mathbf{e} + 2\mathbf{d} - \mathbf{a} = = 0.5(-4\mathbf{i} + 2\mathbf{j}) + 2(-\mathbf{i} + \mathbf{j}) - (2\mathbf{i} + \mathbf{j})$
$= (-2\mathbf{i} + \mathbf{j}) + (-2\mathbf{i} + 2\mathbf{j}) - (2\mathbf{i} + \mathbf{j}) = -6\mathbf{i} + 2\mathbf{j}$

Q5 **a)**

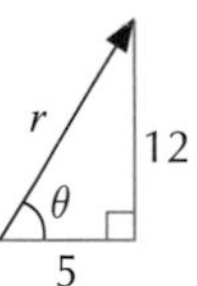

(i) $r = \sqrt{5^2 + 12^2} = \sqrt{169} = 13$

(ii) $\theta = \tan^{-1}\left(\frac{12}{5}\right) = 67.4°$ (3 s.f.)
above the positive horizontal

b)

4 θ 5 r

(i) $r = \sqrt{4^2 + 5^2} = \sqrt{41} = 6.40$ (3 s.f.)

(ii) $\theta = \tan^{-1}\left(\frac{5}{4}\right) = 51.3°$ (3 s.f.)
below the positive horizontal

c)

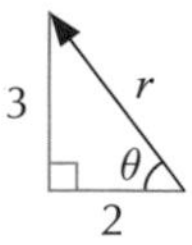

(i) $r = \sqrt{2^2 + 3^2} = \sqrt{13} = 3.61$ (3 s.f.)

(ii) $\theta = \tan^{-1}\left(\frac{3}{2}\right) = 56.3°$ (3 s.f.) above the negative horizontal

d)

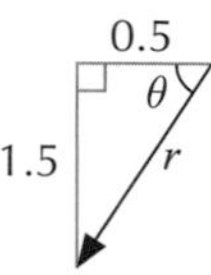

(i) $r = \sqrt{0.5^2 + 1.5^2} = \sqrt{2.5} = 1.58$ (3 s.f.)

(ii) $\theta = \tan^{-1}\left(\frac{1.5}{0.5}\right) = 71.6°$ (3 s.f.) below the negative horizontal

Q6 Magnitude $= \sqrt{7^2 + 9^2} = \sqrt{130} = 11.4$ N (3 s.f.)
direction $= \tan^{-1}\left(\frac{9}{7}\right) = 52.1°$ (3 s.f.)
above the positive horizontal

Q7

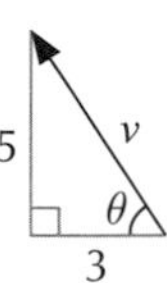

Speed, $v = \sqrt{3^2 + 5^2} = \sqrt{34} = 5.83$ ms^{-1} (3 s.f.)
$\theta = \tan^{-1}\left(\frac{5}{3}\right) = 59.03...°$
So the bearing is $270° + 059.03...° = 329.03...°$
$= 329°$ (3 s.f.)

Q8 $|\mathbf{b}| = \sqrt{3^2 + 4^2} = \sqrt{25} = 5$
So $\mathbf{a} = 3\mathbf{b} = 3(3\mathbf{i} + 4\mathbf{j}) = 9\mathbf{i} + 12\mathbf{j}$

Q9 $|\mathbf{Q}| = \sqrt{(-4)^2 + 8^2} = \sqrt{80} = 4\sqrt{5}$
So $\mathbf{Q} = 2\mathbf{P} \Rightarrow \mathbf{P} = \frac{1}{2}(-4\mathbf{i} + 8\mathbf{j}) = (-2\mathbf{i} + 4\mathbf{j})$ N

2. Resolving Vectors

Exercise 2.1 — Resolving a vector horizontally and vertically

Q1 a) Horizontal component:
$x = -18\cos 40° = -13.8$ (3 s.f.)
Vertical component:
$y = 18\sin 40° = 11.6$ (3 s.f.)
So the vector is $-13.8\mathbf{i} + 11.6\mathbf{j}$

b) $x = 2\cos 30° = \frac{2\sqrt{3}}{2} = \sqrt{3}$
$y = 2\sin 30° = 1$
So the vector is $\sqrt{3}\mathbf{i} + \mathbf{j}$

c) $x = 42\cos 70° = 14.4$ (3 s.f.)
$y = -42\sin 70° = -39.5$ (3 s.f.)
So the vector is $14.4\mathbf{i} - 39.5\mathbf{j}$

Q2 a) $x = 3\cos 60° = 1.5$
$y = 3\sin 60° = 1.5\sqrt{3}$
So $\mathbf{a} = 1.5(\mathbf{i} + \sqrt{3}\mathbf{j})$ N

b) $x = 8\cos 45° = \frac{8}{\sqrt{2}} = 4\sqrt{2}$
$y = -8\sin 45° = -\frac{8}{\sqrt{2}} = -4\sqrt{2}$
So $\mathbf{p} = 4\sqrt{2}(\mathbf{i} - \mathbf{j})$ ms^{-2}

c) $x = -17\cos 70° = -5.81$ (3 s.f.)
$y = 17\sin 70° = 16.0$ (3 s.f.)
So $\mathbf{d} = (-5.81\mathbf{i} + 16.0\mathbf{j})$ ms^{-1}

d) $x = -12\cos 15° = -11.6$ (3 s.f.)
$y = -12\sin 15° = -3.11$ (3 s.f.)
So $\mathbf{k} = (-11.6\mathbf{i} - 3.11\mathbf{j})$ kmh^{-1}

Q3

$x = 3\cos 20° = 2.82$ km (3 s.f.)
$y = -3\sin 20° = -1.03$ km (3 s.f.)

Q4

$x = 13\cos 40° = 9.96$ (3 s.f.)
$y = 13\sin 40° = 8.36$ (3 s.f.)
So $\mathbf{v} = (9.96\mathbf{i} + 8.36\mathbf{j})$ ms^{-1}
You could've found the components using the 50° angle — $x = 13\sin 50°$ and $y = 13\cos 50°$. The answer would've been the same.

Q5 $x = -24\cos 30° = -\frac{24\sqrt{3}}{2} = -12\sqrt{3}$
$y = 24\sin 30° = 12$
So the vector is $12(-\sqrt{3}\mathbf{i} + \mathbf{j})$

Q6

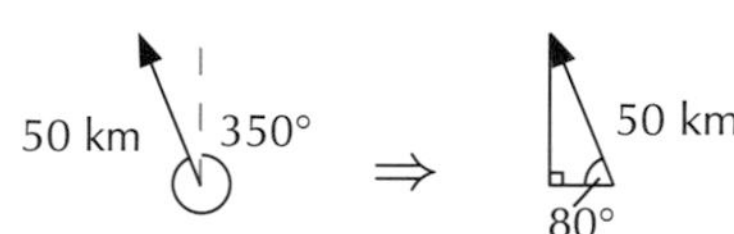

$x = -50\cos 80° = -8.68$ (3 s.f.)
$y = 50\sin 80° = 49.2$ (3 s.f.)
So the displacement is $(-8.68\mathbf{i} + 49.2\mathbf{j})$ km
Again, you could've set up your triangle differently and found the components using a different angle. E.g. $x = -50\sin 10°$, $y = 50\cos 10°$.

Q7

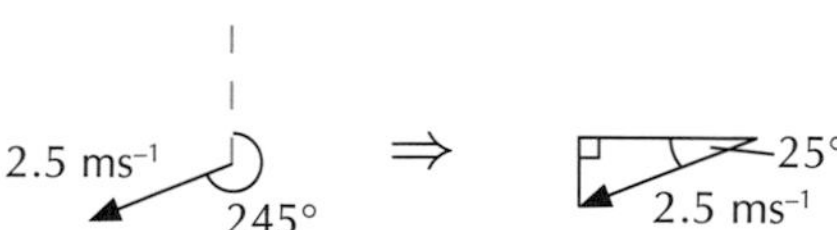

$x = -2.5\cos 25° = -2.27$ (3 s.f.)
$y = -2.5\sin 25° = -1.06$ (3 s.f.)
So the velocity is $(-2.27\mathbf{i} - 1.06\mathbf{j})$ ms^{-1}
Here, you could've done $x = -2.5\sin 65°$, $y = -2.5\cos 65°$.

Q8

42°
2 ms^{-1}
42°

$x = 2\cos 42° = 1.49$ (3 s.f.)
$y = -2\sin 42° = -1.34$ (3 s.f.)
So the velocity is $(1.49\mathbf{i} - 1.34\mathbf{j})$ ms^{-1}

Exercise 2.2 — Resolving to find a resultant vector

Q1

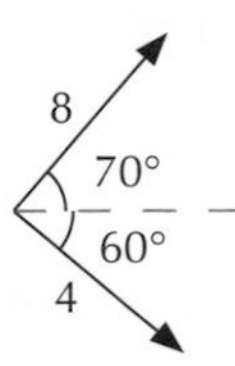

Resolving horizontally (taking right as positive):
$8\cos 70° + 4\cos 60° = 4.736...$
Resolving vertically (taking up as positive):
$8\sin 70° - 4\sin 60° = 4.053...$
Use these components to draw a right-angled triangle:

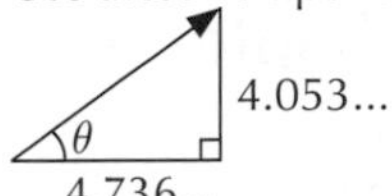

magnitude = $\sqrt{4.736...^2 + 4.053...^2} = 6.23$ (3 s.f.)
$\theta = \tan^{-1}\left(\frac{4.053...}{4.736...}\right)$
= 40.6° (3 s.f.) above the positive horizontal

Q2

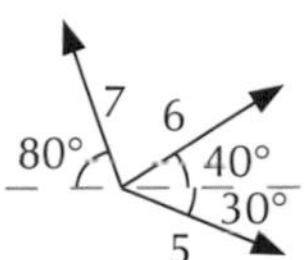

Resolving horizontally (taking right as positive):
$6\cos 40° + 5\cos 30° - 7\cos 80° = 7.710...$
Resolving vertically (taking up as positive):
$7\sin 80° + 6\sin 40° - 5\sin 30° = 8.250...$
Use these components to draw a right-angled triangle:

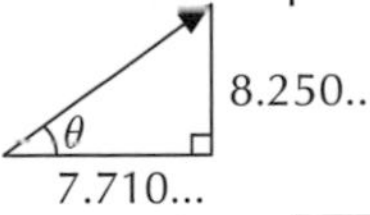

magnitude = $\sqrt{7.710...^2 + 8.250...^2} = 11.3$ (3 s.f.)
$\theta = \tan^{-1}\left(\frac{8.250...}{7.710...}\right)$
= 46.9° (3 s.f.) above the positive horizontal

Q3

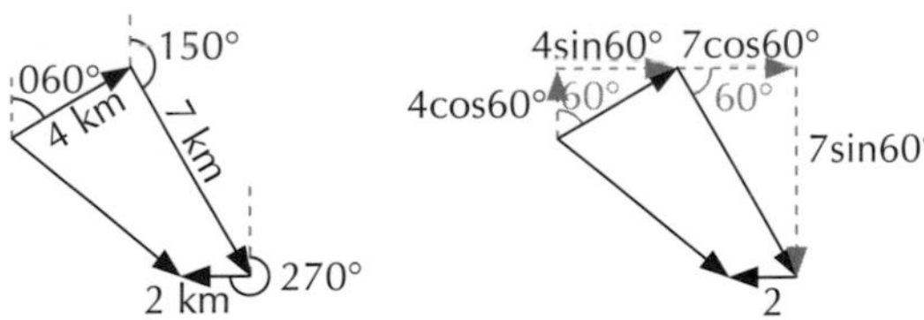

Resolving east:
$4\sin 60° + 7\cos 60° - 2 = 4.964...$
Resolving north:
$4\cos 60° - 7\sin 60° = -4.062...$
Use these components to draw a right-angled triangle:

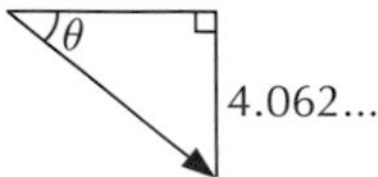

Distance = $\sqrt{4.964...^2 + 4.062...^2} = 6.41$ km (3 s.f.)
$\theta = \tan^{-1}\left(\frac{4.062...}{4.964...}\right) = 39.293...°$
$090° + 39.293...° = 129.293...°$
So the final displacement is 6.41 km on a bearing of 129°.
Don't forget that displacement is a vector quantity, so you should give a direction as well as a distance.

Q4 a)

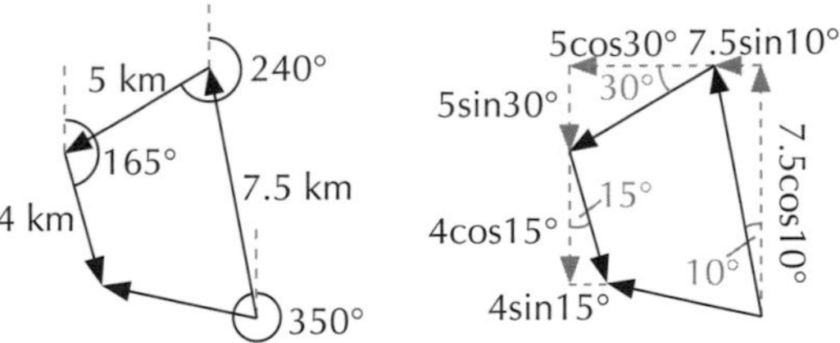

Resolving east:
$-7.5\sin 10° - 5\cos 30° + 4\sin 15° = -4.597...$
Resolving north:
$7.5\cos 10° - 5\sin 30° - 4\cos 15° = 1.022...$
Use these components to draw a right-angled triangle:

1.022... θ
4.597...

Distance = $\sqrt{4.597...^2 + 1.022...^2} = 4.709...$
= 4.71 km (3 s.f.)

b) $\theta = \tan^{-1}\left(\frac{1.022...}{4.597...}\right) = 12.537...°$
Add this to 90° to find the bearing he needs to walk back along:
$90° + 12.537...° = 102.537...°$
So the bearing is 103°

3. Applications of Vectors

Exercise 3.1 — Displacement, velocity and acceleration vectors

Q1 $\mathbf{s} = \mathbf{v}t$
$\mathbf{s} = (\mathbf{i} + 2\mathbf{j}) \times 4$
$\mathbf{s} = (4\mathbf{i} + 8\mathbf{j})$ m
Add this to the initial position vector:
$(4\mathbf{i} - 3\mathbf{j}) + (4\mathbf{i} + 8\mathbf{j}) = (8\mathbf{i} + 5\mathbf{j})$ m
$t = 4$ because you're finding the particle's position at time $t = 6$ s, which is 4 s after $t = 2$ s.

Q2 $\mathbf{s} = (3\mathbf{i} + 12\mathbf{j}) - (6\mathbf{i} - 3\mathbf{j}) = (-3\mathbf{i} + 15\mathbf{j})$
$\mathbf{s} = \mathbf{v}t$
$\Rightarrow (-3\mathbf{i} + 15\mathbf{j}) = (-2t\mathbf{i} + 10t\mathbf{j})$
Equating horizontal components: $-3 = -2t$
$\Rightarrow t = 1.5$ h

Q3 **a)** $\mathbf{s} = (-5\mathbf{i} + 2\mathbf{j}) - (4\mathbf{i} - 7\mathbf{j})$
$\mathbf{s} = (-9\mathbf{i} + 9\mathbf{j})$ m
$\mathbf{s} = \mathbf{v}t$
$\Rightarrow (-9\mathbf{i} + 9\mathbf{j}) = 3\mathbf{v}$
$\Rightarrow \mathbf{v} = (-3\mathbf{i} + 3\mathbf{j})$ ms^{-1}

b) speed $= \sqrt{(-3)^2 + 3^2} = \sqrt{18} = 4.24$ ms^{-1} (3 s.f.)

c)

$\tan\theta = \left(\frac{3}{3}\right)$
$\theta = 45°$ above the negative horizontal

Q4 $\mathbf{u} = 4\mathbf{i} + 5\mathbf{j}$, $t = 6$, $\mathbf{s} = 33\mathbf{i} + 48\mathbf{j}$, $\mathbf{a} = \mathbf{a}$
Using $\mathbf{s} = \mathbf{u}t + \frac{1}{2}\mathbf{a}t^2$:
$33\mathbf{i} + 48\mathbf{j} = 6(4\mathbf{i} + 5\mathbf{j}) + \frac{1}{2}\mathbf{a}(6^2)$
$33\mathbf{i} + 48\mathbf{j} = 24\mathbf{i} + 30\mathbf{j} + 18\mathbf{a}$
$9\mathbf{i} + 18\mathbf{j} = 18\mathbf{a}$
So $\mathbf{a} = (0.5\mathbf{i} + \mathbf{j})$ ms^{-2}

Q5 $\mathbf{u} = 8\mathbf{i} + \mathbf{j}$, $\mathbf{v} = -3\mathbf{i} + 2\mathbf{j}$, $\mathbf{a} = (-5.5\mathbf{i} + 0.5\mathbf{j})$, $t = t$
Using $\mathbf{v} = \mathbf{u} + \mathbf{a}t$:
$-3\mathbf{i} + 2\mathbf{j} = 8\mathbf{i} + \mathbf{j} + (-5.5\mathbf{i} + 0.5\mathbf{j})t$
$-11\mathbf{i} + \mathbf{j} = (-5.5t\mathbf{i} + 0.5t\mathbf{j})$
Equating horizontal components: $-11 = -5.5t$
$\Rightarrow t = 2$ s

Q6 **a)** Find the particle's displacement from O:
$\mathbf{u} = \mathbf{0}$, $\mathbf{a} = (2\mathbf{i} - 8\mathbf{j})$, $\mathbf{s} = \mathbf{s}$, $t = t$
$\mathbf{s} = \mathbf{u}t + \frac{1}{2}\mathbf{a}t^2$
$\mathbf{s} = \frac{1}{2}(2\mathbf{i} - 8\mathbf{j})t^2$
$\mathbf{s} = (\mathbf{i} - 4\mathbf{j})t^2$ m
The particle sets off from O, so $\mathbf{p} = \mathbf{s}$:
$\mathbf{p} = (\mathbf{i} - 4\mathbf{j})t^2$ m

b) $\mathbf{s} = (2\mathbf{i} + 2\mathbf{j}) - (-4\mathbf{i} + 6\mathbf{j}) = (6\mathbf{i} - 4\mathbf{j})$ m
$\mathbf{s} = \mathbf{v}t$
$(6\mathbf{i} - 4\mathbf{j}) = 2\mathbf{v}$
$\Rightarrow \mathbf{v} = (3\mathbf{i} - 2\mathbf{j})$ ms^{-1}

c) Find the displacement of Q:
$\mathbf{s} = \mathbf{v}t = (3\mathbf{i} - 2\mathbf{j})t$
Add this to its initial position vector:
$\mathbf{q} = [(-4\mathbf{i} + 6\mathbf{j}) + (3\mathbf{i} - 2\mathbf{j})t]$ m

d) At $t = 8$:
$\mathbf{p} = (\mathbf{i} - 4\mathbf{j}) \times 8^2 = (64\mathbf{i} - 256\mathbf{j})$ m
$\mathbf{q} = (-4\mathbf{i} + 6\mathbf{j}) + 8(3\mathbf{i} - 2\mathbf{j}) = (20\mathbf{i} - 10\mathbf{j})$ m
$\mathbf{p} - \mathbf{q} = (64\mathbf{i} - 256\mathbf{j}) - (20\mathbf{i} - 10\mathbf{j}) = (44\mathbf{i} - 246\mathbf{j})$ m
Distance $= \sqrt{(44)^2 + (-246)^2} = 249.90...$ m
$= 250$ m (3 s.f.)

Q7 **a)** Find the snowmobile's displacement during the first hour and a half:
$\mathbf{s} = \mathbf{v}t = (8\mathbf{i} - 14\mathbf{j}) \times 1.5 = (12\mathbf{i} - 21\mathbf{j})$ km
This is its position vector at 1030 hours.
It then starts travelling with velocity $-20\mathbf{i}$ kmh^{-1}
So its position vector at t hours after 1030 is:
$[(12\mathbf{i} - 21\mathbf{j}) + (-20\mathbf{i})t]$ km
When it is due south of O, the horizontal component of its position vector is zero:
$12 - 20t = 0$
$12 = 20t$
$t = 0.6$ hours $= 0.6 \times 60 = 36$ minutes
So it is due south of O 36 minutes after 1030.
So the time is 1106 hours.

b) At 1200, the first snowmobile has position vector:
$(12\mathbf{i} - 21\mathbf{j}) - (20\mathbf{i} \times 1.5)$
$= 12\mathbf{i} - 21\mathbf{j} - 30\mathbf{i}$
$= (-18\mathbf{i} - 21\mathbf{j})$ km
The second snowmobile travels from O to this point in 1 hour.
$\mathbf{s} = \mathbf{v}t$
$-18\mathbf{i} - 21\mathbf{j} = \mathbf{v} \times 1$
$\Rightarrow \mathbf{v} = (-18\mathbf{i} - 21\mathbf{j})$ kmh^{-1}

Review Exercise — Chapter 3

Q1 Displacement $= (15 \times 0.25) - (10 \times 0.75) = -3.75$ km
Time taken = 1 hour
Average velocity $= -3.75$ kmh^{-1}
(i.e. 3.75 kmh^{-1} south)

Q2 $\mathbf{a} + 2\mathbf{b} - 3\mathbf{c} = (3\mathbf{i} + 7\mathbf{j}) + 2(-2\mathbf{i} + 2\mathbf{j}) - 3(\mathbf{i} - 3\mathbf{j})$
$= (3 - 4 - 3)\mathbf{i} + (7 + 4 + 9)\mathbf{j} = -4\mathbf{i} + 20\mathbf{j}$

Q3 **a), b)** The grid is divided into unit squares:

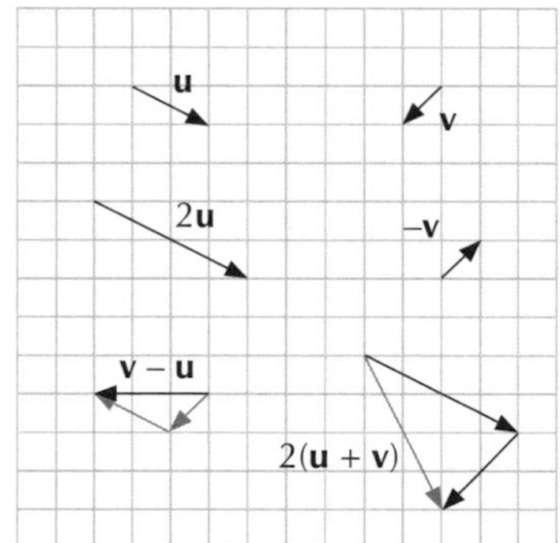

c) $|\mathbf{u}| = \sqrt{2^2 + (-1)^2} = \sqrt{5}$ (= 2.24 (3 s.f.))

d) $\theta = \tan^{-1}\left(\frac{4}{2}\right)$
$= 63.4°$ (3 s.f.) below the positive horizontal

Q4 $|\mathbf{p}| = \sqrt{5^2 + (-12)^2} = \sqrt{169} = 13$
$\Rightarrow \mathbf{q} = 5\mathbf{p} = 5(5\mathbf{i} - 12\mathbf{j})$
$\mathbf{q} = 25\mathbf{i} - 60\mathbf{j}$

Q5

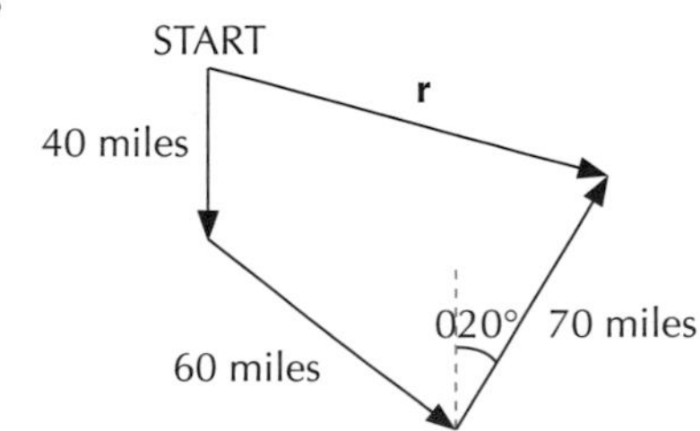

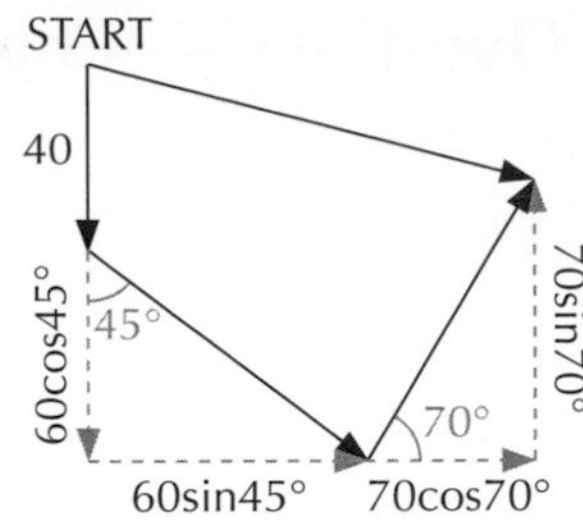

Resolving East:
$60\sin 45° + 70\cos 70° = 66.367...$ miles
Resolving North:
$-40 - 60\cos 45° + 70\sin 70° = -16.647...$ miles
$|\mathbf{r}| = \sqrt{66.367...^2 + (-16.647...)^2}$
$= 68.423... = 68.4$ miles (3 s.f.)

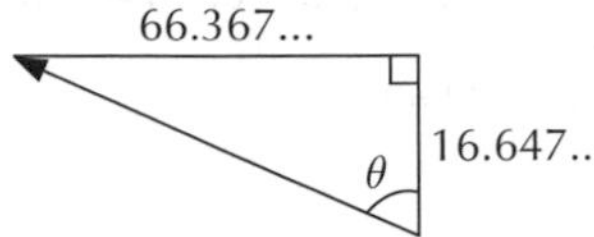

$\theta = \tan^{-1}\left(\frac{66.367...}{16.647...}\right) = 75.918...°$

$360° - 75.918...° = 284.081...°$

So bearing is 284°

Q6

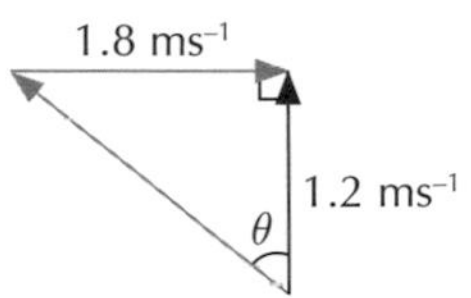

speed $= \sqrt{1.8^2 + 1.2^2} = 2.163...$
$= 2.16$ ms^{-1} (3 s.f.)
$\theta = \tan^{-1}\left(\frac{1.8}{1.2}\right) = 56.309...°$
So he has to swim at an angle of 56.3° (3 s.f.) to the perpendicular to the river bank (upstream).

Q7 Draw a diagram to show the journey:

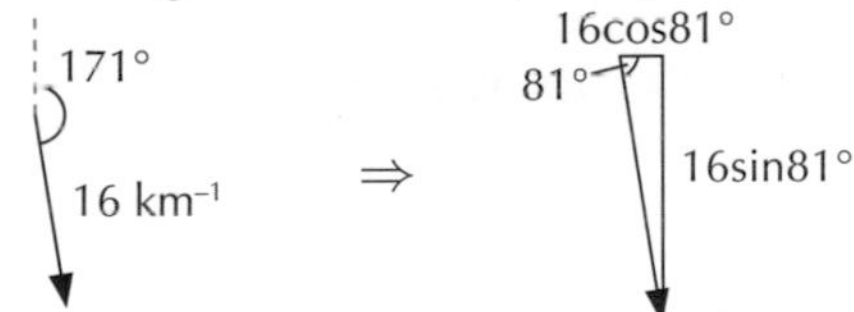

Horizontal component of velocity:
$16\cos 81° = 2.502... = 2.50$ (3 s.f.)
Vertical component of velocity:
$-16\sin 81° = -15.803... = -15.8$ (3 s.f.)
So her velocity is $(2.50\mathbf{i} - 15.8\mathbf{j})$ kmh^{-1}
You could've done this question using the 9° angle instead.

Q8 a) Resolving horizontally (taking right as positive):
$-32\cos 30° + 28\cos 65° + 21\cos 50° = -2.380...$
Resolving vertically (taking up as positive):
$32\sin 30° + 28\sin 65° - 21\sin 50° = 25.289...$
Draw a triangle to show the components:

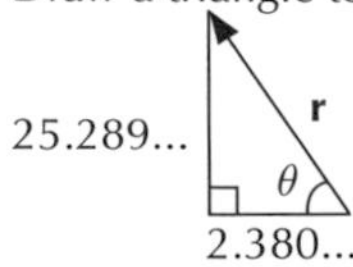

$|\mathbf{r}| = \sqrt{25.289...^2 + 2.380...^2} = 25.401...$
$= 25.4$ (3 s.f.)
$\theta = \tan^{-1}\left(\frac{25.289...}{2.380...}\right) = 84.621...°$
$= 84.6°$ (3 s.f.) above the negative horizontal

b) Resolving horizontally (taking right as positive):
$-66\cos 85° - 58\cos 70° + 39\cos 75° = -15.495...$
Resolving vertically (taking up as positive):
$66\sin 85° - 58\sin 70° - 39\sin 75° = -26.424...$
Draw a triangle to show the components:

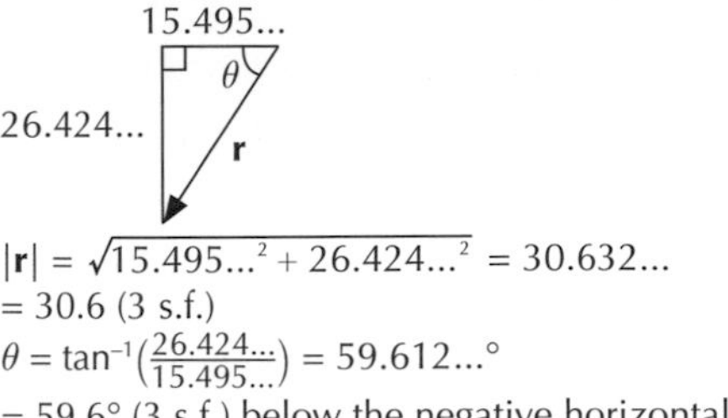

$|\mathbf{r}| = \sqrt{15.495...^2 + 26.424...^2} = 30.632...$
$= 30.6$ (3 s.f.)
$\theta = \tan^{-1}\left(\frac{26.424...}{15.495...}\right) = 59.612...°$
$= 59.6°$ (3 s.f.) below the negative horizontal

Q9 a)

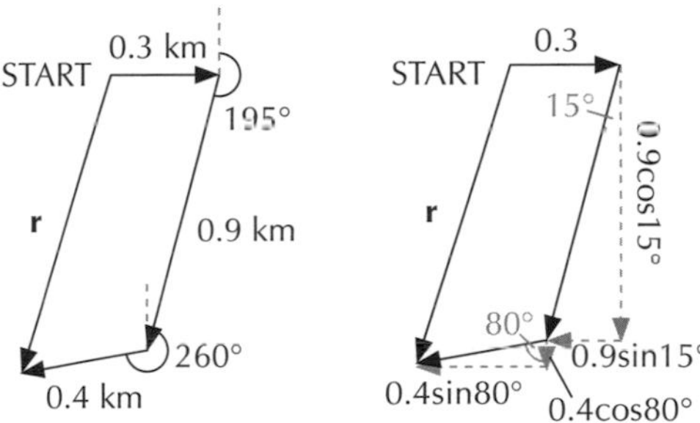

Resolving east:
$0.3 - 0.9\sin 15° - 0.4\sin 80° = -0.326...$
Resolving north:
$-0.9\cos 15° - 0.4\cos 80° = -0.938...$
Draw a triangle to show the components:

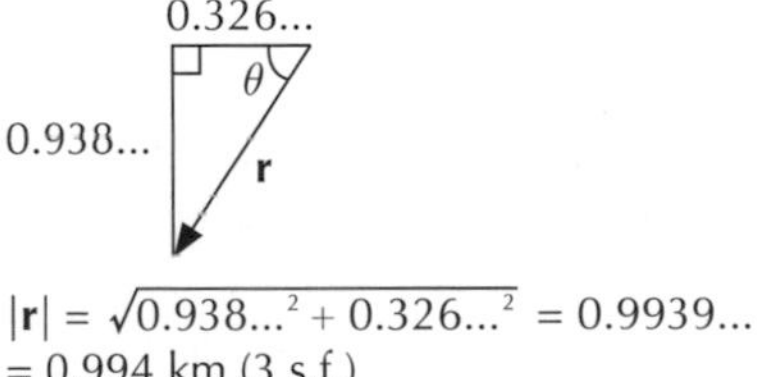

$|\mathbf{r}| = \sqrt{0.938...^2 + 0.326...^2} = 0.9939...$
$= 0.994$ km (3 s.f.)

b) From resolving east and north in part a), the dog's final displacement is $(-0.327\mathbf{i} - 0.939\mathbf{j})$ km (3 s.f.)

Q10 Using $\mathbf{s} = \mathbf{v}t$:
$\mathbf{s} = (3\mathbf{i} + 5\mathbf{j}) \times 6$
$\mathbf{s} = (18\mathbf{i} + 30\mathbf{j})$ m
Now using Pythagoras' theorem:
distance $= \sqrt{18^2 + 30^2} = \sqrt{1224} = 35.0$ m (3 s.f.)

Q11 Using $\mathbf{s} = \mathbf{v}t$:
$\mathbf{s} = 5(7\mathbf{i} - 3\mathbf{j}) = 35\mathbf{i} - 15\mathbf{j}$
$\mathbf{y} - \mathbf{x} = 35\mathbf{i} - 15\mathbf{j}$
$2\mathbf{i} + 5\mathbf{j} - \mathbf{x} = 35\mathbf{i} - 15\mathbf{j}$
$\mathbf{x} = -33\mathbf{i} + 20\mathbf{j}$

Q12 $\mathbf{u} = 5\mathbf{i} + 2\mathbf{j}$, $\mathbf{a} = \mathbf{i} + 2\mathbf{j}$, $t = 8$, $\mathbf{v} = \mathbf{v}$
Using $\mathbf{v} = \mathbf{u} + \mathbf{a}t$:
$\mathbf{v} = (5\mathbf{i} + 2\mathbf{j}) + 8(\mathbf{i} + 2\mathbf{j}) = 5\mathbf{i} + 2\mathbf{j} + 8\mathbf{i} + 16\mathbf{j}$
$\mathbf{v} = 13\mathbf{i} + 18\mathbf{j}$
speed $= \sqrt{13^2 + 18^2} = \sqrt{493} = 22.2$ ms^{-1} (3 s.f.)

$\theta = \tan^{-1}\left(\frac{18}{13}\right)$
$= 54.2°$ (3 s.f.) above the positive horizontal

Q13 $\mathbf{s} = (-6\mathbf{i} + 3\mathbf{j}) - (3\mathbf{i} + 5\mathbf{j}) = -9\mathbf{i} - 2\mathbf{j}$
$t = 5$, $\mathbf{u} = 2\mathbf{i} + \mathbf{j}$, $\mathbf{v} = \mathbf{v}$
Using $\mathbf{s} = \left(\frac{\mathbf{u}+\mathbf{v}}{2}\right)t$:
$-9\mathbf{i} - 2\mathbf{j} = 5\left(\frac{2\mathbf{i} + \mathbf{j} + \mathbf{v}}{2}\right)$
$-18\mathbf{i} - 4\mathbf{j} = 10\mathbf{i} + 5\mathbf{j} + 5\mathbf{v}$
$-28\mathbf{i} - 9\mathbf{j} = 5\mathbf{v}$
$\mathbf{v} = (-5.6\mathbf{i} - 1.8\mathbf{j})$ ms^{-1}

Q14 $\mathbf{s} = (8\mathbf{i} - 2\mathbf{j}) - (4\mathbf{i} + 7\mathbf{j}) = 4\mathbf{i} - 9\mathbf{j}$
$\mathbf{u} = 2\mathbf{i} - 3\mathbf{j}$, $\mathbf{v} = -1.5\mathbf{j}$, $t = t$
Using $\mathbf{s} = \left(\frac{\mathbf{u}+\mathbf{v}}{2}\right)t$:
$4\mathbf{i} - 9\mathbf{j} = \left(\frac{2\mathbf{i} - 3\mathbf{j} - 1.5\mathbf{j}}{2}\right)t$
$4\mathbf{i} - 9\mathbf{j} = (t\mathbf{i} - 2.25t\mathbf{j})$
Equating horizontal components: $t = 4$ s

Q15 $\mathbf{s} = (-5\mathbf{i} + 10\mathbf{j}) - (9\mathbf{i} - 6\mathbf{j}) = -14\mathbf{i} + 16\mathbf{j}$
$t = 4$, $\mathbf{u} = \mathbf{i} + 2\mathbf{j}$, $\mathbf{a} = \mathbf{a}$
Using $\mathbf{s} = \mathbf{u}t + \frac{1}{2}\mathbf{a}t^2$:
$-14\mathbf{i} + 16\mathbf{j} = 4\mathbf{i} + 8\mathbf{j} + \frac{1}{2}\mathbf{a}(4^2)$
$-18\mathbf{i} + 8\mathbf{j} = 8\mathbf{a}$
$\Rightarrow \mathbf{a} = (-2.25\mathbf{i} + \mathbf{j})$ ms^{-2}
$|\mathbf{a}| = \sqrt{(-2.25)^2 + 1^2} = 2.46$ ms^{-2} (3 s.f.)

Q16 a) $\mathbf{u} = 7\mathbf{i} - 2\mathbf{j}$, $\mathbf{a} = -3\mathbf{i} - 2\mathbf{j}$, $t = 2$, $\mathbf{s} = \mathbf{s}$
Using $\mathbf{s} = \mathbf{u}t + \frac{1}{2}\mathbf{a}t^2$:
$\mathbf{s} = 2(7\mathbf{i} - 2\mathbf{j}) + \frac{1}{2}(-3\mathbf{i} - 2\mathbf{j})(2^2)$
$\mathbf{s} = 14\mathbf{i} - 4\mathbf{j} + 2(-3\mathbf{i} - 2\mathbf{j})$
$\mathbf{s} = 14\mathbf{i} - 4\mathbf{j} - 6\mathbf{i} - 4\mathbf{j}$
$\mathbf{s} = (8\mathbf{i} - 8\mathbf{j})$ m

b) distance $= \sqrt{8^2 + (-8)^2} = \sqrt{128}$
$= 11.3$ m (3 s.f.)

c) Using $\mathbf{v} = \mathbf{u} + \mathbf{a}t$ with $t = 5$:
$\mathbf{v} = 7\mathbf{i} - 2\mathbf{j} + 5(-3\mathbf{i} - 2\mathbf{j})$
$\mathbf{v} = 7\mathbf{i} - 2\mathbf{j} - 15\mathbf{i} - 10\mathbf{j}$
$\mathbf{v} = (-8\mathbf{i} - 12\mathbf{j})$ ms^{-1}

Exam-Style Questions — Chapter 3

1

magnitude $= \sqrt{3^2 + 2^2} = \sqrt{13} = 3.61$ ms^{-1} (3 s.f.)
$\theta = \tan^{-1}\left(\frac{3}{2}\right) = 56.309...°$
So the angle to the riverbank is $90° - 56.309...°$
$= 33.690...° = 33.7°$ (3 s.f.)
[4 marks available in total]:
- ***1 mark for correct workings to find magnitude***
- ***1 mark for correct value of magnitude***
- ***1 mark for correct workings to find angle***
- ***1 mark for correct value of angle***

2 Add the vectors together to find the resultant velocity:
$(4\mathbf{i} + 6\mathbf{j}) + (\mathbf{i} - 2\mathbf{j}) + (-3\mathbf{j}) = (5\mathbf{i} + \mathbf{j})$ ms^{-1}
magnitude $= \sqrt{5^2 + 1^2} = \sqrt{26} = 5.099...$
$= 5.10$ ms^{-1} (3 s.f.)
$\theta = \tan^{-1}\left(\frac{1}{5}\right) = 11.309...°$
$= 11.3°$ (3 s.f.) above **i**
[5 marks available in total]:
- ***1 mark for finding resultant velocity***
- ***1 mark for correct workings for magnitude***
- ***1 mark for correct value of magnitude***
- ***1 mark for correct workings for direction***
- ***1 mark for correct direction***

3 a)

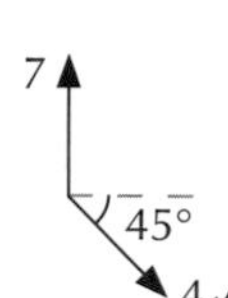

Resolving horizontally (taking right as positive):
$4\sqrt{2}\cos 45° = 4$
Resolving vertically (taking up as positive):
$7 - 4\sqrt{2}\sin 45° = 3$
So $\mathbf{r} = 4\mathbf{i} + 3\mathbf{j}$
[2 marks available in total]:
- ***1 mark for resolving horizontally and vertically***
- ***1 mark for correct expression for r***

b) $|\mathbf{r}| = \sqrt{4^2 + 3^2} = 5$
$\Rightarrow \mathbf{s} = 7\mathbf{r}$
So $\mathbf{s} = 7(4\mathbf{i} + 3\mathbf{j}) = 28\mathbf{i} + 21\mathbf{j}$
[3 marks available in total]:
- ***1 mark for finding magnitude of r***
- ***1 mark for correct working to find s***
- ***1 mark for correct expression for s***

4 Using $\mathbf{s} = \mathbf{v}t$ for the first particle:
$\mathbf{s} = 8(3\mathbf{i} + \mathbf{j}) = 24\mathbf{i} + 8\mathbf{j}$
So position vector of $A = (\mathbf{i} + 2\mathbf{j}) + (24\mathbf{i} + 8\mathbf{j})$
$= (25\mathbf{i} + 10\mathbf{j})$ m
Using $\mathbf{s} = \mathbf{v}t$ for the second particle:
$\mathbf{s} = 5(-4\mathbf{i} + 2\mathbf{j}) = -20\mathbf{i} + 10\mathbf{j}$
So position vector of $B = (25\mathbf{i} + 10\mathbf{j}) + (-20\mathbf{i} + 10\mathbf{j})$
$= (5\mathbf{i} + 20\mathbf{j})$ m

[5 marks available in total]:
- ***1 mark for correct use of s = vt***
- ***1 mark for correct workings for A***
- ***1 mark for correct value of A***
- ***1 mark for correct workings for B***
- ***1 mark for correct value of B***

5 a)

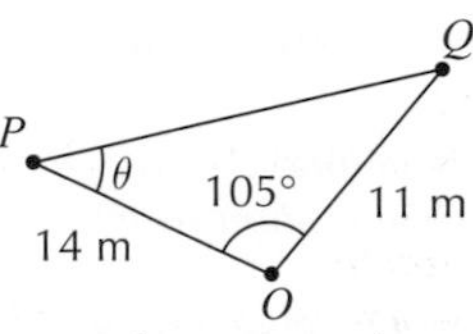

Using the cosine rule:
$PQ^2 = 14^2 + 11^2 - (2 \times 14 \times 11)\cos 105°$
$PQ^2 = 396.716...$
$\Rightarrow PQ = 19.917... = 19.9$ m (3 s.f.)
[2 marks available in total]:
- ***1 mark for correct use of cosine rule***
- ***1 mark for correct value of PQ***

b) Using the sine rule:
$\frac{\sin 105°}{19.917...} = \frac{\sin\theta}{11}$
$\Rightarrow \sin\theta = 11 \times \frac{\sin 105°}{19.917...} = 0.533...$
$\Rightarrow \theta = 32.239...° = 32.2°$ (3 s.f.)
[2 marks available in total]:
- ***1 mark for correct use of sine rule***
- ***1 mark for correct value for angle***

6 a) Speed $= \sqrt{7^2 + (-3)^2} = \sqrt{58}$
$= 7.62$ ms^{-1} (3 s.f.)
[2 marks available in total]:
- ***1 mark for correct workings***
- ***1 mark for correct value***

b)

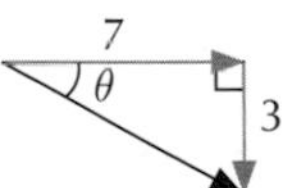

$\theta = \tan^{-1}\left(\frac{3}{7}\right) = 23.198...°$
$90° + 23.198...° = 113.198...°$
So the bearing is 113°
[3 marks available in total]:
- ***1 mark for correct workings***
- ***1 mark for calculating angle from i***
- ***1 mark for correct bearing***

c) Using $\mathbf{s} = \mathbf{v}t$ with $\mathbf{v} = 7\mathbf{i} - 3\mathbf{j}$ and $t = 4$:
$\mathbf{s} = (\mathbf{i} + 5\mathbf{j}) + 4(7\mathbf{i} - 3\mathbf{j}) = (29\mathbf{i} - 7\mathbf{j})$
So at $t = 4$, P has position vector $(29\mathbf{i} - 7\mathbf{j})$ m
$15\mathbf{i} - (29\mathbf{i} - 7\mathbf{j}) = (-14\mathbf{i} + 7\mathbf{j})$ m
So during the next 3.5 seconds, the displacement of P is $(-14\mathbf{i} + 7\mathbf{j})$ m
Now using $\mathbf{s} = \mathbf{v}t$ with $\mathbf{s} = -14\mathbf{i} + 7\mathbf{j}$ and $t = 3.5$:
$-14\mathbf{i} + 7\mathbf{j} = 3.5\mathbf{v}$
$\Rightarrow \mathbf{v} = \frac{1}{3.5}(-14\mathbf{i} + 7\mathbf{j}) = (-4\mathbf{i} + 2\mathbf{j})$ ms^{-1}
So $a = -4$ and $b = 2$
[4 marks available in total]:
- ***1 mark for calculating position at t = 4***
- ***1 mark for calculating displacement to 15i***
- ***1 mark for correct workings***
- ***1 mark for correct values of a and b***

7 a)

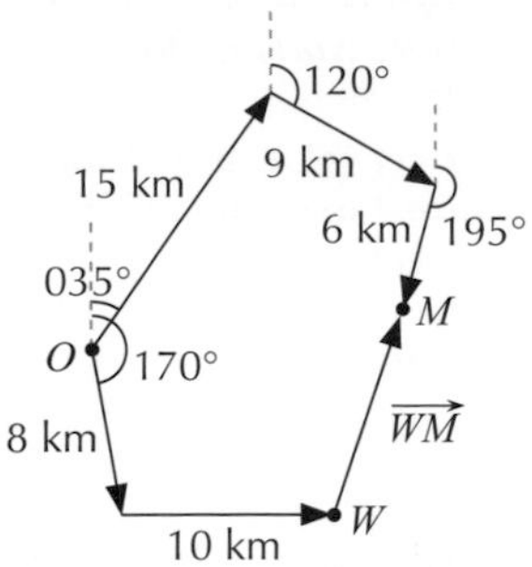

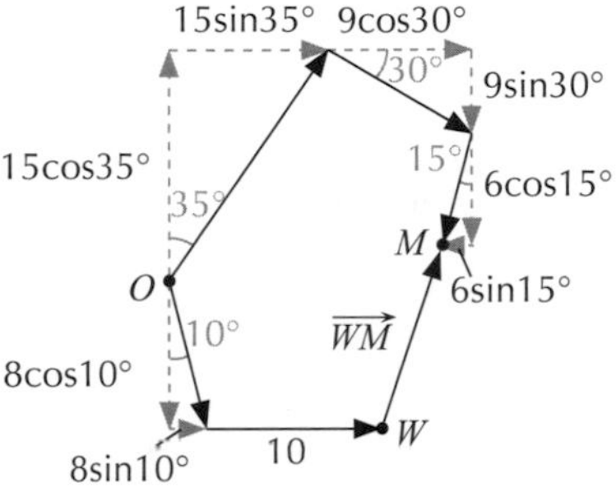

For the man, resolving east:
$15\sin 35° + 9\cos 30° - 6\sin 15° = 14.844...$
Resolving north:
$15\cos 35° - 9\sin 30° - 6\cos 15° = 1.991...$
So the position vector of the man is:
$\overrightarrow{OM} = (14.844...\mathbf{i} + 1.991...\mathbf{j})$ km
For the woman, resolving east:
$8\sin 10° + 10 = 11.389...$
Resolving north:
$-8\cos 10° = -7.878...$
So the position vector of the woman is:
$\overrightarrow{OW} = (11.389...\mathbf{i} - 7.878...\mathbf{j})$ km
So $\overrightarrow{WM}$, the position vector of the man relative to the woman, is:
$\overrightarrow{WM} = \overrightarrow{OM} - \overrightarrow{OW}$
$= (14.844...\mathbf{i} + 1.991...\mathbf{j}) - (11.389...\mathbf{i} - 7.878...\mathbf{j})$
$= (3.455...\mathbf{i} + 9.870...\mathbf{j})$ km
Using Pythagoras' Theorem to find the distance between them, and trigonometry to find the direction:

distance $= \sqrt{3.455...^2 + 9.870...^2} = 10.457...$
$= 10.5$ km (3 s.f.)
$\theta = \tan^{-1}\left(\frac{9.870...}{3.455...}\right) = 70.703...°$
$90° - 70.703...° = 19.296...°$
So the bearing is 019°
[10 marks available in total]:
- ***1 mark for resolving east for the man***
- ***1 mark for resolving north for the man***
- ***1 mark for resolving east for the woman***

• 1 mark for resolving north for the woman
• 1 mark for correct workings to find $\overrightarrow{WM}$ (or $\overrightarrow{MW}$)
• 1 mark for correct value of $\overrightarrow{WM}$ (or $\overrightarrow{MW}$)
• 1 mark for correct workings to find distance
• 1 mark for correct distance
• 1 mark for correct workings to find angle θ
• 1 mark for correct bearing

8 a) $\mathbf{u} = \mathbf{0}$, $\mathbf{a} = \mathbf{a}$, $\mathbf{s} = (9\mathbf{i} - 18\mathbf{j})$, $t = 3$
$\mathbf{s} = \mathbf{u}t + \frac{1}{2}\mathbf{a}t^2$
$(9\mathbf{i} - 18\mathbf{j}) = \frac{1}{2} \times \mathbf{a} \times 3^2$
$(9\mathbf{i} - 18\mathbf{j}) = 4.5\mathbf{a}$
$\Rightarrow \mathbf{a} = (2\mathbf{i} - 4\mathbf{j})\ \text{ms}^{-2}$
[3 marks available in total]:
• 1 mark for using correct equation of motion
• 1 mark for correct workings
• 1 mark for correct acceleration

b) $\mathbf{u} = \mathbf{0}$, $\mathbf{a} = 2\mathbf{i} - 4\mathbf{j}$, $\mathbf{s} = \mathbf{s}$, $t = t$
$\mathbf{s} = \mathbf{u}t + \frac{1}{2}\mathbf{a}t^2$
$\mathbf{s} = \frac{1}{2}(2\mathbf{i} - 4\mathbf{j})t^2$
$\mathbf{s} = (\mathbf{i} - 2\mathbf{j})t^2$ m
The particle starts at O, so its position vector is equal to its displacement:
$\mathbf{p} = (\mathbf{i} - 2\mathbf{j})t^2$ m
[3 marks available in total]:
• 1 mark for using correct equation of motion
• 1 mark for correct workings
• 1 mark for correct expression for p

c) Find an expression for the second particle's displacement after t seconds:
$\mathbf{s} = \mathbf{v}t$
$\mathbf{s} = (3\mathbf{i} - 5\mathbf{j})t$
So the second particle's position vector at time t is:
$\mathbf{q} = (a\mathbf{i} + b\mathbf{j}) + (3\mathbf{i} - 5\mathbf{j})t$
When they collide, their position vectors are equal:
$(\mathbf{i} - 2\mathbf{j})t^2 = (a\mathbf{i} + b\mathbf{j}) + (3\mathbf{i} - 5\mathbf{j})t$
$t = 8$, so:
$64(\mathbf{i} - 2\mathbf{j}) = (a\mathbf{i} + b\mathbf{j}) + 8(3\mathbf{i} - 5\mathbf{j})$
$64\mathbf{i} - 128\mathbf{j} - 24\mathbf{i} + 40\mathbf{j} = a\mathbf{i} + b\mathbf{j}$
$40\mathbf{i} - 88\mathbf{j} = a\mathbf{i} + b\mathbf{j}$
So $a = 40$ and $b = -88$
[4 marks available in total]:
• 1 mark for finding expression for second particle's position in terms of t
• 1 mark for making expressions for particles' positions equal to each other
• 1 mark for correct value of a
• 1 mark for correct value of b

d) Using $\mathbf{p} = (\mathbf{i} - 2\mathbf{j})t^2$ with $t = 8$:
$\mathbf{p} = (\mathbf{i} - 2\mathbf{j}) \times 64 = (64\mathbf{i} - 128\mathbf{j})$ m
So distance $= \sqrt{64^2 + (-128)^2} = 143$ m (3 s.f.)
You could've used the expression for q instead — the answer is the same.
[2 marks available in total]:
• 1 mark for finding position vector of particles
• 1 mark for correct distance

e) At $t = 11$:
$\mathbf{p} = (\mathbf{i} - 2\mathbf{j}) \times 121 = (121\mathbf{i} - 242\mathbf{j})$ m
$\mathbf{q} = (40\mathbf{i} - 88\mathbf{j}) + 11(3\mathbf{i} - 5\mathbf{j})$
$= (73\mathbf{i} - 143\mathbf{j})$ m
Position vector of **q** relative to **p** is:
$\mathbf{p} - \mathbf{q} = (121\mathbf{i} - 242\mathbf{j}) - (73\mathbf{i} - 143\mathbf{j})$
$= (48\mathbf{i} - 99\mathbf{j})$ m
So distance $= \sqrt{48^2 + (-99)^2} = 110.02...$
$= 110$ m (3 s.f.)
[4 marks available in total]:
• 1 mark for finding position vector of first particle
• 1 mark for finding position vector of second particle
• 1 mark for finding position vector of one particle relative to the other
• 1 mark for correct distance

Chapter 4: Forces and Statics

1. Forces

Exercise 1.1 — Treating forces as vectors

Q1 a) Horizontal component $(\rightarrow) = 6.5$ N
Vertical component $(\uparrow) = 0$ N

b) Horizontal component $(\rightarrow) = 20\cos 40°$
$= 15.3$ N (3 s.f.)
Vertical component $(\uparrow) = 20\sin 40°$
$= 12.9$ N (3 s.f.)

c) Horizontal component $(\rightarrow) = 17\sin 25°$
$= 7.18$ N (3 s.f.)
Vertical component $(\uparrow) = 17\cos 25°$
$= 15.4$ N (3 s.f.)

d) Horizontal component $(\rightarrow) = -5\cos 10°$
$= -4.92$ N (3 s.f.)
Vertical component $(\uparrow) = 5\sin 10°$
$= 0.868$ N (3 s.f.)

e) Horizontal component $(\rightarrow) = 3\cos 30°$
$= 2.60$ N (3 s.f.)
Vertical component $(\uparrow) = -3\sin 30° = -1.5$ N

f) Horizontal component $(\rightarrow) = -13\sin 60°$
$= -11.3$ N (3 s.f.)
Vertical component $(\uparrow) = -13\cos 60° = -6.5$ N

Q2 a) $10\mathbf{j}$ N

b) $-3.2\mathbf{i}$ N

c) $21\cos 45°\mathbf{i} + 21\sin 45°\mathbf{j}$ $(= \frac{21}{2}\sqrt{2}\mathbf{i} + \frac{21}{2}\sqrt{2}\mathbf{j})$

Q3

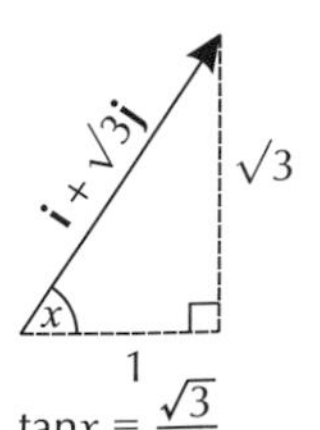

$\tan x = \frac{\sqrt{3}}{1}$
$x = \tan^{-1}(\sqrt{3}) = 60°$

Q4 a)

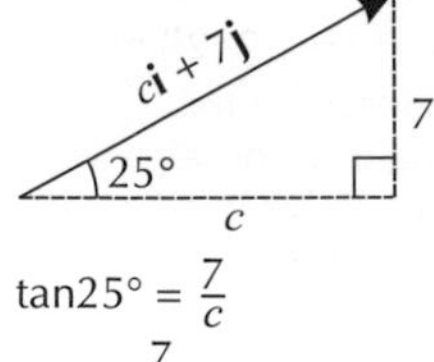

$\tan 25° = \frac{7}{c}$

$c = \frac{7}{\tan 25°}$

$= 15.011... = 15.0$ (to 3 s.f.)

b) magnitude $= \sqrt{(15.011...)^2 + 7^2}$

$= 16.56...$ N $= 16.6$ N (to 3 s.f.)

Q5

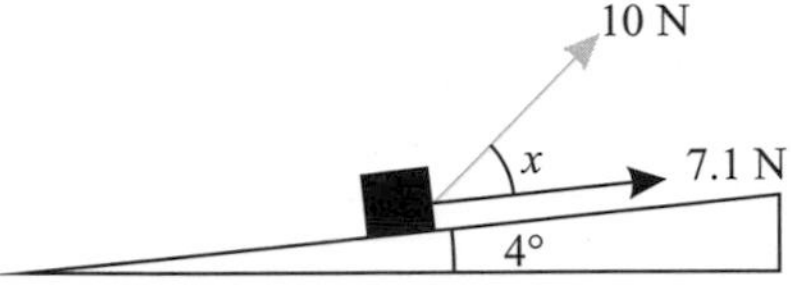

a) $10\cos x = 7.1$

$x = \cos^{-1}\left(\frac{7.1}{10}\right) = 44.8°$ (to 3 s.f.)

b) $10\cos(x + 4) = 6.59$ N (to 3 s.f.)

Q6

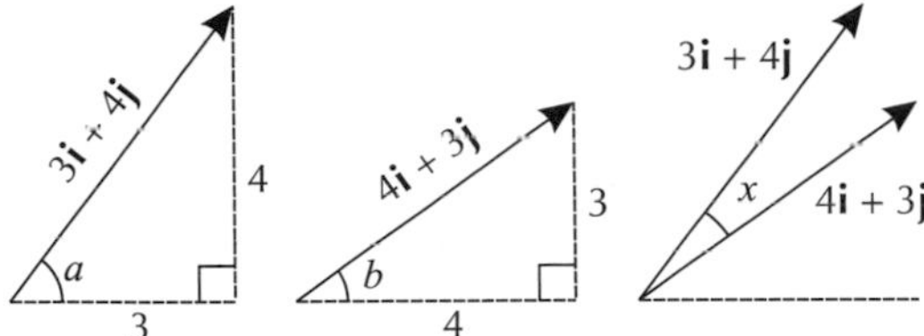

$a = \tan^{-1}\left(\frac{4}{3}\right)$ $b = \tan^{-1}\left(\frac{3}{4}\right)$

So the angle between the two forces

$x = a - b = 16.3°$ (to 3 s.f.)

Exercise 1.2 — Resultant forces

Q1 a)

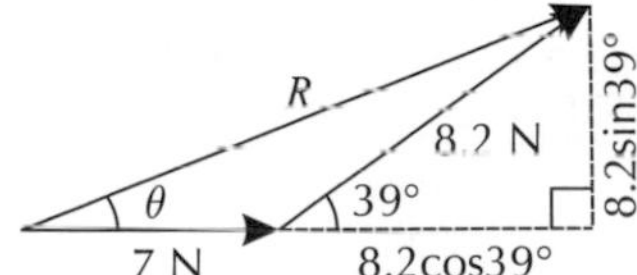

$\theta = \tan^{-1}\left(\frac{8.2\sin 39°}{7 + 8.2\cos 39°}\right)$

$= 21.1°$ (3 s.f.) above the positive horizontal

$R = \sqrt{(7 + 8.2\cos 39°)^2 + (8.2\sin 39°)^2}$

$= 14.3$ N (3 s.f.)

b)

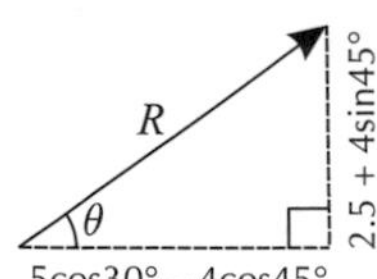

Resolving horizontally:

$R(\rightarrow) = 5\cos 30° - 4\cos 45°$

Resolving vertically:

$R(\uparrow) = 5\sin 30° + 4\sin 45°$

$= 2.5 + 4\sin 45°$

$\theta = \tan^{-1}\left(\frac{2.5 + 4\sin 45°}{5\cos 30° - 4\cos 45°}\right)$

$= 74.3°$ (3 s.f.) above the positive horizontal

$R = \sqrt{(2.5 + 4\sin 45°)^2 + (5\cos 30° - 4\cos 45°)^2}$

$= 5.54$ N (3 s.f.)

Q2 a)

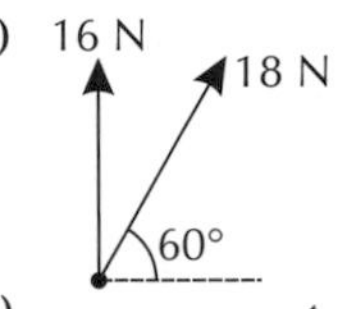

b)

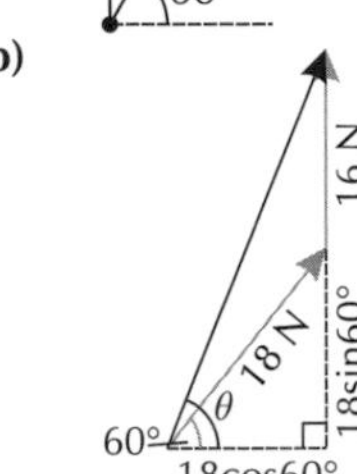

$\theta = \tan^{-1}\left(\frac{16 + 18\sin 60°}{18\cos 60°}\right)$

$= 74.1°$ (3 s.f.) above the positive horizontal

$R = \sqrt{(18\cos 60°)^2 + (16 + 18\sin 60°)^2}$

$= 32.8$ N (3 s.f.)

Q3 $(8 + 3)\mathbf{i} + (5 - 2)\mathbf{j} = 11\mathbf{i} + 3\mathbf{j}$ N

$R = \sqrt{11^2 + 3^2}$

$= \sqrt{130}$

$= 11.4$ N (3 s.f.)

$\theta = \tan^{-1}\left(\frac{3}{11}\right)$

$= 15.3°$ (3 s.f.) above the positive horizontal

Q4 a) Resolving horizontally:

$R(\rightarrow) = 10 - 11\cos 75° - 12\cos 80°$

$= 5.069...$ N

Resolving vertically:

$R(\uparrow) = 11\sin 75° - 12\sin 80°$

$= -1.192...$ N

$R = \sqrt{(5.069...)^2 + (-1.192...)^2}$

$= 5.21$ N (to 3 s.f.)

$\theta = \tan^{-1}\left(\frac{-1.192...}{5.069...}\right) = -13.2°$ (to 3 s.f.)

i.e. 13.2° (3 s.f.) below the positive horizontal

b) Resolving horizontally:

$R(\rightarrow) = 6.5\cos 69° + 10\cos 47° - 8\sin 61°$

$= 2.152...$ N

Resolving vertically:

$R(\uparrow) = 6.5\sin 69° + 8\cos 61° - 10\sin 47°$

$= 2.633...$ N

$= \sqrt{(2.152...)^2 + (2.633...)^2}$

$= 3.40$ N (to 3 s.f.)

$\theta = \tan^{-1}\left(\frac{2.633...}{2.152...}\right)$

$= 50.7°$ (to 3 s.f.)

above the positive horizontal

Q5 Resolving vertically (↑):

$3\cos 20° + 2\cos 30° - T = 0$

$T = 3\cos 20° + 2\cos 30°$
$= 4.55$ N (to 3 s.f.)

Q6

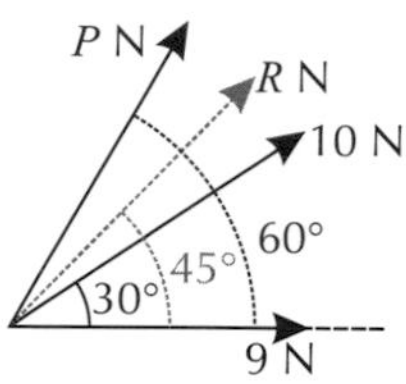

Resolving horizontally (→):

$P\cos 60° + 10\cos 30° + 9 = R\cos 45°$ ①

Resolving vertically (↑):

$P\sin 60° + 10\sin 30° = R\sin 45°$ ②

Because the resultant acts at 45°, its horizontal and vertical components are equal.
i.e. $\cos 45° = \sin 45° \Rightarrow R\cos 45° = R\sin 45°$
So, equating the left hand sides of ① and ②:
$P\cos 60° + 10\cos 30° + 9 = P\sin 60° + 10\sin 30°$
$P\cos 60° - P\sin 60° = 10\sin 30° - 10\cos 30° - 9$
$\Rightarrow P = \frac{10\sin 30° - 10\cos 30° - 9}{\cos 60° - \sin 60°} = 34.6$ N (3 s.f.)

Q7

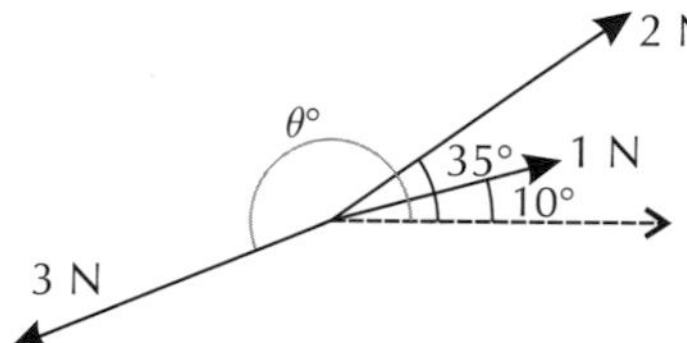

a) Resolving horizontally (→):
$1\cos 10° + 2\cos 35° + 3\cos\theta = 0$
$\theta = \cos^{-1}\left(\frac{-\cos 10° - 2\cos 35°}{3}\right)$
$= 150.970...° = 151°$ (to 3 s.f.)

θ must lie in the range $180° \leq \theta \leq 360°$
$\cos\theta = \cos(360° - \theta)$, therefore
$\theta = 360° - 150.970...° = 209.029...°$
$= 209°$ (to 3 s.f.)

b) $R = 1\sin 10° + 2\sin 35° + 3\sin(209.029...°)$
$= -0.135$ N (to 3 s.f.)
So, R has magnitude 0.135 N (to 3 s.f.)
(and acts in the negative **j**-direction)

Exercise 1.3 — Forces in equilibrium

Q1

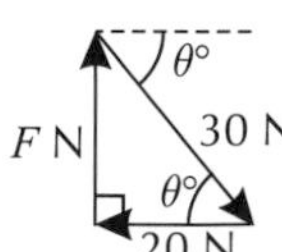

$F = \sqrt{30^2 - 20^2}$
$= \sqrt{500}$
$= 22.4$ N (to 3 s.f.)

$\theta = \cos^{-1}\left(\frac{20}{30}\right) = 48.2°$ (to 3 s.f.)

Q2

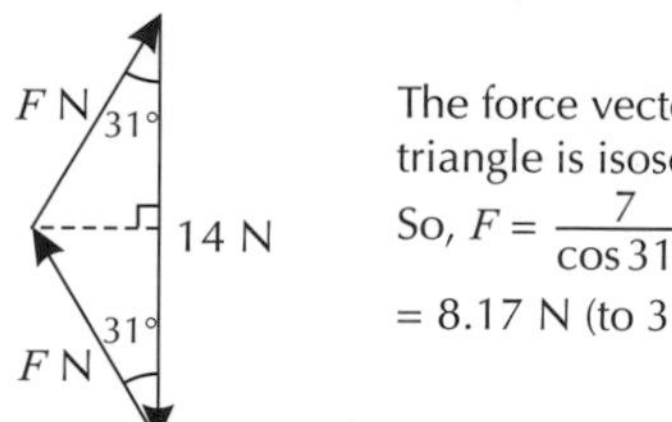

The force vector triangle is isosceles.
So, $F = \frac{7}{\cos 31°}$
$= 8.17$ N (to 3 s.f.)

Q3 Resolving horizontally (→):
$F\sin 50° - 5\sin 10° = 0$
$F = \frac{5\sin 10°}{\sin 50°}$
$= 1.133...$ N
$= 1.13$ N (to 3 s.f.)

Resolving vertically (↑):
$F\cos 50° + 5\cos 10° - G = 0$
$G = F\cos 50° + 5\cos 10°$
$= (1.133...)\cos 50° + 5\cos 10°$
$= 5.65$ N (to 3 s.f.)

Q4 Resolving horizontally:
$2P = 20\sin\theta$ ①

Resolving vertically:
$P = 20\cos\theta$ ②

Divide ① by ②:
$\tan\theta = \frac{2P}{P} = 2$,
$\theta = \tan^{-1}(2) = 63.43...° = 63.4°$ (to 3 s.f.)

Substituting into ② gives
$P = 20\cos\theta$
$= 20\cos(63.43...°)$
$= 8.94$ N (to 3 s.f)

Exercise 1.4 — Equilibrium problems

Q1 a) Resolving horizontally:
$T\cos 50° = 14$ N
$T = \frac{14}{\cos 50°} = 21.78... = 21.8$ N (to 3 s.f.)
Resolving vertically:
$T\sin 50° = mg$
$m = \frac{T\sin 50°}{g} = \frac{21.78...\sin 50°}{9.8}$
$= 1.70$ kg (to 3 s.f.)

b) Resolving horizontally:
$T = 8\sin 25° = 3.380... = 3.38$ N (to 3 s.f.)
Resolving vertically:
$mg = 8\cos 25°$
$m = \frac{8\cos 25°}{g} = 0.740$ kg (to 3 s.f.)

Q2 Resolving horizontally:
$15\sin x = 13\sin 32°$
$x = \sin^{-1}\left(\frac{13\sin 32°}{15}\right) = 27.339...° = 27.3°$ (to 3 s.f.)

Resolving vertically:
$W = 13\cos 32° + 15\cos(27.339...°)$
$= 24.3$ N (to 3 s.f.)

Q3 a)

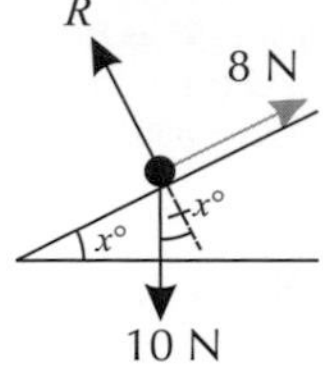

Resolving parallel to the plane:

$10\sin x = 8$

$x = \sin^{-1}\left(\frac{8}{10}\right) = 53.130... = 53.1°$ (to 3 s.f.)

b) Resolving perpendicular to the plane:

$R = 10\cos x$

$= 6$ N

Q4

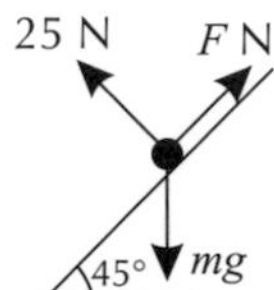

a) Resolving parallel to the plane:
$F = mg\sin 45°$
Resolving perpendicular to the plane:
$25 = mg\cos 45°$
$\cos 45° = \sin 45°$, therefore $F = 25$ N

b) Resolving perpendicular to the plane:
$mg\cos 45° = 25$

$m = \frac{25}{g\cos 45°}$

$= \frac{25}{9.8 \times \cos 45°}$

$= 3.61$ kg (to 3 s.f.)

Q5

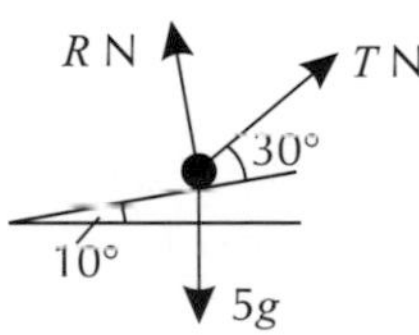

a) Magnitude of the tension in the string = T
normal reaction force = R
Resolving parallel to the plane:

$T\cos 30° = 5g\sin 10°$

$T = \frac{(5 \times 9.8 \times \sin 10°)}{\cos 30°}$

$= 9.83$ N (to 3 s.f.)

b) Resolving perpendicular to the plane:
$R + T\sin 30° = 5g\cos 10°$
$R = 5g\cos 10° - T\sin 30°$
$= 43.3$ N (to 3 s.f.)

Q6

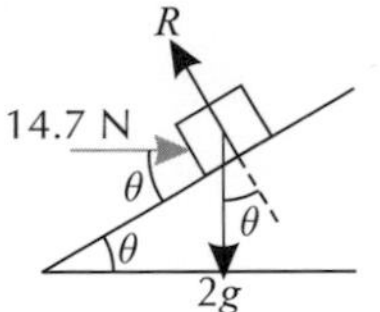

Resolving the forces on the block parallel to the plane:
$14.7\cos\theta = 2g\sin\theta$

$\frac{\sin\theta}{\cos\theta} = \frac{14.7}{2g}$

$\tan\theta = \frac{14.7}{(2 \times 9.8)} = 0.75$

Q7

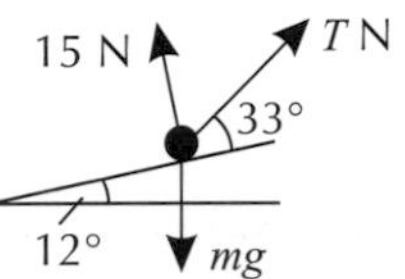

a) The string is inclined at $45° - 12° = 33°$ to the plane.
Resolving parallel to the plane:

$T\cos 33° = mg\sin 12°$,

$mg = \frac{T\cos 33°}{\sin 12°}$ ①

Resolving perpendicular to the plane:
$15 + T\sin 33° = mg\cos 12°$ ②

Substituting ① into ②:

$15 + T\sin 33° = \frac{T\cos 33°}{\sin 12°}\cos 12°$

$15 = T\left(\left(\frac{\cos 33°}{\sin 12°}\cos 12°\right) - \sin 33°\right)$

$T = \frac{15}{\left(\left(\frac{\cos 33°}{\sin 12°}\cos 12°\right) - \sin 33°\right)}$

$= 4.41$ N (to 3.s.f)

b) Rearrange ① and substitute the values for T and g (= 9.8 ms^{-2}):

$m = \frac{T\cos 33°}{g\sin 12°}$

$= 1.82$ kg (to 3 s.f.)

Q8

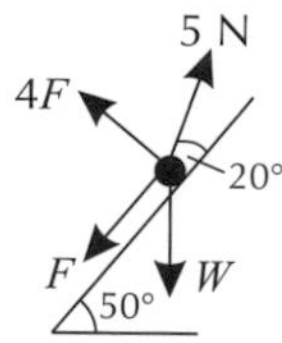

The string makes an angle of
$70° - 50° = 20°$ with the plane.
Resolving perpendicular to the plane:
$R + 5\sin 20° = W\cos 50°$
$R = 4F$, so:
$4F + 5\sin 20° = W\cos 50°$ ①

Resolving parallel to the plane:
$F + W\sin 50° = 5\cos 20°$
$F = 5\cos 20° - W\sin 50°$ ②

Substituting ② into ①,
$20\cos 20° - 4W\sin 50° + 5\sin 20° = W\cos 50°$,
$W = \dfrac{20\cos 20° + 5\sin 20°}{4\sin 50° + \cos 50°} = 5.53$ N (to 3 s.f.)

2. Friction

Exercise 2.1 — Friction

Q1 The particle is on the point of slipping, so $F = \mu R$.
Resolving vertically: $R = W$, so using $F = \mu W$:

a) $F = 0.25 \times 5 = 1.25$ N

b) $F = 0.3 \times 8 = 2.4$ N

c) $F = 0.75 \times 15 = 11.25$ N

Q2

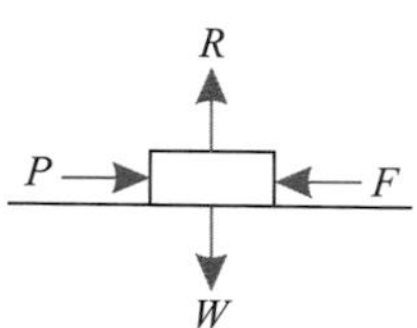

Resolving vertically: $R = W$

Resolving horizontally: $P = F$, so using $F = \mu R$, $\mu = \dfrac{P}{W}$

a) $\mu = \dfrac{5}{20} = 0.25$

b) $\mu = \dfrac{8}{15} = 0.53$ (to 2 d.p.)

Q3

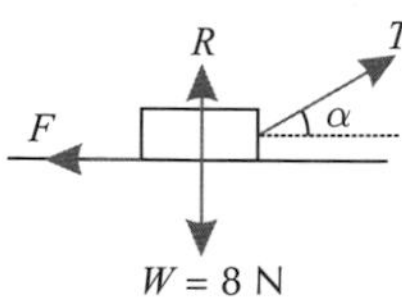

Resolving vertically: $R + T\sin\alpha = 8$

Resolving horizontally: $T\cos\alpha = F$

T will be greatest when the object is in limiting equilibrium: $F = \mu R$

a) $\alpha = 0 \Rightarrow R = W$ and $T = F = \mu R = 8\mu$
$T = 0.61 \times 8 = 4.88$ N

b) $\alpha = 35°$
Resolving vertically: $R + T\sin 35° = 8$
$R = 8 - T\sin 35°$ ①
Resolving horizontally:
$T\cos 35° = F$
$F = \mu R$, $R = \dfrac{F}{\mu} = \dfrac{T\cos 35°}{0.61}$ ②
Substitute the value of R from ① into ②:
$8 - T\sin 35° = \dfrac{T\cos 35°}{0.61}$
$0.61(8 - T\sin 35°) = T\cos 35°$

$T(\cos 35° + 0.61\sin 35°) = 4.88$
$T = \dfrac{4.88}{\cos 35° + 0.61\sin 35°}$
$= 4.17$ N (to 3 s.f.)

Q4

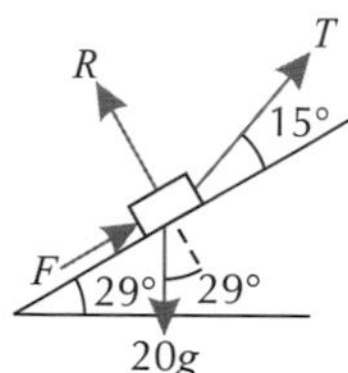

Resolving parallel to the plane:
$T\cos 15° + F = 20g\sin 29°$ ①

Resolving perpendicular to the plane:
$R + T\sin 15° = 20g\cos 29°$
$R = -T\sin 15° + 20g\cos 29°$ ②

T is only just large enough to hold the sledge at rest, so the sledge is in limiting equilibrium
and $F = \mu R = 0.1R$. Substituting this and ② into ①:

$T\cos 15° + 0.1(-T\sin 15° + 20g\cos 29°) = 20g\sin 29°$
$T = \dfrac{20g\sin 29° - 2g\cos 29°}{\cos 15° - 0.1\sin 15°}$
$T = 82.8$ N (to 3 s.f.)

Q5 **a)**

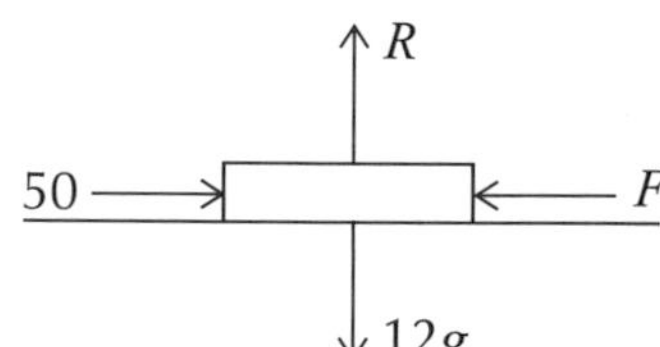

Resolving vertically: $R = 12g$
Find the frictional force, F:
$F \leq \mu R$
$F \leq 0.5 \times 12g$
$F \leq 58.8$ N
50 N isn't big enough to overcome friction — so the particle won't move.

b) Maximum force is when $F = \mu R$, so max force is 58.8 N

Q6

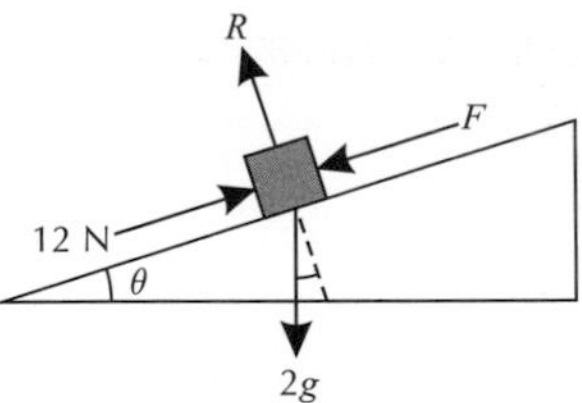

Resolving parallel to the plane:
$12 = F + 2g\sin\theta$
$F = 12 - 2g\sin\theta$
Resolving perpendicular to the plane:
$R = 2g\cos\theta$
The object is on the point of moving, so $F = \mu R$.

$$\mu = \frac{F}{R} = \frac{(12 - 2g\sin\theta)}{2g\cos\theta}$$

$\cos\theta = \frac{4}{5}$, so, drawing a right-angled triangle, the side adjacent the angle will be 4, and the hypotenuse will be 5. Then, by Pythagoras' theorem, the opposite side will be 3.

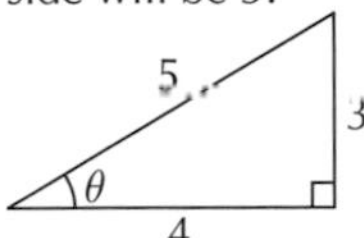

Therefore, $\sin\theta = \frac{3}{5}$

$$\mu = \frac{\left(12 - \left(2 \times 9.8 \times \frac{3}{5}\right)\right)}{\left(2 \times 9.8 \times \frac{4}{5}\right)} = 0.015 \text{ (to 2 s.f.)}$$

Q7

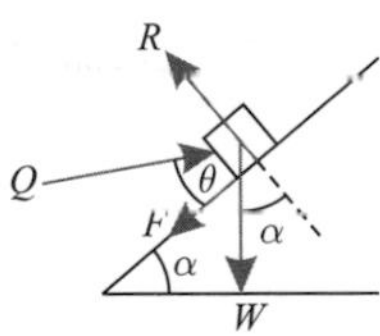

Resolving parallel to the plane:
$Q\cos\theta = F + W\sin\alpha$
$Q\cos\theta = \mu R + W\sin\alpha$ ①
Resolving perpendicular to the plane (↖):
$R = W\cos\alpha + Q\sin\theta$ ②
Substituting ② into ① and rearranging:
$Q\cos\theta = \mu(W\cos\alpha + Q\sin\theta) + W\sin\alpha$

$$\mu = \frac{Q\cos\theta - W\sin\alpha}{W\cos\alpha + Q\sin\theta}$$

a) $\mu = \frac{(10 - 4)}{8\cos 30^\circ}$
$= 0.87$ (to 2 d.p.)

b) $\mu = \frac{5\cos 30^\circ - 6\sin 25^\circ}{6\cos 25^\circ + 2.5}$
$= 0.23$ (to 2 d.p.)

Q8 a) Resolving horizontally:
$F = 4\cos 25^\circ$
Friction is limiting, so, using $F = \mu R$:
$4\cos 25^\circ = 0.15R$
$\Rightarrow R = 24.168... = 24.2$ N (3 s.f.)

b) Resolving vertically:
$R = mg + 4\sin 25^\circ$
$mg = 24.168... - 4\sin 25^\circ = 22.477...$
So $m = 22.477... \div 9.8 = 2.29$ kg (3 s.f.)

Q9

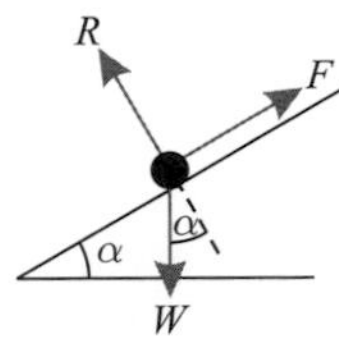

Resolving perpendicular to the plane:
$R = W\cos\alpha$ ①
Resolving parallel to the plane:
$F = W\sin\alpha$ ②
$F \leq \mu R$ when the object is at rest on the plane.
Substituting in values for F and R from ① and ②:
$W\sin\alpha \leq \mu W\cos\alpha$

$$\frac{W\sin\alpha}{W\cos\alpha} \leq \mu$$

$\Rightarrow \tan\alpha \leq \mu$

Review Exercise — Chapter 4

Q1 a)

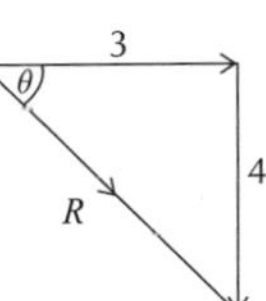

$R = \sqrt{4^2 + 3^3} = 5\text{ N}$
$\tan\theta = \frac{4}{3}$
$\theta = 53.1^\circ$ (to 3.s.f.)
below the positive horizontal

b)

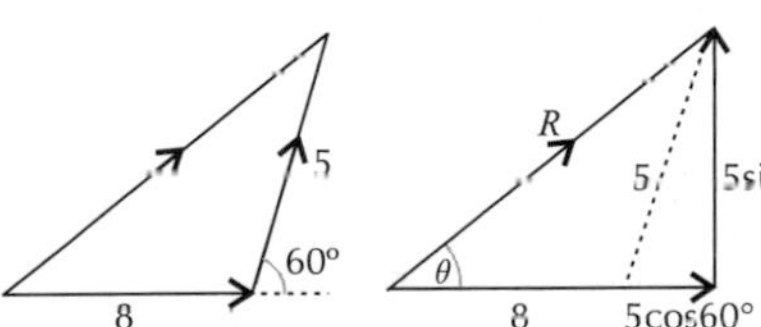

$R = \sqrt{(8 + 5\cos 60^\circ)^2 + (5\sin 60^\circ)^2}$
$= 11.4$ N (to 3 s.f.)
$\tan\theta = \frac{5\sin 60^\circ}{8 + 5\cos 60^\circ} = 0.412...$
So $\theta = 22.4^\circ$ (to 3 s.f.)
above the positive horizontal

c) Total force upwards = $6 - 4\sin 10^\circ - 10\sin 20^\circ$
$= 1.885...$ N
Total force left $= 10\cos 20^\circ - 4\cos 10^\circ$
$= 5.457...$ N

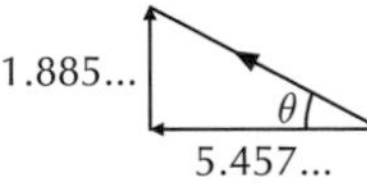

$R = \sqrt{1.885...^2 + 5.457...^2} = 5.77$ N (3 s.f.)
$\theta = \tan^{-1}\left(\frac{1.885...}{5.457...}\right)$
$= 19.1^\circ$ (3 s.f.) above the negative horizontal

Q2 Use the force (2**i** + 7**j**) N — it acts in the same direction as (x**i** + y**j**) N.

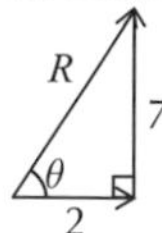

$\theta = \tan^{-1}\left(\frac{7}{2}\right) = 74.05...°$

So the angle made with **j** is:

90 ° – 74.05...° = 15.9° (3 s.f.)

Q3

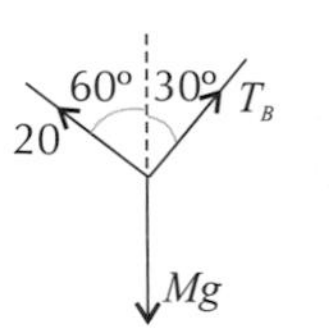

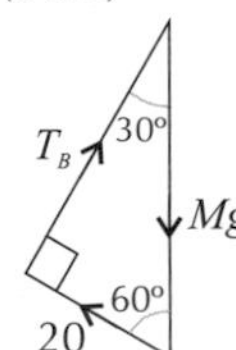

a) $\tan 30° = \frac{20}{T_B}$

$T_B = \frac{20}{\tan 30°}$

$= 34.6 \text{ N (3 s.f.)}$

b) $\sin 30° = \frac{20}{Mg}$

$M = \frac{20}{g \sin 30°} = 4.08 \text{ kg (3 s.f.)}$

Q4

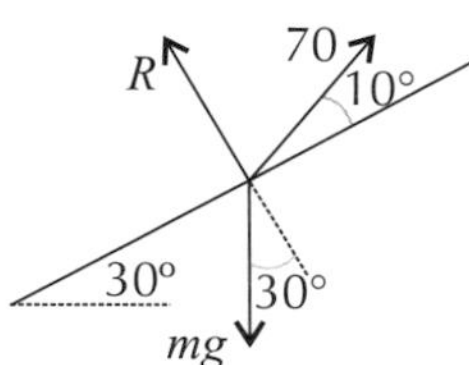

Using sine rule:

$\frac{mg}{\sin 100°} = \frac{70}{\sin 30°}$

So $mg = \frac{70 \sin 100°}{\sin 30°}$

$m = 14.1 \text{ kg (3 s.f.)}$

$\frac{R}{\sin 50°} = \frac{70}{\sin 30°}$

So $R = \frac{70 \sin 50°}{\sin 30°} = 107 \text{ N (3 s.f.)}$

Who knew triangles could be so useful? You could also have answered this question by resolving forces parallel and perpendicular to the plane.

Q5 a)

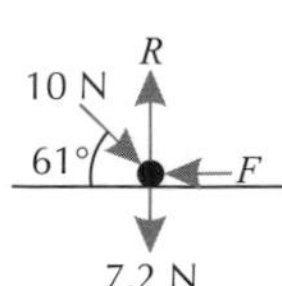

Resolving vertically:

$R = 7.2 + 10\sin 61°$

Resolving horizontally:

$F = 10\cos 61°$

$F = \mu R$, so:

$\mu = \frac{10 \cos 61°}{7.2 + 10 \sin 61°} = 0.30$ (to 2 d.p.)

b)

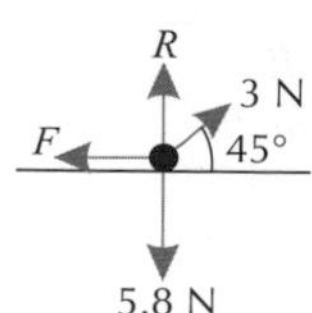

Resolving vertically:

$R + 3\sin 45° = 5.8$

$R = 5.8 - 3\sin 45°$

Resolving horizontally:

$F = 3\cos 45°$

$F = \mu R$, so:

$\mu = \frac{3 \cos 45°}{5.8 - 3 \sin 45°} = 0.58$ (to 2 d.p.)

Exam-Style Questions — Chapter 4

1 Resolve horizontally (→): 0 + 5cos30° = 4.330... N

Resolve vertically (↑): 4 – 5sin30° = 1.5 N

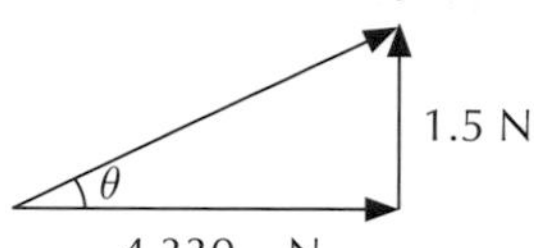

$\theta = \tan^{-1}\left(\frac{1.5}{4.330...}\right) = 19.106...°$

i.e. θ = 19.1° (3 s.f.) above the positive horizontal

Magnitude = $\sqrt{1.5^2 + 4.330...^2}$ = 4.58 N (3 s.f.)

[4 marks available in total]:
- ***1 mark for resolving horizontally***
- ***1 mark for resolving vertically***
- ***1 mark for calculating the direction***
- ***1 mark for calculating the magnitude***

2 a)

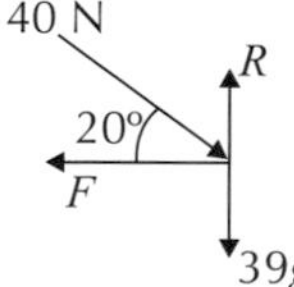

[2 marks available in total]:
- ***1 mark for drawing 4 correct arrows***
- ***1 mark for correctly labelling the arrows***

b) Resolve vertically (↑):

$R = 39g + 140\sin 20° = 430$ N (3 s.f.)

Resolve horizontally (→):

$F = 140\cos 20° = 132$ N (3 s.f.)

[4 marks available in total]:
- ***1 mark for resolving vertically***
- ***1 mark for resolving horizontally***
- ***1 mark for correct reaction magnitude***
- ***1 mark for correct friction magnitude***

No need to panic if friction is involved — it's just another thing to consider when resolving (and an extra arrow to draw).

3 a) **R** = **A** + **B** = (2**i** – 11**j**) + (7**i** + 5**j**) = (9**i** – 6**j**) N

[2 marks available in total]:
- ***1 mark for correct workings***
- ***1 mark for correct resultant***

b) $|\mathbf{R}| = \sqrt{9^2 + (-6)^2} = 10.8$ N (3 s.f.)
[2 marks available in total]:
- ***1 mark for correct workings***
- ***1 mark for correct magnitude***

$|\mathbf{R}|$ just means the magnitude of **R**.

4 a)

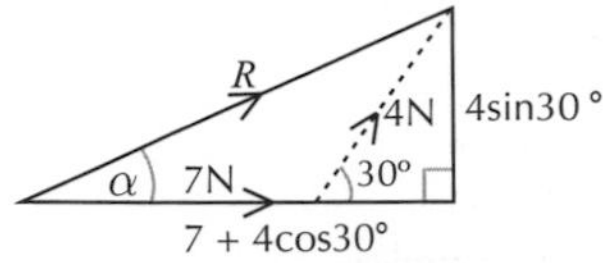

Resolve vertically (↑):
$4\sin 30° = 2$
Resolve horizontally (→):
$7 + 4\cos 30° = 10.464...$
$R = \sqrt{2^2 + 10.464...^2}$
$= 10.6$ N (3 s.f.)
[3 marks available in total]:
- ***1 mark for resolving vertically***
- ***1 mark for resolving horizontally***
- ***1 mark for correct magnitude***

b) $\tan\alpha = \frac{2}{10.464...} = 0.1911...$
$\alpha = 10.8°$ (3 s.f.)
[2 marks available in total]:
- ***1 mark for correct workings***
- ***1 mark for correct value of α***

5

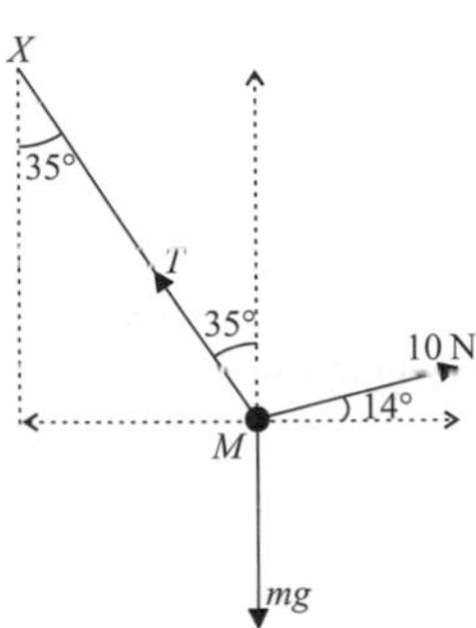

Resolving vertically: $mg = 10\sin 14° + T\cos 35°$
Resolving horizontally: $T\sin 35° = 10\cos 14°$
So, $T = \frac{10\cos 14°}{\sin 35°} = 16.916...$ N
So $mg = 10\sin 14° + (16.916...)\cos 35°$
$= 16.276...$ N
So the mass of $M = \frac{16.276...}{g} = 1.66$ kg (3 s.f.)
[4 marks available in total]:
- ***1 mark for resolving vertically***
- ***1 mark for resolving horizontally***
- ***1 mark for correct value of T***
- ***1 mark for correct mass of M***

Drawing a good clear diagram will help no end with this question.

6 a)

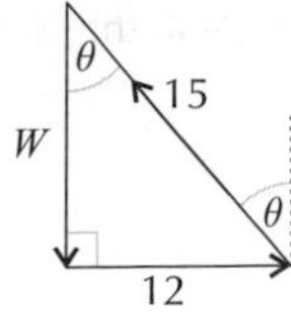

$\sin\theta = \frac{12}{15}$, so, $\theta = 53.1°$ (3 s.f.)
[2 marks available in total]:
- ***1 mark for correct workings***
- ***1 mark for the correct value of θ***

b) $15^2 = W^2 + 12^2$
$W = \sqrt{15^2 - 12^2} = 9$ N
[2 marks available in total]:
- ***1 mark for correct workings***
- ***1 mark for correct value of W***

c) Remove W and the particle moves in the opposite direction to W, i.e. upwards. This resultant of the two remaining forces is 9 N upwards, because the particle was in equilibrium beforehand.
[2 marks available in total]:
- ***1 mark for correct magnitude***
- ***1 mark for correct direction***

The word 'state' in an exam question means that you shouldn't need to do any extra calculation to answer it.

7

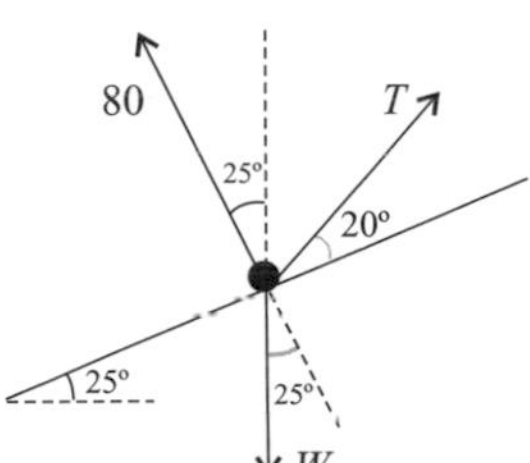

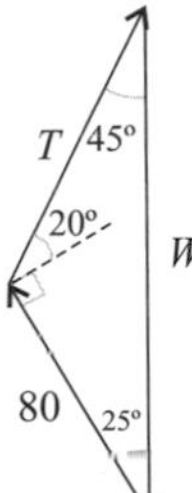

a) $\frac{T}{\sin 25°} = \frac{80}{\sin 45°}$

So, $T = \frac{80\sin 25°}{\sin 45°} = 47.8$ N (3 s.f.)
[3 marks available in total]:
- ***1 mark for diagram***
- ***1 mark for correct workings***
- ***1 mark for correct value of T***

b) $\frac{W}{\sin 110°} = \frac{80}{\sin 45°}$

So, $W = \frac{80\sin 110°}{\sin 45°} = 106$ N (3 s.f.)
[2 marks available in total]:
- ***1 mark for correct workings***
- ***1 mark for correct value of W***

You could answer this question by resolving forces, rather than using the sine rule.

8 **a)** Resolving horizontally:

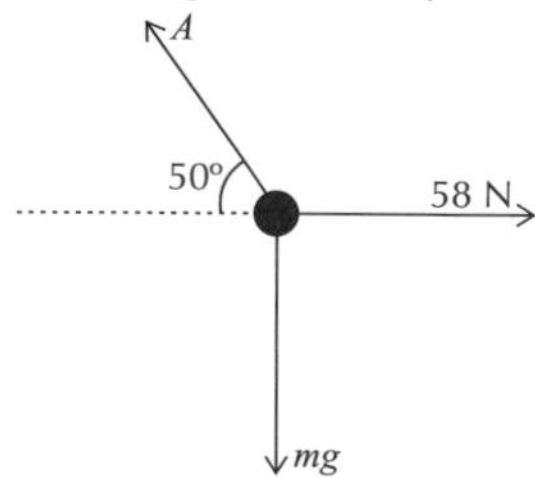

$A\cos 50° = 58$ N

so, $A = \frac{58}{\cos 50°} = 90.231... = 90.2$ N (3 s.f.)

[2 marks available in total]:
- ***1 mark for resolving horizontally***
- ***1 mark for correct value of A***

b) Resolving vertically:
$mg = A\sin 50° = (90.231...)\sin 50°$
so, $mg = 69.121...$ and $m = 7.05$ kg (3 s.f.)

[2 marks available in total]:
- ***1 mark for resolving vertically***
- ***1 mark for correct value of m***

9 Resolving horizontally: $S\cos 40° = F$
Resolving vertically: $R = 2g + S\sin 40°$
It's limiting friction so $F = \mu R$
So, $S\cos 40° = 0.3(2g + S\sin 40°)$
$S\cos 40° = 0.6g + 0.3S\sin 40°$
$S\cos 40° - 0.3S\sin 40° = 0.6g$
$S(\cos 40° - 0.3\sin 40°) = 0.6g$
$S = 10.3$ N (3 s.f.)

[4 marks available in total]:
- ***1 mark for resolving horizontally***
- ***1 mark for resolving vertically***
- ***1 mark for correct workings***
- ***1 mark for correct value of S***

A ring on a rod — it might be a car on a road, or a sled on snow... it's all the same mathematically.

Chapter 5: Dynamics

1. Newton's Laws of Motion

Exercise 1.1 — Using Newton's laws

Q1 $F_{net} = ma$
$F_{net} = 15 \times 4 = 60$ N

Q2 **a)** $F_{net} = ma$
$10 = 5a$
$a = 2$ ms^{-2}

b) Use a constant acceleration equation.
$u = 0, v = v, a = 2, t = 8$
$v = u + at$
$v = 0 + (2 \times 8) = 16$ ms^{-1}

Q3

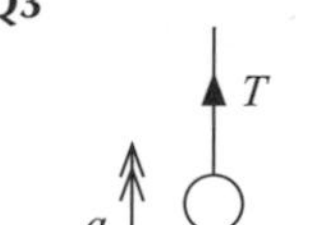

Resolving vertically:
$F_{net} = ma$
$T - 18g = 18 \times 0.4$
$T = 7.2 + 176.4 = 183.6$ N

Q4 **a)** $F_{net} = ma$
$18 = 5m$
$m = 18 \div 5 = 3.6$ kg

b) $u = 0, v = v, a = 5, t = 4$
$v = u + at$
$v = 0 + (5 \times 4) = 20$ ms^{-1}

c) Resolving vertically:
$R - mg = 0$
$R = mg = 3.6 \times 9.8 = 35.28$ N

Q5 **a)** Resolving horizontally:
$F_{net} = ma$
$10\cos 45° = 3a$
$a = 7.071... \div 3 = 2.357...$
$a = 2.36$ ms^{-2} (3 s.f.)

b) Resolving vertically:
$F_{net} = ma$
$R + 10\sin 45° - 3g = 0$
$R = 3g - 10\sin 45° = 22.328...$
$R = 22.3$ N (3 s.f.)

Q6 **a)** Resolving horizontally:
$F_{net} = ma$
$16\cos 20° - 7 = (49 \div 9.8) \times a$
$a = 8.035... \div 5 = 1.607...$
$a = 1.61$ ms^{-2} (3 s.f.)

b) Use a constant acceleration equation.
$u = 0, v = v, a = 1.607..., t = 7$
$v = u + at$
$v = 0 + (1.607... \times 7) = 11.2$ ms^{-1} (3 s.f.)

c) Resolving vertically:
$R + 16\sin 20° - 49 = 0$
$R = 49 - 16\sin 20° = 43.527...$
$R = 43.5$ N (3 s.f.)

Q7 **a)** $u = 0, v = 2.5, a = a, t = 4$
$v = u + at$
$2.5 = 0 + 4a$
$a = 0.625$ ms^{-2}

b)

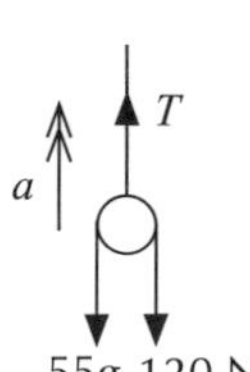

Resolving vertically:
$F_{net} = ma$
$T - 120 - 55g = 55 \times 0.625$
$T = 34.375 + 120 + 539 = 693$ N (3 s.f.)

Q8

1.5 N

a

$0.3g$

Resolving vertically:
$0.3g - 1.5 = 0.3a$
$a = 1.44 \div 0.3 = 4.8 \text{ ms}^{-2}$
$u = 0, a = 4.8, s = s, t = 12$
$s = ut + \frac{1}{2}at^2$
$s = 0 + (\frac{1}{2} \times 4.8 \times 12^2) = 345.6 \text{ m}$
Remember that if something is dropped, its initial velocity is zero.

Q9 a) Resultant, $R = (5\mathbf{i} + 2\mathbf{j}) + (3\mathbf{i} - 4\mathbf{j}) = (8\mathbf{i} - 2\mathbf{j})$ N
$\mathbf{F} = m\mathbf{a}$
$8\mathbf{i} - 2\mathbf{j} = 10\mathbf{a}$
$\mathbf{a} = 0.8\mathbf{i} - 0.2\mathbf{j}$

b) $|\mathbf{a}| = \sqrt{0.8^2 + (-0.2)^2} = 0.8246...$
$= 0.825 \text{ ms}^{-2}$ (3 s.f.)

c) $u = 0, v = v, a = 0.8246..., t = 6$
$v = u + at$
$v = 0 + (0.8246... \times 6) = 4.947...$
$= 4.95 \text{ ms}^{-1}$ (3 s.f.)

Q10 a) $\mathbf{u} = (0\mathbf{i} + 0\mathbf{j}), \mathbf{v} = (30\mathbf{i} + 20\mathbf{j}), \mathbf{a} = \mathbf{a}, t = 10$
$\mathbf{v} = \mathbf{u} + \mathbf{a}t$
$(30\mathbf{i} + 20\mathbf{j}) = (0\mathbf{i} + 0\mathbf{j}) + 10\mathbf{a}$
$\Rightarrow \mathbf{a} = (3\mathbf{i} + 2\mathbf{j}) \text{ ms}^{-2}$
$\mathbf{F}_{net} = m\mathbf{a} = 2(3\mathbf{i} + 2\mathbf{j})$
$= (6\mathbf{i} + 4\mathbf{j})$ N

b) $(10\mathbf{i} - 3\mathbf{j}) + \mathbf{x} = 6\mathbf{i} + 4\mathbf{j}$
$\mathbf{x} = (6 - 10)\mathbf{i} + (4 + 3)\mathbf{j}$
$= (-4\mathbf{i} + 7\mathbf{j})$ N
$|\mathbf{x}| = \sqrt{(-4)^2 + 7^2} = 8.062... = 8.06$ N (3 s.f.)

Q11 $u = 0, v = 6, a = a, t = 2$
$v = u + at$
$6 = 0 + 2a$
$\Rightarrow a = 3 \text{ ms}^{-2}$
Resultant force, $\mathbf{R} = (6\mathbf{i} + 3\mathbf{j}) + (2\mathbf{i} + 3\mathbf{j}) = (8\mathbf{i} + 6\mathbf{j})$ N
$|\mathbf{R}| = \sqrt{8^2 + 6^2} = 10$ N
$F_{net} = ma$
$10 = 3m$
$m = 10 \div 3 = 3.33$ kg (3 s.f.)

Q12 a) Resultant, $\mathbf{R} = (6\mathbf{i} - 10\mathbf{j}) + (4\mathbf{i} + 5\mathbf{j}) = (10\mathbf{i} - 5\mathbf{j})$ N
$|\mathbf{R}| = \sqrt{10^2 + (-5)^2} = \sqrt{125}$ N
$F_{net} = ma$
$\sqrt{125} = 5a$
$a = \sqrt{125} \div 5 = 2.236...$
$= 2.24 \text{ ms}^{-2}$ (3 s.f.)

b) $\mathbf{R}_{new} = (10\mathbf{i} - 5\mathbf{j}) + (-6\mathbf{i} + 2\mathbf{j}) = (4\mathbf{i} - 3\mathbf{j})$ N
$|\mathbf{R}_{new}| = \sqrt{4^2 + (-3)^2} = 5$ N
$F_{net} = ma$
$5 = 5a \Rightarrow a = 1 \text{ ms}^{-2}$
So the acceleration decreases by 1.24 ms^{-2} (3 s.f.)

Q13 a) $7\mathbf{i} + \mathbf{j} = (6\mathbf{i} - 2\mathbf{j}) + (5\mathbf{i} + 5\mathbf{j}) + \mathbf{x}$
$\mathbf{x} = (7 - 6 - 5)\mathbf{i} + (1 + 2 - 5)\mathbf{j} = (-4\mathbf{i} - 2\mathbf{j})$ N

b) $u = 2, v = 6, a = a, t = 8$
$v = u + at$
$6 = 2 + 8a$
$a = 4 \div 8 = 0.5 \text{ ms}^{-2}$
$|\mathbf{F}_{net}| = |7\mathbf{i} + \mathbf{j}| = \sqrt{7^2 + 1^2} = \sqrt{50}$ N
$F_{net} = ma$
$\sqrt{50} = 0.5m$
$\Rightarrow m = 14.142... = 14.1$ kg (3 s.f.)

c) The new resultant force is $(7\mathbf{i} + \mathbf{j}) + (-7\mathbf{i} - \mathbf{j}) = 0$ N
So there is no resultant force, and hence the particle does not accelerate (i.e. it continues to move at whatever velocity it had when the force began to act).

Exercise 1.2 — Friction and inclined planes

Q1 a) Resolving parallel to the plane (↙):
$F_{net} = ma$
$1.5g\sin25° = 1.5a$
$a = 9.8\sin25° = 4.141... = 4.14 \text{ ms}^{-2}$ (3 s.f.)

b) $u = 0, v = v, a = 4.141..., t = 3$
$v = u + at$
$v = 0 + (4.141... \times 3) = 12.4 \text{ ms}^{-1}$ (3 s.f.)

Q2 a) Resolving parallel to the plane (↗):
$F_{net} = ma$
$P\cos45° - 3g\sin45° = 3 \times 0.7$
$P = (2.1 + 3g\sin45°) \div \cos45°$
$= 32.369... = 32.4$ N (3 s.f.)

b) Resolving parallel to the plane (↗):
$F_{net} = ma$
$-3g\sin45° = 3a \Rightarrow a = -g\sin45°$
$u = 2, v = 0, a = -g\sin45°, t = t$
$v = u + at$
$0 = 2 - tg\sin45°$
$t = 2 \div g\sin45° = 0.289$ s (3 s.f.)

Q3 a)

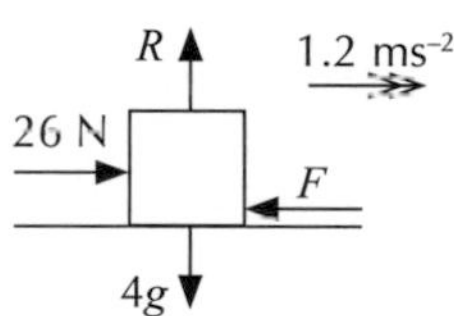

b) Resolving vertically:
$R - 4g = 0$
$R = 4g = 39.2$ N

c) Resolving horizontally:
$F_{net} = ma$
$26 - F = 4 \times 1.2$
$F = 21.2$ N

d) The frictional force takes its maximum possible value.

e) Friction is at its maximum, so $F = \mu R$:
$21.2 = 39.2\mu$
$\Rightarrow \mu = 0.54$ (2 d.p.)

Q4 a)

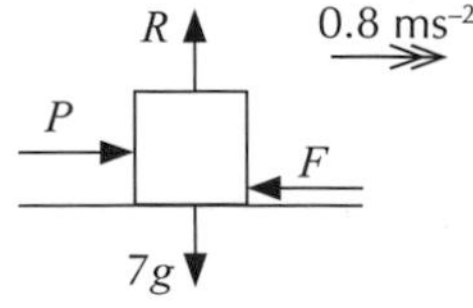

b) Resolving vertically:
$R - 7g = 0 \Rightarrow R = 7g = 68.6$ N

c) Resolving horizontally:
$F_{net} = ma$
$P - F = 7 \times 0.8$
$P - \mu R = 5.6$
$P = 5.6 + (0.2 \times 68.6) = 19.32$ N

Q5 a)

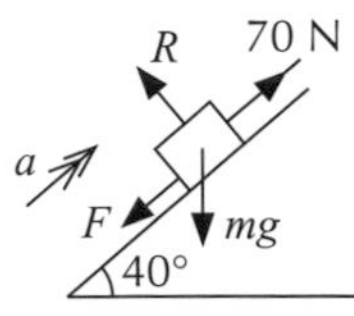

b) Resolving perpendicular to the plane (↖):
$R - mg\cos40° = 0$
$\Rightarrow R = mg\cos40°$
Resolving parallel to the plane (↗):
$F_{net} = ma$
$70 - F - mg\sin40° = 3.2m$
$70 - \mu R - mg\sin40° = 3.2m$
$70 - 0.35(mg\cos40°) - mg\sin40° = 3.2m$
$70 = m(3.2 + 0.35g\cos40° + g\sin40°)$
$m = 70 \div 12.126... = 5.77$ kg (3 s.f.)

Q6 Resolving parallel to the plane (↗):
$F_{net} = ma$
$50\cos\theta - 6g\sin30° = 6 \times 0.6$
$50\cos\theta = 3.6 + 3g$
$\cos\theta = 33 \div 50$
$\theta = \cos^{-1}(0.66) = 48.7°$ (3 s.f.)

Q7 a)

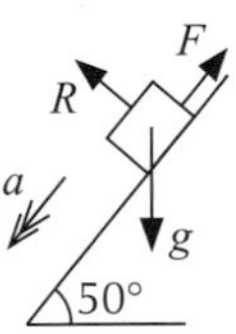

b) Resolving perpendicular to the plane (↖):
$R = g\cos50°$
Resolving parallel to the plane (↙):
$F_{net} = ma$
$g\sin50° - F = a$
$g\sin50° - \mu R = a$
$g\sin50° - (0.4 \times g\cos50°) = a$
$\Rightarrow a = 4.9875...$
$u = 0, a = 4.9875..., s = 2, t = t$
$s = ut + \frac{1}{2}at^2$
$2 = \frac{1}{2}(4.9875...)t^2$
$t^2 = 0.8020...$
$\Rightarrow t = 0.896$ s (3 s.f.)

Q8 Resolving perpendicular to the plane (↖):
$R = 5000\cos10°$
Resolving parallel to the plane (↗):
$F_{net} = ma$
$T - F - 5000\sin10° = (5000 \div 9.8) \times 0.35$
$T - \mu R - 5000\sin10° = 178.57...$
$T - (0.1 \times 5000\cos10°) - 5000\sin10° = 178.57...$
$\Rightarrow T = 1539.21... = 1540$ N (3 s.f.)

Q9 a)

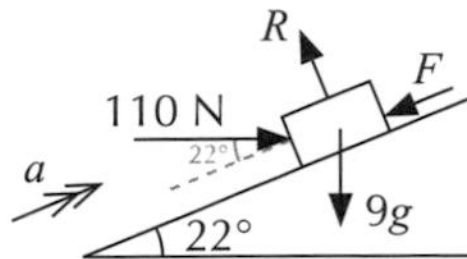

b) Resolving perpendicular to the plane (↖):
$R = 9g\cos22° + 110\sin22° = 122.98...$
Resolving parallel to the plane (↗):
$F_{net} = ma$
$110\cos22° - F - 9g\sin22° = 9 \times 1.3$
$110\cos22° - \mu 122.98... - 9g\sin22° = 11.7$
$\mu 122.98... = 110\cos22° - 9g\sin22° - 11.7$
$\Rightarrow \mu = 57.24... \div 122.98... = 0.47$ (2 d.p.)

2. Connected Particles

Exercise 2.1 — Connected particles

Q1 a)

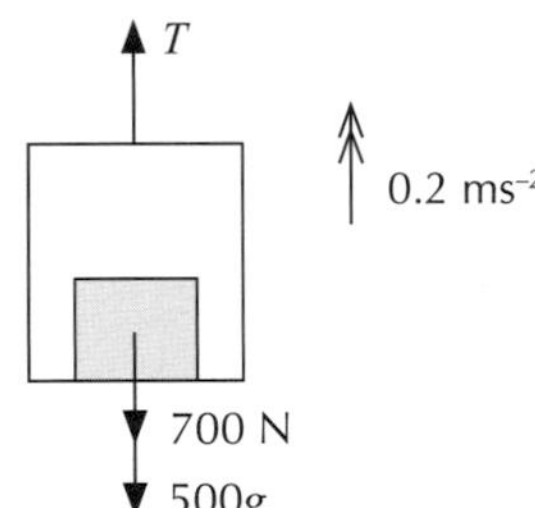

Resolving vertically for the whole system:
$F_{net} = ma$
$T - 500g - 700 = (500 + (700 \div 9.8)) \times 0.2$
$\Rightarrow T = 5714.285... = 5710$ N (3 s.f.)

b)

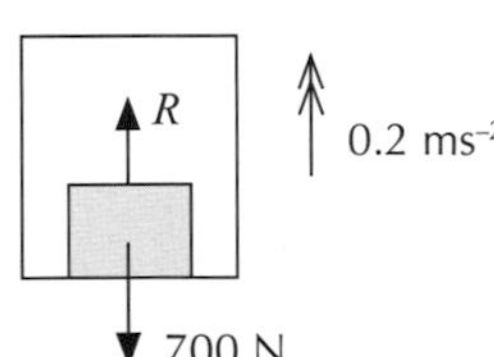

Resolving vertically for the load:
$F_{net} = ma$
$R - 700 = (700 \div 9.8) \times 0.2$
$\Rightarrow R = 714.285... = 714$ N (3 s.f.)

Q2 a)

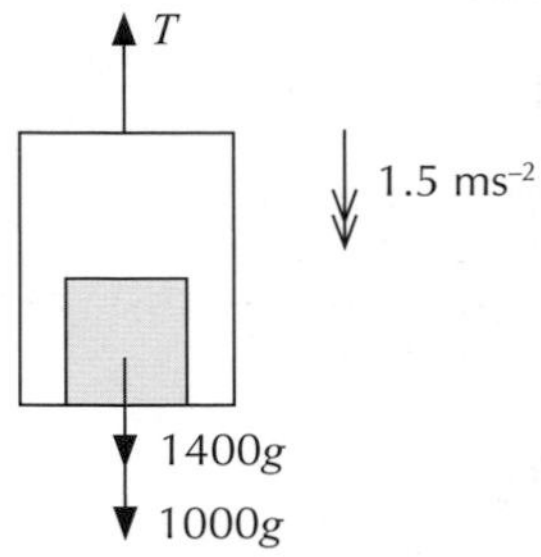

Resolving vertically for whole system:
$2400g - T = 2400 \times 1.5$
$\Rightarrow T = 19\,920$ N

b)

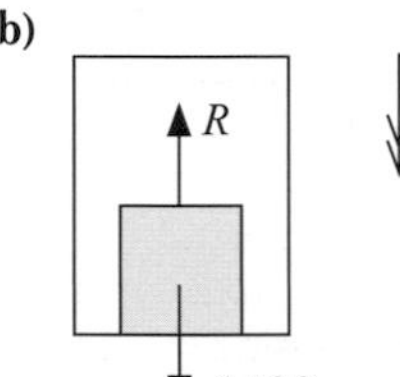

Resolving vertically for the load:
$1400g - R = 1400 \times 1.5$
$\Rightarrow R = 11\,620$ N

c) The lift is now falling freely under gravity, so $a = g$:
$u = 0, v = v, a = 9.8, s = 30$
$v^2 = u^2 + 2as$
$v^2 = 2 \times 9.8 \times 30 = 588$
$v = 24.2$ ms^{-1} (3 s.f.)

Q3 a) Resolving horizontally for the whole system, taking the direction of acceleration as positive:
$F_{net} = ma$
$P = 3500 \times 0.3 = 1050$ N
The tractor and trailer are decelerating, so this means you need to take the direction opposite to the direction of motion as being positive.

b) Resolving horizontally for the trailer:
$F_{net} = ma$
$T = 1500 \times 0.3 = 450$ N

c) E.g. The tractor and trailer are modelled as particles, there are no external forces (e.g. air resistance) acting, the coupling is horizontal, the braking force generated by the tractor is constant, the tractor and trailer are moving in a straight line on horizontal ground.

Q4 a)

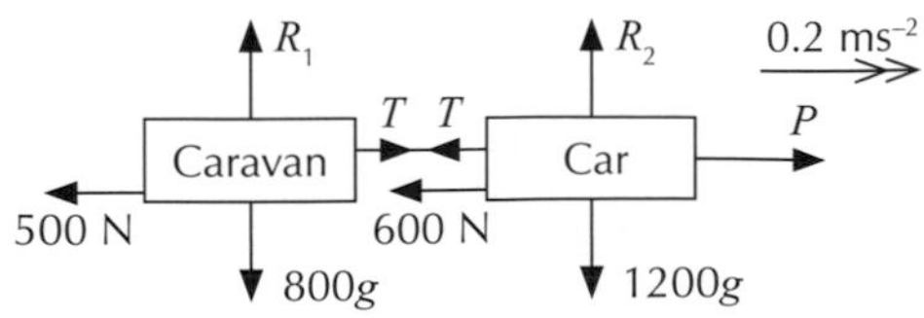

Resolving horizontally for the whole system:
$F_{net} = ma$
$P - 500 - 600 = 2000 \times 0.2$
$\Rightarrow P = 1500$ N

b) Resolving horizontally for the caravan:
$T - 500 = 800 \times 0.2$
$\Rightarrow T = 660$ N

c) $F_{net} = ma$
$-500 = 800a \Rightarrow a = -0.625$ ms^{-2}
$u = 20, v = 0, a = -0.625, t = t$
$v = u + at$
$0 = 20 - 0.625t$
$\Rightarrow t = 32$ s

Q5 a)

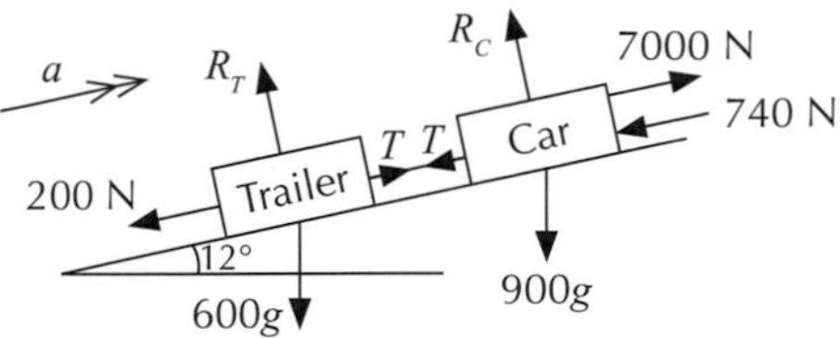

b) Resolving parallel to the plane (↗) for the whole system:
$F_{net} = ma$
$7000 - 740 - 200 - 1500g\sin 12° = 1500a$
$\Rightarrow a = 2.0024... = 2.00$ ms^{-2} (3 s.f.)

c) Resolving parallel to the plane (↗) for the trailer:
$T - 200 - 600g\sin 12° = 600 \times 2.0024...$
$\Rightarrow T = 2624$ N

d) An inextensible rope means that the tension in the rope is constant, and the acceleration of the car and the trailer are always the same.

Q6 a) Resolving perpendicular to the plane (↖) for A:
$R_A = 2000g\cos 20°$
So, using $F = \mu R$:
$F_A = 0.3 \times 2000g\cos 20° = 600g\cos 20°$
Resolving perpendicular to the plane (↖) for B:
$R_B = 1600g\cos 20°$
So, using $F = \mu R$:
$F_B = 0.4 \times 1600g\cos 20° = 640g\cos 20°$
Resolving parallel to the plane (↙) for A:
$F_{net} = ma$
$2000g\sin 20° - T - F_A = 2000a$
$2000g\sin 20° - T - 600g\cos 20° = 2000a$ **eqn1**
Resolving parallel to the plane (↙) for B:
$F_{net} = ma$
$1600g\sin 20° + T - F_B = 1600a$
$1600g\sin 20° + T - 640g\cos 20° = 1600a$ **eqn2**
Multiplying **eqn2** by 1.25:
$2000g\sin 20° + 1.25T - 800g\cos 20° = 2000a$ **eqn3**
Subtracting **eqn1** from **eqn3**:
$2.25T - 200g\cos 20° = 0$
$\Rightarrow T = 200g\cos 20° \div 2.25 = 818.576...$
$= 819$ N (3 s.f.)

b) Substitute your value of T from part a) into **eqn 1** (or **eqn 2**) to find the acceleration of the system:
$2000g\sin 20° - 818.576... - 600g\cos 20° = 2000a$
$\Rightarrow a = 359.626... \div 2000 = 0.1798...$ ms^{-2}
$u = 0, s = 25, t = t$
Using $s = ut + \frac{1}{2}at^2$:
$25 = \frac{1}{2} \times 0.1798... \times t^2$
$t^2 = 278.06...$
$\Rightarrow t = 16.67... = 16.7$ s (3 s.f.)

Exercise 2.2 — Introduction to pegs and pulleys

Q1 a)

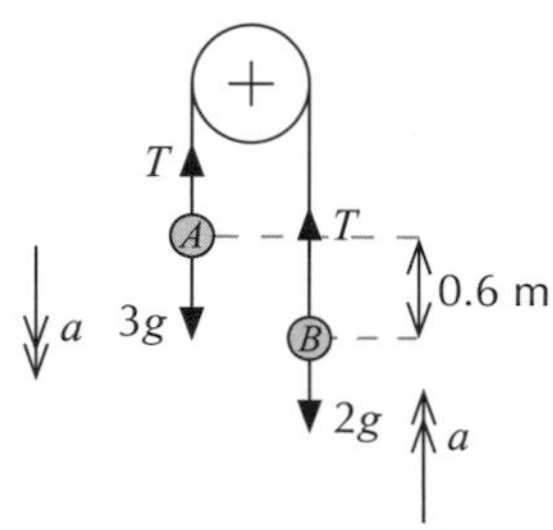

b) Resolving vertically (↓) for A:
$F_{net} = ma$
$3g - T = 3a$ **eqn1**
Resolving vertically (↑) for B:
$F_{net} = ma$
$T - 2g = 2a$ **eqn2**
Adding **eqn1** and **eqn2**:
$g = 5a \Rightarrow a = 9.8 \div 5 = 1.96 \text{ ms}^{-2}$
The particles will become level when they have each moved 0.3 m.
$u = 0, a = 1.96, s = 0.3, t = t$
$s = ut + \frac{1}{2}at^2$
$0.3 = \frac{1}{2} \times 1.96 \times t^2$
$t^2 = 0.306...$
$\Rightarrow t = 0.5532... = 0.553 \text{ s (3 s.f.)}$

Q2 a) $u = 0, a = a, s = 5, t = 2$
$s = ut + \frac{1}{2}at^2$
$5 = \frac{1}{2} \times a \times 2^2$
$\Rightarrow a = 5 \div 2 = 2.5 \text{ ms}^{-2}$
Resolving vertically (↓) for A:
$F_{net} = ma$
$35g - T = 35 \times 2.5$
$\Rightarrow T = 343 - 87.5 = 255.5 \text{ N}$

b) Resolving vertically (↑) for B:
$F_{net} = ma$
$T - Mg = 2.5M$
$255.5 = 12.3M$
$\Rightarrow M = 20.8 \text{ kg (3 s.f.)}$

Q3 a) Resolving horizontally (→) for A:
$F_{net} = ma$
$T = 5a$ **eqn1**
Resolving vertically (↓) for B:
$7g - T = 7a$ **eqn2**
Substituting **eqn1** into **eqn2**:
$7g - 5a = 7a$
$7g = 12a$
$a = 7g \div 12 = 5.716... = 5.72 \text{ ms}^{-2} \text{ (3 s.f.)}$

b) Using **eqn1**:
$T = 5a = 5 \times 5.716... = 28.583...$
$= 28.6 \text{ N (3 s.f.)}$

c) String is light and inextensible, pulley is fixed and smooth, horizontal surface is smooth, no other external forces are acting, A doesn't hit the pulley, B doesn't hit the floor, string doesn't break, pulley doesn't break, string between A and the pulley is horizontal, string is initially taut, acceleration due to gravity is constant at 9.8 ms^{-2}.

Q4 a)

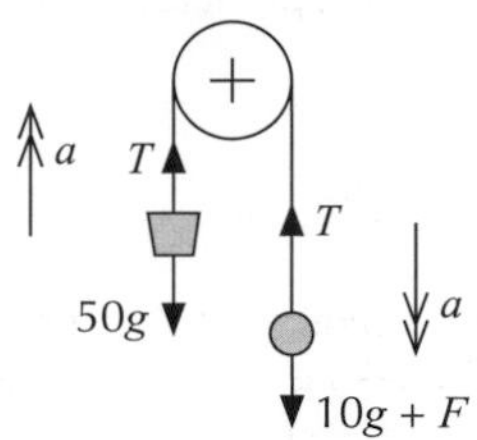

b) First find the acceleration.
$u = 0, s = 12, a = a, t = 20$
$s = ut + \frac{1}{2}at^2$
$12 = \frac{1}{2} \times a \times 20^2$
$\Rightarrow a = 0.06 \text{ ms}^{-2}$
Now resolving vertically (↑) for the bucket:
$F_{net} = ma$
$T - 50g = 50 \times 0.06$
$\Rightarrow T = 493 \text{ N}$

c) Resolving vertically (↓) for the counterweight:
$F_{net} = ma$
$10g + F - T = 10 \times 0.06$
$\Rightarrow F = 0.6 - 98 + 493 = 395.6 \text{ N}$

d)

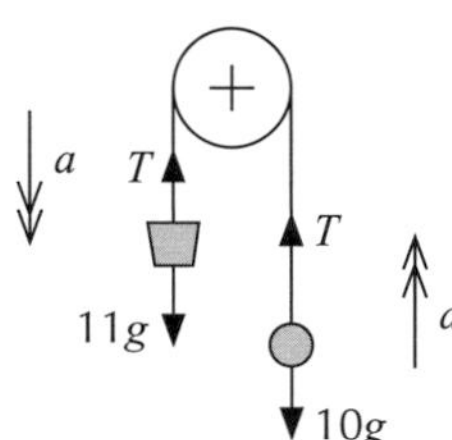

Resolving vertically (↓) for the bucket:
$11g - T = 11a$ **eqn1**
Resolving vertically (↑) for the counterweight:
$T - 10g = 10a$ **eqn2**
Adding **eqn1** and **eqn2**:
$g = 21a$
$\Rightarrow a = 0.466... \text{ ms}^{-2}$
$u = 0, v = v, s = 12$
$v^2 = u^2 + 2as$
$v^2 = 2 \times 0.466... \times 12 = 11.2$
$\Rightarrow v = 3.35 \text{ ms}^{-1} \text{ (3 s.f.)}$

Q5 a) A has a greater mass than B, so A will accelerate downwards and B will accelerate upwards.
Resolving vertically (↓) for A:
$15g - T = 15a$ **eqn1**
Resolving vertically (↑) for B:
$T - 12g = 12a$ **eqn2**
Adding **eqn1** and **eqn2**:
$3g = 27a$
$\Rightarrow a = 1.088... = 1.09 \text{ ms}^{-2} \text{ (3 s.f.)}$

b) The force exerted on the pulley by the string is $2T$.
Using **eqn2**:
$T = 12a + 12g = (12 \times 1.088...) + (12 \times 9.8)$
$T = 130.66...$
So $2T = 261.33... = 261 \text{ N (3 s.f.)}$

c) First find the speed of the particles when A hits the ground:
$u = 0, v = v, a = 1.088..., s = 6$
$v^2 = u^2 + 2as$
$v^2 = 2 \times 1.088... \times 6 = 13.066...$
$v = 3.614...$
Now considering the motion of B as it moves freely under gravity, taking upwards as positive:
$u = 3.614..., v = 0, a = -9.8, t = t$
$v = u + at$
$0 = 3.614... - 9.8t$
$\Rightarrow t = 0.368... = 0.369$ s (3 s.f.)

Q6 Split the motion into two parts. The first part is from the particles being released to P striking the pulley.
Resolving vertically (↓) for Q:
$F_{net} = ma$
$10g - T = 10a$ **eqn1**
Resolving horizontally (→) for P:
$F_{net} = ma$
$T = 8a$ **eqn2**
Substituting **eqn2** into **eqn1**:
$10g - 8a = 10a$
$10g = 18a$
$a = 5.444...$
Use this to find the time between the point that the particles are released and the point that P hits the pulley:
$u = 0, a = 5.444..., s = 4, t = t$
$s = ut + \frac{1}{2}at^2$
$4 = \frac{1}{2} \times 5.444... \times t^2$
$t^2 = 1.469...$
$t = 1.212...$
Also find the speed of the particles at this point:
$v = u + at$
$v = 0 + (5.444... \times 1.212...) = 6.599...$
Now consider the second part of the motion — Q falling freely under gravity:
$u = 6.599..., a = 9.8, s = 9 - 4 = 5, t = t$
$s = ut + \frac{1}{2}at^2$
$5 = (6.599...)t + 4.9t^2$
$4.9t^2 + (6.599...)t - 5 = 0$
Using the quadratic formula:
$$t = \frac{-6.599... \pm \sqrt{(6.599...)^2 - (4 \times 4.9 \times -5)}}{9.8}$$
So $t = 0.540...$ or $t = -1.887...$
t must be positive, so take $t = 0.540...$
So the total time taken is:
$1.212... + 0.540... = 1.752...$
$= 1.75$ s (3 s.f.)

Exercise 2.3 — Harder problems involving pegs and pulleys

Q1 a) Resolving vertically (↑) for A:
$R = 6g$
Now using $F = \mu R$:
$F = 0.2 \times 6g = 1.2g$
Resolving horizontally (→) for A:
$T - F = 6a$
$12 - 1.2g = 6a$
$\Rightarrow a = 0.04$ ms^{-2}

b) Resolving vertically (↓) for B:
$F_{net} = ma$
$Mg - T = 0.04M$
$M(g - 0.04) = 12$
$\Rightarrow M = 1.23$ kg (3 s.f.)

Q2 a) Resolving vertically (↑) for B:
$F_{net} = ma$
$T - 2g = 2 \times 1.6$
$\Rightarrow T = 22.8$ N

b) Resolving perpendicular to the plane (↖) for A:
$F_{net} = ma$
$R - 12g\cos30° = 0$
$R = 12g\cos30°$
Resolving parallel to the plane (↙) for A:
$F_{net} = ma$
$12g\sin30° - F - T = 12 \times 1.6$
$6g - F - 22.8 = 19.2$
$F = 16.8$ N
Using $F = \mu R$:
$16.8 = \mu(12g\cos30°)$
$\mu = 16.8 \div 12g\cos30° = 0.16$ (2 d.p.)

c) Considering the motion of either particle:
$u = 0, a = 1.6, s = s, t = 3$
$s = ut + \frac{1}{2}at^2$
$s = \frac{1}{2} \times 1.6 \times 3^2 = 7.2$ m

d) E.g. B does not hit the pulley; A does not reach the end of the slope.

Q3 a) Resolving vertically (↓) for B:
$F_{net} = ma$
$9g - T = 9 \times 0.4$
$\Rightarrow T = 84.6$ N
Resolving vertically (↑) for A:
$R + 60\sin40° = 8g$
$\Rightarrow R = 39.832...$ N
Resolving horizontally (→) for A:
$F_{net} = ma$
$T - F - 60\cos40° = 8 \times 0.4$
$F = 84.6 - 60\cos40° - 3.2 = 35.437...$ N
$F = \mu R \Rightarrow \mu = 35.437... \div 39.832...$
$= 0.89$ (2 d.p.)

b) $u = 0, v = v, a = 0.4, s = 0.2$
$v^2 = u^2 + 2as$
$v^2 = 2 \times 0.4 \times 0.2 = 0.16$
$v = 0.4$ ms^{-1}

c) When A hits the pulley, A and B are both travelling at 0.4 ms^{-1}.
$u = 0.4, v = v, a = 9.8, s = 0.6 - 0.2 = 0.4$
$v^2 = u^2 + 2as$
$v^2 = 0.4^2 + (2 \times 9.8 \times 0.4) = 8$
$v = 2.83$ ms^{-1} (3 s.f.)

Q4 a) Resolving perpendicular to the plane (↖) for P:
$R = 60g\cos50°$
Using $F = \mu R$:
$F = 0.1 \times 60g\cos50° = 6g\cos50°$
Resolving parallel to the plane (↙) for P:
$F_{net} = ma$
$60g\sin50° - F - T = 0$
$T = 60g\sin50° - 6g\cos50° = 412.63...$ N
Resolving vertically (↑) for Q:
$F_{net} = ma$
$T - 20g - K = 0$
$K = 412.63... - 20g = 216.63...$
$K = 217$ N (3 s.f.)

b) Resolving vertically (↑) for Q:
$F_{net} = ma$
$T - 20g = 20a$ **eqn1**
Resolving parallel to the plane (↙) for P:
$60g\sin50° - F - T = 60a$
$60g\sin50° - 6g\cos50° - T = 60a$ **eqn2**
Adding **eqn1** and **eqn2**:
$60g\sin50° - 6g\cos50° - 20g = 80a$
$\Rightarrow a = 2.707...$ ms^{-2}
$u = 0, v = v, t = 5$
$v = u + at$
$v = 0 + (2.707... \times 5) = 13.539...$
$v = 13.5$ ms^{-1} (3 s.f.)

Q5 a) $u = 0, a = a, s = 10, t = 30$
$s = ut + \frac{1}{2}at^2$
$10 = \frac{1}{2} \times a \times 30^2$
$a = 0.0222...$
Resolving parallel to the plane (↗) for the car:
$F_{net} = ma$
$T - 800g\sin25° = 800 \times 0.0222...$
$\Rightarrow T = 3331.10... = 3330$ N (3 s.f.)

b) Resolving vertically (↑) for the truck:
$R_T = 2000g$
You're told you can assume that friction is at its maximum value, so using $F = \mu R$:
$F = 0.8 \times 2000g = 1600g$ N
Resolving horizontally (→) for the truck:
$F_{net} = ma$
$W - F - T = 2000 \times 0.022...$
$W = 44.44... + 1600g + 3331.10...$
$= 19\,055.54... = 19\,100$ N (3 s.f.)

c) Resolving horizontally (→) for the truck:
$F_{net} = ma$
$W - F = 2000a$
$19\,055.54... - 1600g = 2000a$
$\Rightarrow a = 1.69$ ms^{-2} (3 s.f.)

Q6 a) Resolving perpendicular to the 40° plane (↖) for A:
$R_A = 0.2g\cos40°$
Using $F = \mu R$:
$F_A = 0.7 \times 0.2g\cos40° = 0.14g\cos40°$
Resolving parallel to the 40° plane (↗) for A:
$T - F_A - 0.2g\sin40° = 0.2a$
$T - 0.14g\cos40° - 0.2g\sin40° = 0.2a$
$\Rightarrow 5T - 0.7g\cos40° - g\sin40° = a$ **eqn1**
Resolving perpendicular to the 20° plane (↗) for B:
$R_B = 0.9g\cos20°$
Using $F = \mu R$:
$F_B = 0.05 \times 0.9g\cos20° = 0.045g\cos20°$
Resolving parallel to the 20° plane (↘) for B:
$F_{net} = ma$
$0.9g\sin20° - F_B - T = 0.9a$
$0.9g\sin20° - 0.045g\cos20° - T = 0.9a$
$\Rightarrow g\sin20° - 0.05g\cos20° - (1.11...)T = a$ **eqn2**
Solving the simultaneous equations **1** and **2**:
$5T - 0.7g\cos40° - g\sin40° =$
$g\sin20° - 0.05g\cos20° - (1.11...)T$
$\Rightarrow (6.11...)T = g\sin20° - 0.05g\cos20° +$
$0.7g\cos40° + g\sin40°$
$\Rightarrow T = 2.363... = 2.36$ N (3 s.f.)

b) Using **eqn1** from part a):
$a = 5T - 0.7g\cos40° - g\sin40°$
$= (5 \times 2.363...) - 0.7g\cos40° - g\sin40°$
$= 0.2648...$
$u = 0, v = v, s = 0.35$
$v^2 = u^2 + 2as$
$v^2 = 2 \times 0.2648... \times 0.35 = 0.185...$
$\Rightarrow v = 0.431$ ms^{-1} (3 s.f.)

3. Momentum and Impulse

Exercise 3.1 — Momentum

Q1 a) Momentum $= mv = 3 \times 6 = 18$ Ns
b) $mv = 6.8 \times 0.4 = 2.72$ Ns
c) $mv = 1000\,000 \times 57 = 57\,000\,000$ Ns

Q2 a) Mass = momentum ÷ velocity = 28 ÷ 7 = 4 kg
b) $m = 0.8 \div 3.2 = 0.25$ kg
c) $m = 584 \div 73 = 8$ kg

Q3 a) Velocity = momentum ÷ mass
= 2000 ÷ 500 = 4 ms^{-1}
b) $v = 8000 \div 4000 = 2$ ms^{-1}
c) $v = 585 \div 3.9 = 150$ ms^{-1}

Exercise 3.2 — Conservation of momentum

Q1 $m_Au_A + m_Bu_B = m_Av_A + m_Bv_B$
$(2 \times 9) + (7 \times 2) = 2v + (7 \times 4)$
$2v = 4$
$v = 2$ ms^{-1}

Q2 a)

Before
18 ms^{-1} 5 ms^{-1}
A B
3 kg 8 kg

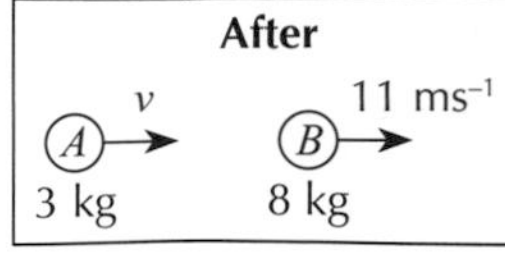

b) $m_Au_A + m_Bu_B = m_Av_A + m_Bv_B$
$(3 \times 18) + (8 \times 5) = 3v + (8 \times 11)$
$3v = 6$
$v = 2 \text{ ms}^{-1}$

Q3 $m_Pu_P + m_Qu_Q = m_Pv_P + m_Qv_Q$
$(6 \times 2.5) + (4 \times 0) = 6v + (4 \times 6)$
$6v = -9$
$v = -1.5 \text{ ms}^{-1}$
i.e. P moves with speed 1.5 ms^{-1} in the opposite direction to its motion before the collision.

Q4 $m_1u_1 + m_2u_2 = m_{(1+2)}v$
$(8 \times 4) + (5 \times 3) = 13v$
$v = 3.62 \text{ ms}^{-1}$ (2 d.p.)
You don't need to convert the masses to kg here — as long as you use the same units of mass (tonnes) throughout your working, then the answer will come out correct.

Q5 $m_1u_1 + m_2u_2 = m_1v_1 + m_2v_2$
$8m + (2 \times -3) = 0$
$8m = 6$
$m = 0.75$ kg

Q6 a) $m_Pu_P + m_Qu_Q = m_{(P+Q)}v$
$(4 \times 3.5) + (2 \times -1) = 6v$
$v = 2 \text{ ms}^{-1}$

b) $m_Pu_P + m_Qu_Q = m_Pv_P + m_Qv_Q$
$(4 \times 3.5) + (2 \times -1) = (4 \times v) + (2 \times 2v)$
$12 = 8v$
$v = 1.5 \text{ ms}^{-1}$
So $v_P = 1.5 \text{ ms}^{-1}$ and $v_Q = 3 \text{ ms}^{-1}$

c) $m_Pu_P + m_Qu_Q = m_Pv_P + m_Qv_Q$
$(4 \times 3.5) + (2 \times -1) = (4 \times -v) + (2 \times 3v)$
$12 = 2v$
$v = 6 \text{ ms}^{-1}$
So $v_P = 6 \text{ ms}^{-1}$ and $v_Q = 18 \text{ ms}^{-1}$

Q7 $m_Au_A + m_Bu_B = m_Av_A + m_Bv_B$
$(m \times 5) + (3m \times u) = (m \times -1) + (3m \times 3)$
Dividing through by m:
$5 + 3u = -1 + 9$
$3u = 3$
$u = 1 \text{ ms}^{-1}$

Q8 $m_1u_1 + m_2u_2 = m_{(1+2)}v$
$5u + (4 \times 1.2) = 9 \times 1.5$
$5u = 8.7$
$u = 1.74 \text{ ms}^{-1}$

Q9 $m_Au_A + m_Bu_B = m_Av_A + m_Bv_B$
$(50 \times 3) + (M \times -2) = (50 \times 0) + (M \times 4)$
$150 = 6M$
$M = 25$ kg

Q10 a) $m_Pu_P + m_Qu_Q = m_Pv_P + m_Qv_Q$
$(0.12 \times 9) + (0.09 \times -11) = 0.12v + (0.09 \times 6)$
$0.12v = -0.45$
$v = -3.75 \text{ kmh}^{-1}$
$(3.75 \times 1000) \div 3600 = 1.0416... \text{ ms}^{-1}$
So the speed of P is 1.04 ms^{-1} (3 s.f.)

b) Following the collision, P moves in the opposite direction to its motion before the collision.

Q11 $m_1u_1 + m_2u_2 = m_1v_1 + m_2v_2$
$(2 \times 4.5) + (2.5 \times -3) = (2 \times -v) + (2.5 \times 2v)$
$1.5 = 3v$
$v = 0.5 \text{ ms}^{-1}$
So the heavier boat moves off at 1 ms^{-1} and the lighter boat moves off at 0.5 ms^{-1}.

Q12 $m_1u_1 + m_2u_2 = m_{(1+2)}v$
$(60 \times 3) + (40 \times -2) = 100v$
$v = 1 \text{ ms}^{-1}$
$s = vt = 1 \times 6 = 6$ m

Q13 a) $m_Au_A + m_Bu_B = m_Av_A + m_Bv_B$
$(2m \times 4u) + (4m \times -6u) = (2m \times -2u) + (4m \times v)$
Cancelling the m's:
$8u - 24u = -4u + 4v$
$4v = -12u$
$v = -3u$

b) No, the direction of B's motion is the same after the collision, as its velocity is still negative relative to u.

Q14 a) Considering the collision between P and Q:
$m_Pu_P + m_Qu_Q = m_Pv_P + m_Qv_Q$
$(1 \times 5) + (m \times 3) = (1 \times -4) + (m \times 4)$
$5 + 3m = -4 + 4m$
$m = 9$ kg

b) Considering the collision between Q and R:
$m_Qu_Q + m_Ru_R = m_{(Q+R)}v$
$(9 \times 4) + (4 \times 1.5) = 13v$
$v = 3.23 \text{ ms}^{-1}$ (3 s.f.)

Q15 a) $m_Au_A + m_Bu_B = m_Av_A + m_Bv_B$
$(5 \times 2.8) + (2 \times 0) = (5 \times -1.2) + 2v$
$2v = 20$
$v = 10 \text{ ms}^{-1}$ in the same direction as A was travelling before the collision.

b) $m_Bu_B + m_Cu_C = m_Bv_B + m_Cv_C$
$(2 \times 10) + (7 \times 0) = 2v + (7 \times 3.5)$
$2v = -4.5$
$v = -2.25 \text{ ms}^{-1}$
The speed of B is now greater than the speed of A, and they are both moving in the same direction. So it is possible for them to collide again.

Exercise 3.3 — Impulse

Q1 $I = Ft = 7 \times 15 = 105$ Ns

Q2 $F = I \div t = 2880 \div 9 = 320$ N

Q3 $I = mv - mu = (2 \times 5) - (2 \times 3) = 4$ Ns

Q4 $I = mv - mu = (0.3 \times 0) - (0.3 \times 4) = -1.2$ Ns
i.e. an impulse of 1.2 Ns in the opposite direction to its motion.

Q5 $I = mv - mu$
$0.6 = 0.08(v - u)$
$\Rightarrow (v - u) = 7.5 \text{ ms}^{-1}$ (in the direction of its motion)

Q6 $I = mv - mu$
$21 = 35v - (35 \times 3.2)$
$\Rightarrow v = 3.8 \text{ ms}^{-1}$

Q7 $I = mv - mu$
$0.9 = 0.15v - (0.15 \times 0)$
$\Rightarrow v = 6 \text{ ms}^{-1}$

Q8 $I = mv - mu$
$-1.8 = m(0 - 4.5)$
$\Rightarrow m = 0.4$ kg

Q9 $I = mv - mu$
$126 = m(2.1 - 1.2)$
$\Rightarrow m = 140$ kg

Q10 $I = mv - mu$
$-0.03125 = 0.0025v - (0.0025 \times 5)$
$\Rightarrow v = -7.5$ ms^{-1}
So its speed is 7.5 ms^{-1}.

Q11 a) $mv - mu = (25\,000 \times 1.8) - (25\,000 \times 30)$
$= -705\,000$ Ns

b) $I = Ft$
$-705\,000 = 20F$
$F = -35\,250$ N

Q12 a) $I = mv - mu = (0.18 \times -15) - (0.18 \times 25)$
$= -7.2$ Ns

b) The impulse exerted on the back of the goal by the puck is equal in magnitude but opposite in direction to the impulse exerted on the puck by the back of the goal.
i.e. 10.8 Ns

Q13 a) Taking downwards as positive:
$u = 0,\ v = v,\ a = 9.8,\ s = 10$
$v^2 = u^2 + 2as$
$v^2 = 0 + (2 \times 9.8 \times 10) = 196$
$v = 14$ ms^{-1}

b) Taking downwards as positive:
$I = mv - mu = (0.3 \times -8) - (0.3 \times 14) = -6.6$ Ns

c) Taking upwards as positive:
$u = 8,\ v = 0,\ a = -9.8,\ s = s$
$v^2 = u^2 + 2as$
$0 = 8^2 + (2 \times -9.8 \times s)$
$s = 64 \div 19.6 = 3.27$ m (3 s.f.)

Q14 a) Taking the direction that B is moving as positive:
$I = mv - mu = (0.3 \times 0) - (0.3 \times 8) = -2.4$ Ns

b) The impulse given to A by B is 2.4 Ns.
$I = mv - mu$
$2.4 = 0.2v - (0.2 \times -5)$
$v = 7$ ms^{-1} (in the opposite direction to its motion before the collision).
You could've done part b) using conservation of momentum. Unless a question tells you to use a particular method, it's up to you.

Q15 a) $I = mv - mu$
$= (1300 \times 6.3 \times 1000 \div 3600) -$
$(1300 \times 5.4 \times 1000 \div 3600) = 325$ Ns

b) Impulse on P is -325 Ns.
$I = mv - mu$
$-325 = 1200v - (1200 \times 7.2 \times 1000 \div 3600)$
$v = 1.729...$ ms^{-1}
$v = 1.729... \times 3600 \div 1000 = 6.225$ kmh^{-1}
You could've done this using conservation of momentum — that way you wouldn't have needed to convert any units.

Q16 The impulse given to A by B acts in the opposite direction to the motion of A.
$I = mv - mu$
$-2.4 = 4.8v - (4.8 \times 2)$
$\Rightarrow v = 1.5$ ms^{-1}
Now use conservation of momentum on both particles:
$m_A u_A + m_B u_B = m_{(A+B)} v$
$(4.8 \times 2) + 2u = 6.8v$
$2u = (6.8 \times 1.5) - 9.6$
$u = 0.3$ ms^{-1}

Q17 a) $m_R u_R + m_B u_B = m_R v_R + m_B v_B$
$0.04u + (0.06 \times 0) = (0.04 \times -0.8) + (0.06 \times 1.4)$
$\Rightarrow u = 1.3$ ms^{-1}

b) Impulse received by blue ball:
$I = mv - mu = (0.06 \times 1.4) - (0.06 \times 0)$
$= 0.084$ Ns
So both balls receive an impulse of magnitude 0.084 Ns.

c) The impulse required to take the blue ball from rest to 1.4 ms^{-1} was 0.084 Ns, so the impulse required to take it back to rest is 0.084 Ns, acting in the opposite direction.
$I = Ft$
$0.084 = 3R$
$\Rightarrow R = 0.028$ N

d) $u = 1.4,\ v = 0,\ s = s,\ t = 3$
$s = \left(\frac{u+v}{2}\right)t$
$s = 0.7 \times 3 = 2.1$ m

Q18 Taking the direction of motion of B following the collision as positive:
For particle A:
$I = mv - mu$
$-\frac{5MU}{2} = -M\frac{U}{2} - Mu_A$
$\Rightarrow u_A = 2U$
For particle B:
$I = mv - mu$
$\frac{5MU}{2} = 2M\frac{U}{4} - 2Mu_B$
$\Rightarrow u_B = -U$

So before the collision, A was moving in the positive direction, and B was moving in the negative direction. So the particles must have been moving in opposite directions, towards each other.
A had speed $2U$ ms^{-1}, and B had speed U ms^{-1}, so A had twice the speed of B.
The most important thing with this question is getting the sign of the impulse right. The sign depends on which direction you take as being positive — if you'd chosen the direction of motion of A following the collision as being positive, then the impulse in each of the two equations would've had the opposite sign, but the result would've been the same in the end.

Review Exercise — Chapter 5

Q1 Resolving horizontally:

$F_{net} = ma$

$2 = 1.5a$

$a = 1.33...\ ms^{-2}$

$v = u + at$

$v = 0 + (1.33... \times 3) = 4\ ms^{-1}$

You could also have done this by calculating the impulse.

Q2 a) $\mathbf{F}_{net} = (24\mathbf{i} + 18\mathbf{j}) + (6\mathbf{i} + 22\mathbf{j}) = (30\mathbf{i} + 40\mathbf{j})$ N

$|\mathbf{F}_{net}| = \sqrt{30^2 + 40^2} = 50$ N

$F_{net} = ma$

$50 = 8a$

$a = 6.25\ ms^{-2}$

$\tan\alpha = \frac{40}{30}$

$\alpha = 53.1°$ (3 s.f.) above **i**

b) $s = ut + \frac{1}{2}at^2$

$s = \frac{1}{2} \times 6.25 \times 3^2 = 28.125$ m

Q3 a)

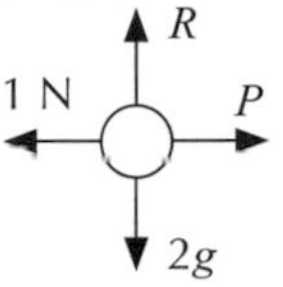

Resolving horizontally:

$F_{net} = ma$

$P - 1 = 2 \times 0.3$

$P = 1.6$ N

b) Resolving vertically:

$R = 2g$

$F = \mu R$, so $1 = \mu \times 2g$

So $\mu = 0.05$ (2 d.p.)

Q4 a)

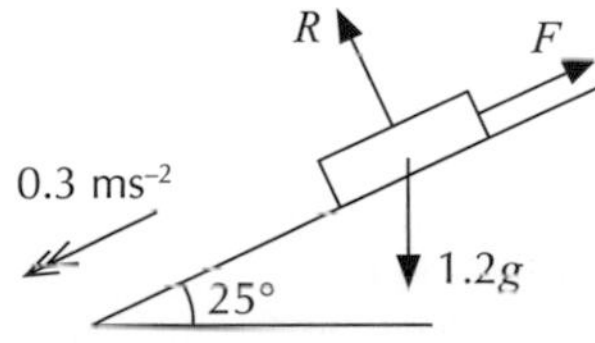

Resolving perpendicular to the plane (↖):

$R = 1.2g\cos25°$

Resolving parallel to the plane (↙):

$F_{net} = ma$

$1.2g\sin25° - F = 1.2 \times 0.3$

$\Rightarrow F = 4.609...$

$F = \mu R$:

$\mu = 4.609... \div 1.2g\cos25° = 0.43$ (2 d.p.)

b) E.g. the brick is a particle, there's no air resistance or other external forces acting, the brick's acceleration is constant, acceleration due to gravity is constant at $9.8\ ms^{-2}$.

Q5 Resolving perpendicular to the plane (↖):

$R = 600\cos30°$

Using $F = \mu R$:

$F = 0.5 \times 600\cos30° = 300\cos30°$

Resolving parallel to plane (↙):

$F_{net} = ma$

$600\sin30° - F = (600 \div 9.8) \times a$

$600\sin30° - 300\cos30° = (600 \div 9.8) \times a$

$\Rightarrow a = 0.6564...\ ms^{-2}$

$u = 0, v = v, s = 20$

$v^2 = u^2 + 2as$

$v^2 = 0 + (2 \times 0.6564... \times 20) = 26.259...$

$v = 5.12\ ms^{-1}$ (3 s.f.)

Q6 a) Taking tractor and trailer together (and calling the resistance force on the trailer F):

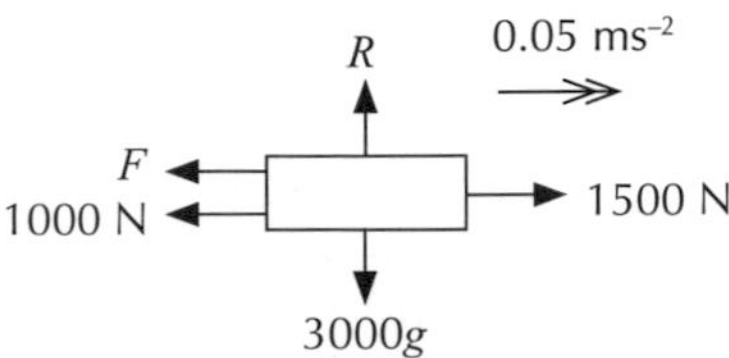

Resolving horizontally: $F_{net} = ma$

$1500 - F - 1000 = 3000 \times 0.05$

$F = 350$ N

b) For trailer alone:

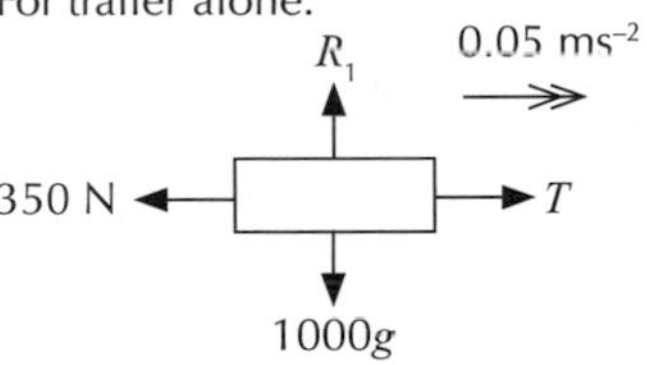

Resolving horizontally:

$F_{net} = ma$

$T - 350 = 1000 \times 0.05$

$T = 400$ N

T could be found instead by looking at the horizontal forces acting on the tractor alone.

Q7

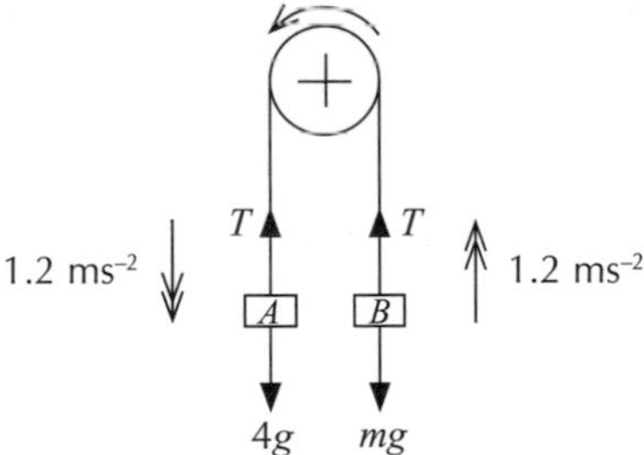

Resolving downwards for A:

$F_{net} = ma$

$4g - T = 4 \times 1.2$

$T = 4g - 4.8$ **eqn1**

Resolving upwards for B:

$F_{net} = ma$

$T - mg = 1.2m$ **eqn2**

Subbing **eqn1** into **eqn2**:

$4g - 4.8 - mg = 1.2m$

$34.4 = m(1.2 + 9.8)$

$m = 3.13$ kg (3 s.f.)

Q8 a)

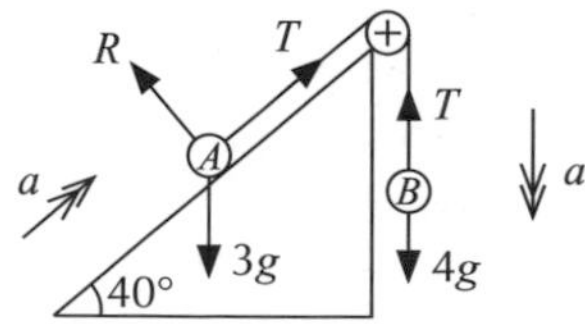

Resolving downwards for B:

$F_{net} = ma$

$4g - T = 4a$

$T = 4g - 4a$ **eqn1**

Resolving parallel to plane (↗) for A:

$T - 3g\sin 40° = 3a$ **eqn2**

Subbing **eqn1** into **eqn2**:

$4g - 4a - 3g\sin 40° = 3a$

$7a = 20.302...$

$a = 2.9002... = 2.90$ ms^{-2} (3 s.f.)

b) Using **eqn1**:

$T = 4g - (4 \times 2.9002...) = 27.598...$

$T = 27.6$ N (3 s.f.)

c) If in equilibrium, then resolving for B:

$T = 4g$

Then for A:

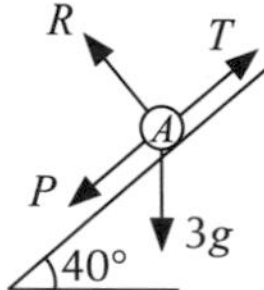

(Where P is the force holding the system in equilibrium).

Resolving parallel to plane (↗):

$F_{net} = ma$

$T - 3g\sin 40° - P = 0$

$P = 4g - 3g\sin 40° = 20.3$ N (3 s.f.)

Q9 a) $(5 \times 3) + (4 \times 1) = (5 \times 2) + (4 \times v)$

$19 = 10 + 4v$

$v = 2.25$ ms^{-1} to the right

b) $(5 \times 3) + (4 \times 1) = 9v$

$19 = 9v$

$v = 2.11$ ms^{-1} (3 s.f.) to the right

c) $(5 \times 3) + (4 \times -2) = (5 \times -v) + (4 \times 3)$

$7 = -5v + 12$

$5v = 5$

$v = 1$ ms^{-1} to the left

d) $(m \times 6) + (8 \times 2) = (m \times 2) + (8 \times 4)$

$6m + 16 = 2m + 32$

$4m = 16$

$m = 4$ kg

Q10 Impulse acts against motion, so $I = -2$ Ns

$I = mv - mu$

$-2 = 0.3v - (0.3 \times 5)$

$v = -1.67$ ms^{-1} (3 s.f.)

Q11 a) Change in momentum = Impulse

$I = Ft = 8400 \times 3 \times 60 = 1\,512\,000$ Ns

b) Change in momentum = $mv - mu$

$1\,512\,000 = 300\,000v$

$v = 5.04$ ms^{-1}

$s = \frac{1}{2}(u + v)t$

$= \frac{1}{2} \times 5.04 \times 180 = 453.6$ m

Q12 You need to find the particle's velocities just before and just after impact.

Falling (down = +ve):

$u = 0,\ v = v,\ a = 9.8,\ s = 2$

$v^2 = u^2 + 2as$

$v^2 = 2 \times 9.8 \times 2 = 39.2$

$v = 6.260...$ ms^{-1}

Rebound (this time, let upwards be positive):

$u = u,\ v = 0,\ a = -9.8,\ s = \frac{4}{3}$

$v^2 = u^2 + 2as$

$0 = u^2 + (2 \times -9.8 \times \frac{4}{3})$

$u^2 = 26.133...$

$u = 5.112...$ ms^{-1}

Taking up as positive:

Impulse = $mv - mu$

$= (0.45 \times 5.112...) - (0.45 \times -6.260...)$

$= 5.12$ Ns (3 s.f.)

Exam-Style Questions — Chapter 5

1 a)

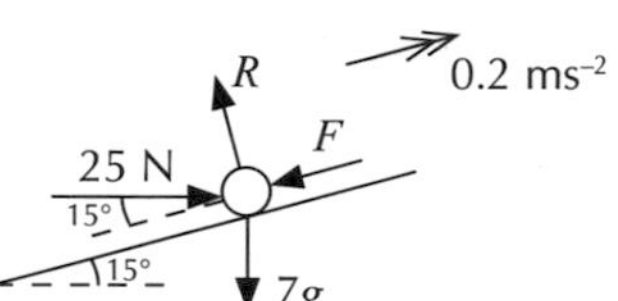

Resolving parallel to the plane (↗):

$F_{net} = ma$

$25\cos 15° - F - 7g\sin 15° = 7 \times 0.2$

$F = 25\cos 15° - 7g\sin 15° - 1.4$

$F = 4.993...$ N

Resolving perpendicular to the plane (↖):

$F_{net} = ma$

$R - 25\sin 15° - 7g\cos 15° = 7 \times 0$

$R = 25\sin 15° + 7g\cos 15° = 72.732...$ N

Using $F = \mu R$:

$4.993... = \mu \times 72.432...$

$\Rightarrow\ \mu = 0.0686... = 0.07$ (2 d.p.)

[5 marks available in total]:

- ***1 mark for resolving in ↗ direction***
- ***1 mark for correct value of F_{net} in ↗ direction***
- ***1 mark for resolving in ↖ direction***
- ***1 mark correct value of R***
- ***1 mark for correct value of μ***

b)

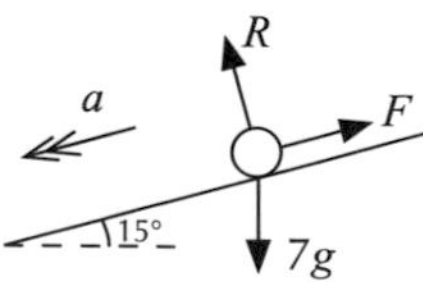

Resolving parallel to the plane (↖):

$R = 7g\cos 15°$

$F = \mu R$

$F = 0.0686... \times 7g\cos 15° = 4.548...$ N

Resolving parallel to the plane (↙):

$7g\sin 15° - F = 7a$

$7g\sin 15° - 4.548... = 7a$

$a = 1.886...$ ms^{-2}

$u = 0,\ s = 3,\ t = t$

$s = ut + \frac{1}{2}at^2$

$3 = \frac{1}{2} \times 1.886... \times t^2$
$t^2 = 3.180...$
$t = 1.78$ s (3 s.f.)

[7 marks available in total]:
- ***1 mark for resolving in ↙ direction***
- ***1 mark for resolving in ↖ direction***
- ***1 mark for finding R***
- ***1 mark for finding F***
- ***1 mark for finding a***
- ***1 mark for correct use of constant acceleration equation***
- ***1 mark for correct value of t***

2 a) Considering the car and the caravan together:

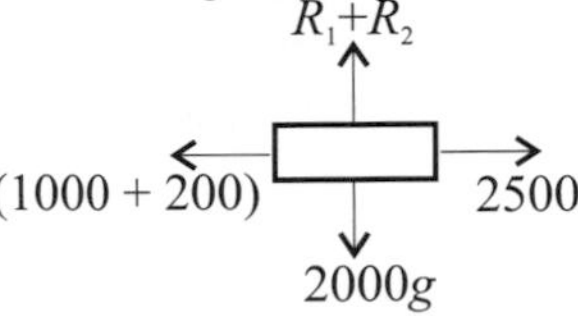

Resolving horizontally:
$F_{net} = ma$
$2500 - 1200 = 2000a$
$a = 0.65$ ms^{-2}

[3 marks available in total]:
- ***1 mark for resolving horizontally***
- ***1 mark for correct workings***
- ***1 mark for correct value of a***

b) Either: *Caravan*

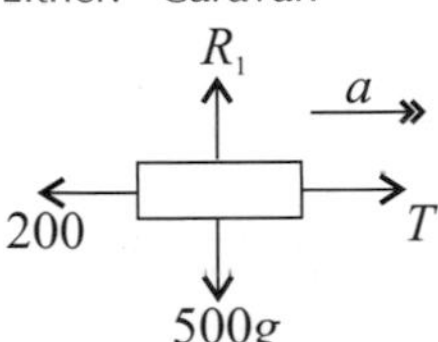

Resolving horizontally:
$F_{net} = ma$
$T - 200 = 500 \times 0.65$
$T = 525$ N

[2 marks available in total]:
- ***1 mark for resolving horizontally***
- ***1 mark for correct value of T***

Or: *Car*

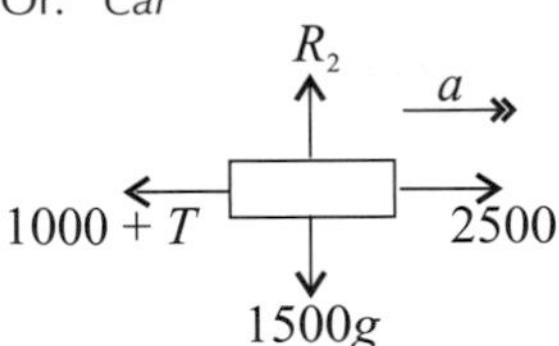

Resolving horizontally:
$F_{net} = ma$
$2500 - (1000 + T) = 1500 \times 0.65$
$2500 - 1000 - T = 975$
$1500 - 975 = T$
$T = 525$ N

[2 marks available in total]:
- ***1 mark for resolving horizontally***
- ***1 mark for correct value of T***

Two different methods, one correct answer. It doesn't matter which you use (but show your diagrams and workings), although it's certainly a bonus if you manage to pick the simpler way and save some time in the exam.

3 a)

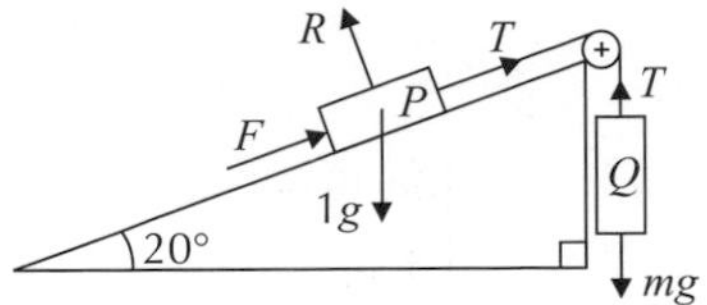

For Q:
$F_{net} = ma$
Resolving vertically:
$mg - T = 0$, so $T = mg$
For P:
$F_{net} = ma$
Resolving in ↖ direction:
$R - 1g\cos20° = 1 \times 0$, so $R = g\cos20°$
Limiting friction:
$F = \mu R = 0.1 \times g\cos20°$
Resolving in ↙ direction:
$1g\sin20° - F - T = 1 \times 0$
$1g\sin20° - 0.1g\cos20° - mg = 0$
$\sin20° - 0.1\cos20° = m$
$m = 0.248$ kg (to 3 s.f.)

[5 marks available in total]:
- ***1 mark for resolving vertically***
- ***1 mark for resolving in ↖ direction***
- ***1 mark for correct value of F***
- ***1 mark for resolving in ↙ direction***
- ***1 mark for correct value of m***

b)

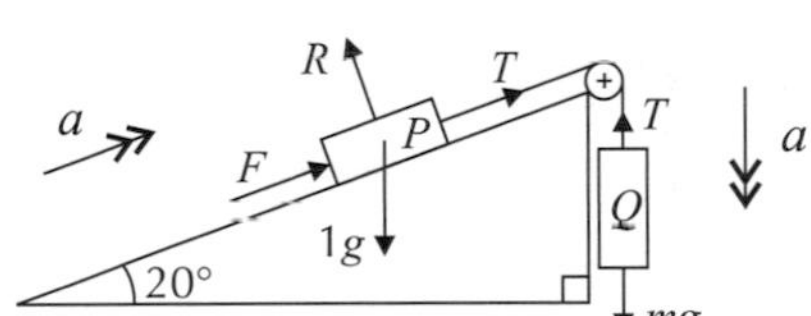

If $Q = 1$ kg:
$F_{net} = ma$
For Q:
Resolving vertically:
$1g - T = 1a$, so $T = g - a$ <u>**eqn 1**</u>
For P:
Resolving in ↖ direction:
$R = g\cos20°$
$F = \mu R = 0.1g\cos20°$
Resolving in ↗ direction:
$T - 1g\sin20° - F = 1a$
$T - 1g\sin20° - 0.1g\cos20° = 1a$ <u>**eqn 2**</u>
Sub <u>**eqn 1**</u> into <u>**eqn 2**</u>:
$(g - a) - g\sin20° - 0.1g\cos20° = a$
$g - g\sin20° - 0.1g\cos20° = 2a$
$5.527... = 2a$, so $a = 2.76$ ms^{-2} (to 3 s.f.)
So P accelerates up the plane and Q accelerates vertically down with an acceleration of 2.76 ms^{-2}.

[5 marks available in total]:
- ***1 mark for resolving vertically***
- ***1 mark for resolving in ↖ direction***
- ***1 mark for resolving in ↗ direction***
- ***1 mark for correctly combining equations***
- ***1 mark for correct value of a and description of motion***

4 Before — After

(0.8) $\xrightarrow{4}$ (1.2) $\xrightarrow{2}$ 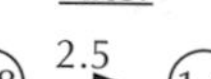 

$(0.8 \times 4) + (1.2 \times 2) = (0.8 \times 2.5) + 1.2v$
$3.2 + 2.4 = 2.0 + 1.2v$
$v = 3 \text{ ms}^{-1}$

Before — After

(1.2) $\xrightarrow{3}$ $\xleftarrow{4}$ (m) — ($1.2 + m$)

$(1.2 \times 3) + (m \times -4) = (1.2 + m) \times 0$
$3.6 = 4m$
$m = 0.9$ kg

[4 marks available in total]:
- ***1 mark for using conservation of momentum***
- ***1 mark for correct value of v***
- ***1 mark for correct workings***
- ***1 mark for correct value of m***

Diagrams are handy for collision questions too, partly because they make the question clearer for you, but also because they make it easier for the examiner to see what you're doing.

5 a) Before — After

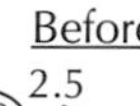

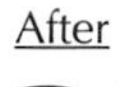

(5000) $\xrightarrow{v}$

$(4000 \times 2.5) + (1000 \times 0) = 5000v$
$v = 2 \text{ ms}^{-1}$

[2 marks available in total]:
- ***1 mark for using conservation of momentum***
- ***1 mark for correct value of v***

b) Impulse $= mv - mu$
$= (4000 \times 2) - (4000 \times 2.5)$
$= -2000$ Ns

[2 marks available in total]:
- ***1 mark for correct workings***
- ***1 mark for correct value of impulse***

c) E.g. track horizontal; no resistance (e.g. friction) to motion; wagons can be modelled as particles.

[2 marks available in total]:
- ***1 mark each for any of the above assumptions or any other relevant assumption***

If you've forgotten what 'any other valid assumption' might be, I recommend you have a look at Chapter 1 again.

6 a) $(8\mathbf{i} - 3\mathbf{j}) = (x\mathbf{i} + y\mathbf{j}) + (5\mathbf{i} + \mathbf{j})$
So, $x\mathbf{i} + y\mathbf{j} = (8\mathbf{i} - 3\mathbf{j}) - (5\mathbf{i} + \mathbf{j})$,
i.e. $x = 3$ and $y = -4$

[2 marks available in total]:
- ***1 mark for correct value of x***
- ***1 mark for correct value of y***

b) Magnitude of resultant force $= \sqrt{8^2 + (-3)^2}$
$= \sqrt{73} = 8.544...$ N
Using $F = ma$:
$8.544... = 2.5a$, so $a = 3.42 \text{ ms}^{-2}$ (to 3 s.f.)

[3 marks available in total]:
- ***1 mark using F = ma***
- ***1 mark for correct workings***
- ***1 mark for correct value of a***

7 a) Resolving forces acting on A:
$7g - T = 7a$
Resolving forces acting on B:
$T - 3g = 3a$, so $T = 3a + 3g$
Substituting T:
$7g - 3a - 3g = 7a$, so $4g = 10a$
hence $a = 3.92 \text{ ms}^{-2}$
Using $v = u + at$:
$u = 0, v = 5.9, a = 3.92, t = t$
$5.9 = 0 + 3.92t$
$\Rightarrow t = 1.505... = 1.51$ s (to 3 s.f.)

[4 marks available in total]:
- ***1 mark for resolving forces***
- ***1 mark for correct value of a***
- ***1 mark for correct workings***
- ***1 mark for correct value of t***

b) Using $v^2 = u^2 + 2as$:
$u = 0, v = 5.9, a = 3.92, s = s$
$5.9^2 = 0^2 + 3.92s$
$\Rightarrow s = 4.440... = 4.44$ m (to 3 s.f.)

[2 marks available in total]:
- ***1 mark for correct workings***
- ***1 mark for correct value of s***

c) When A hits the ground,
speed of A = speed of $B = 5.9 \text{ ms}^{-1}$
B will then continue to rise, momentarily stop and then fall freely under gravity. String will be taut again when displacement of $B = 0$.
So, $a = -9.8$, $s = 0$, $u = 5.9$
Using $s = ut + \frac{1}{2}at^2$:
$0 = 5.9t + \frac{1}{2}(-9.8)t^2 = 5.9t - 4.9t^2$
Solve for t:
$5.9t - 4.9t^2 = 0 \Rightarrow t(5.9 - 4.9t) = 0$
$\Rightarrow t = 0$ or $t = 5.9 \div 4.9 = 1.204...$
So the string becomes taut again at
$t = 1.20$ s (to 3 s.f.)

[4 marks available in total]:
- ***1 mark for using*** $s = ut + \frac{1}{2}at^2$
- ***1 mark for correct workings***
- ***1 mark for solving for t***
- ***1 mark for correct value of t***

Chapter 6: Moments

1. Moments

Exercise 1.1 — Moments

Q1 a) Moment = Force × Perpendicular Distance
$= 3 \times 2.5 = 7.5$ Nm anticlockwise

b) Moment $= 6\sin 30° \times 4 = 12$ Nm clockwise

c) Moment $= 23 \times 0.8\cos 18°$
$= 17.5$ Nm (3 s.f.) clockwise

Q2 a) Taking clockwise as positive:
$(2 \times 9) - (7 \times 2) = 4$ Nm clockwise

b) Taking clockwise as positive:
$(19 \times 1.5) - (14 \times 2) = 0.5$ Nm clockwise

c) Taking clockwise as positive:
$(12.6 \times 5) - (4.5 \times 2) - (6 \times 9) = 0$
(i.e. There is no moment about X.)

d) Taking clockwise as positive:
$(3 \times 2) + (12 \times 4) - (22 \times 2.5) = -1$ Nm
i.e. 1 Nm anticlockwise.

e) Taking clockwise as positive:
$(7\sin30° \times 3) - (15 \times 1.5) = -12$ Nm
i.e. 12 Nm anticlockwise

f) Taking clockwise as positive:
$(10\sin30° \times 3) + (8\sin45° \times 4) = (15 + 16\sqrt{2})$ Nm
= 37.6 Nm (3 s.f.) clockwise

g) Taking clockwise as positive:
$(18\sin25° \times 13) - (24\sin32° \times 13)$
= –66.4 Nm (3 s.f.), i.e. 66.4 Nm anticlockwise

h) Taking clockwise as positive:
$(6\sin105° \times 10) + (2\sin50° \times 8)$
$- (3\sin28° \times 10) - (1 \times 8)$
= 48.1 Nm (3 s.f.) clockwise.

Q3 Find the sum of the moments about O, taking clockwise as positive:
$(13 \times 3) + (X \times 1) - (21 \times 3) = X - 24$
For the rod to rotate clockwise, the sum of the moments must be positive:
$X - 24 > 0$
$\Rightarrow X > 24$

Q4 Find the sum of the moments about O, taking clockwise as positive:
$4(d + 1) + (38 \times 2) - (25 \times 1) -$
$(24\sin150° \times 5) = 4d - 5$
For the rod to rotate anticlockwise, the sum of the moments must be negative:
$4d - 5 < 0$
$\Rightarrow d < 1.25$
Also, d must be greater than or equal to zero, otherwise the 25 N force will be applied to a point which isn't on the rod, and so the rod will rotate clockwise. So:
$0 \le d < 1.25$

Q5 Find the sum of the moments about O, taking anticlockwise as positive:
$(4\sqrt{3}\sin60° \times 3) + 5l - (8 \times 1)$
$- (4\sqrt{2}\sin45° \times [3 + l]) = l - 2$
Sum of moments is 0.5 Nm, so:
$0.5 = l - 2$
$\Rightarrow l = 2.5$ m

Q6 Find the sum of moments about O, taking clockwise as positive, and resolving forces perpendicular to the rod:
$(27\sin\theta \times 3) + (9\sin\theta \times 1) - (7 \times 6)$
$= 90\sin\theta - 42$
Sum of moments is 3 Nm, so:
$3 = 90\sin\theta - 42$
$45 = 90\sin\theta$
$0.5 = \sin\theta$
$\Rightarrow \theta = 30°$

Exercise 1.2 — Moments in equilibrium

Q1 Taking moments about A:
Moments clockwise = Moments anticlockwise
$1.5S + (2 \times 8) = 16 \times 5.5$
$1.5S = 72$
$S = 48$ N
Resolving vertically:
$R + 16 = S + 2$
$R = 50 - 16 = 34$ N

Q2 Resolving vertically:
$10 + 6 = 13 + M$
$M = 3$ N
Taking moments about C:
$10l + 2M = 6 \times 5$
$10l = 30 - 6$
$l = 2.4$ m

Q3 a) Mass acts at centre of rod, i.e. 2.5 m from A, 1 m from C and 0.5 m from D.
Taking moments about the midpoint:
$0.5R_D = 49 \times 1$
$R_D = 98$ N

b) Resolving vertically:
$Mg = 49 + R_D$
$M = (49 + 98) \div 9.8 = 15$ kg

Q4 When the rod is about to tilt about D, $T_C = 0$.
The rod is uniform, so its mass acts at its midpoint, x m from D.
Taking moments about D:
$3g \times 1.5 = 9g \times x$
$x = 44.1 \div 88.2 = 0.5$
So the distance from B to the midpoint is $1.5 + 0.5 = 2$ m, and so the length of the rod is $2 \times 2 = 4$ m

Q5 a)

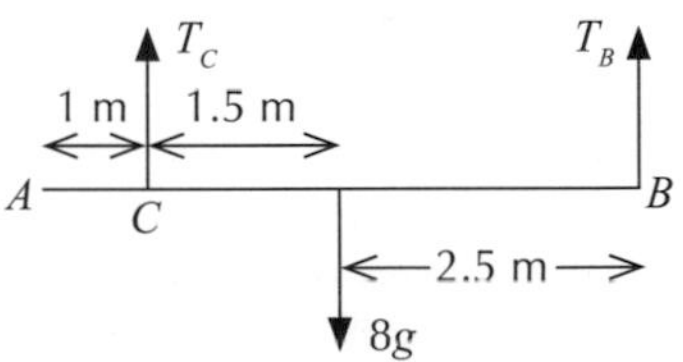

Taking moments about C:
$8g \times 1.5 = 4T_B$
$T_B = 117.6 \div 4 = 29.4$ N
Resolving vertically:
$T_C + T_B = 8g$
$T_C = 78.4 - 29.4 = 49$ N

b) When the beam is about to tilt about C, $T_B = 0$.
Taking moments about C:
$8g \times 1.5 = 16g \times x$
$x = 117.6 \div 156.8 = 0.75$
So the distance of the particle from A is $1 - 0.75 = 0.25$ m

Q6 a) Resolving vertically:
$T_C + T_D = 240$
$T_C = 2T_D$
$\Rightarrow 2T_D + T_D = 240$
$3T_D = 240$
$T_D = 80$ N
$\Rightarrow T_C = 2 \times 80 = 160$ N

b) Taking moments about A:
$(T_C \times 1) + (T_D \times 8) = 240x$
$160 + 640 = 240x$
$\Rightarrow x = 3.33$ m (3 s.f.)

Q7 a)

R, 2R, 2.5 m, 1 m, 2 m, 1.5 m, 1.5 m, A, B, X, 36g, 4R, mg, 25g

b) Taking moments about X:
$(4R \times 0.5) + 3.5R + (25g \times 1) =$
$(36g \times 2.5) + (2R \times 2.5)$
$\Rightarrow 2R + 3.5R + 25g = 90g + 5R$
$\Rightarrow 0.5R = 65g$
$R = 1274$ N
Resolving vertically:
$R + 2R + 4R = 36g + 25g + mg$
$\Rightarrow 7 \times 1274 = 597.8 + 9.8m$
$\Rightarrow m = 849$ kg

c) The plank is modelled as a non-uniform rod, the children are modelled as particles, the reaction forces act perpendicular to the plank, there are no other external forces acting on the plank, the plank is horizontal, acceleration due to gravity is constant at 9.8 ms^{-2}.

Q8 a) The painter stands at the plank's COM, so the weight acting at this point is his weight plus the plank's weight, i.e. $80g + 20g = 100g$.

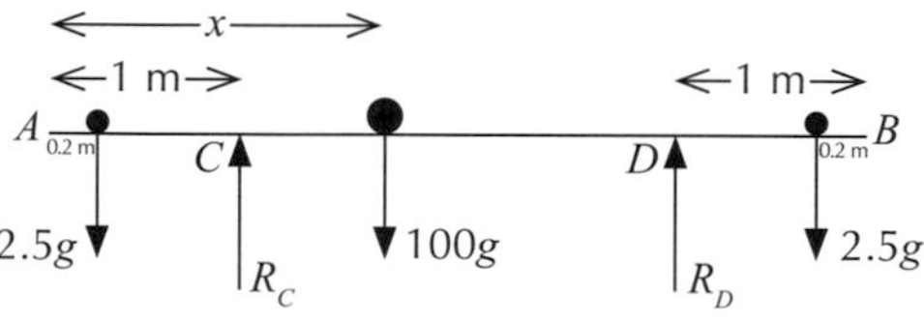

The reaction at C is 4 times the reaction at D, i.e. $R_C = 4R_D$
Resolving vertically:
$2.5g + 100g + 2.5g = R_C + R_D$
$105g = 4R_D + R_D$
$105g = 5R_D$
$\Rightarrow R_D = 21g$ N $\Rightarrow R_C = 84g$ N
Taking moments about A:
$(2.5g \times 0.2) + (100g \times x) + (2.5g \times 3.8) = R_C + 3R_D$
$10g + 100gx = 84g + 63g$
$10g + 100gx = 147g$
$x = (147 - 10) \div (100) = 1.37$ m

b) The distance between the plank's COM and the point D is $4 - 1 - 1.37 = 1.63$ m

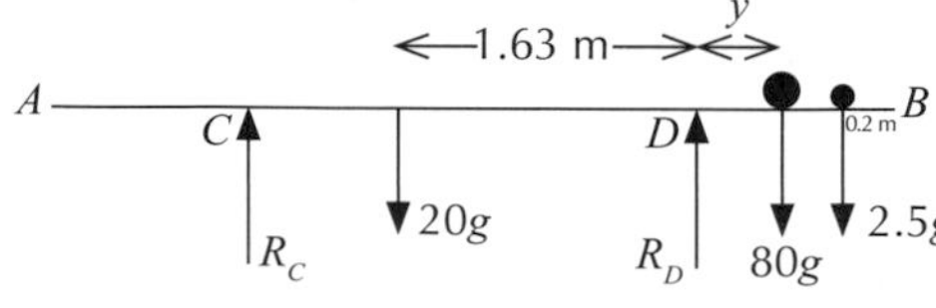

When the plank is about to tilt about D, $R_C = 0$.
Taking moments about D:
$20g \times 1.63 = (80g \times y) + (2.5g \times 0.8)$
$y = (319.48 - 19.6) \div 784 = 0.3825$
So the distance from B is:
$1 - 0.3825 = 0.6175$ m

Review Exercise — Chapter 6

Q1 a) $8 \times 1.5 = 12$ Nm anticlockwise

b) $5\sin(180° - 130°) \times 3.8 = 14.55...$
$= 14.6$ Nm (3 s.f.) clockwise

c) $48 \times 7.5\cos 25° = 326.27...$
$= 326$ Nm (3 s.f.) clockwise

Q2 Assuming that A is on the left and B is on the right, taking clockwise as positive:
$(1.6g \times 6) - (23 \times 12) = -181.92$ Nm
The sum of the moments is negative, so the rod will turn anticlockwise.
Don't forget that the weight of a uniform rod acts at its centre.

Q3 Taking moments about D:
$(21 \times 10) = 14P$
$\Rightarrow P = 210 \div 14 = 15$ N
Resolving vertically:
$21 + 25 = P + Q$
$Q = 46 - 15 = 31$ N

Q4 Resolving vertically:
$20 + 15 = U + 11 + 3U$
$4U = 24$
$\Rightarrow U = 6$ N
Taking moments about C:
$20l + (11 \times 1) + (3U \times 3) = 15 \times 7$
$20l + 11 + 54 = 105$
$\Rightarrow l = 2$ m

Q5 Taking moments about B:
$60g \times 3 = 8T_2$
$T_2 = 1764 \div 8 = 220.5$ N
Resolving vertically:
$T_1 + T_2 = 60g$
$T_1 = 588 - 220.5 = 367.5$ N

Q6 Call the length of the rod l. Then the rod's weight will act a distance of $\frac{l}{2}$ from each end.
Taking moments about one end of the rod:
$205.8 = 3.5g \times \frac{l}{2}$
$\Rightarrow l = 2(205.8 \div 34.3) = 12$ m
The only forces acting on the rod are the reaction at the pivot, which doesn't effect the moment, and the rod's weight, which acts at its centre, i.e. the same distance from each end. So it doesn't matter which end the rod is pivoted at.

Q7 a) When the rod is about to tilt about B, the reaction at A is zero.
Resolving vertically:
$44 = 1.5g + F$
$\Rightarrow F = 44 - 14.7 = 29.3$ N

b) Taking moments about B:
$1.5g \times 2.5 = 29.3x$
$\Rightarrow x = 36.75 \div 29.3 = 1.25$ m (3 s.f.)

Q8 a) Resolving vertically:
$70.16 = 12 + mg + 17$
$\Rightarrow m = 41.16 \div 9.8 = 4.2$ kg

b) Taking moments about midpoint:
$17 \times 6.5 = mgl + (12 \times 6.5)$
$4.2gl = 32.5$
$\Rightarrow l = 32.5 \div 41.16 = 0.7896...$
$= 0.790$ m (3 s.f.)

Q9 a) Resolving vertically:
$15g = 3Y + 2Y$
$147 = 5Y$
$\Rightarrow Y = 29.4$ N

b) Taking moments about M:
$3Y \times x = 2Y \times 4.5$
$\Rightarrow x = 9Y \div 3Y = 3$ m

Exam-Style Questions — Chapter 6

1

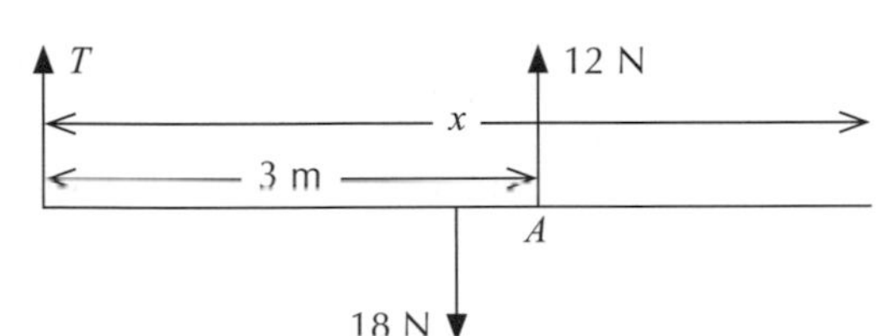

Taking moments about end string:
$12 \times 3 = 18 \times \frac{x}{2}$
$36 = 9x$
$x = 4$ m
[2 marks available in total]:
- ***1 mark for taking moments***
- ***1 mark for showing that x = 4 m***

2 a)

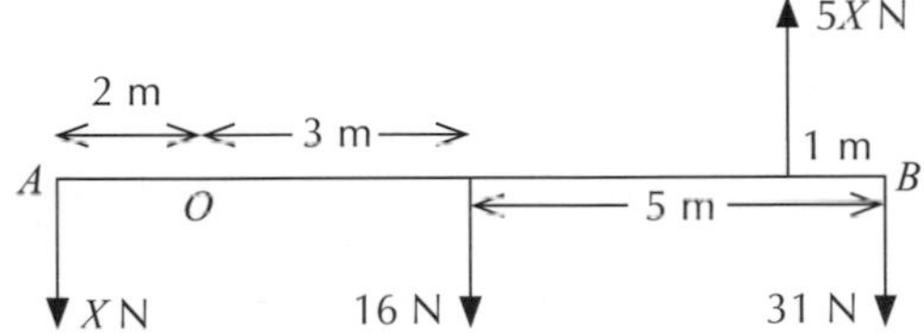

[2 marks available in total]:
- ***1 mark for diagram***
- ***1 mark for correct labelling***

b) Taking moments about O, with clockwise positive:
$(16 \times 3) + (31 \times 8) - 2X - (5X \times 7) = 296 - 37X$
For A to move downwards and B to move upwards (i.e. for the beam to rotate anticlockwise when viewed as in the diagram above), the sum of the moments must be negative:
$296 - 37X < 0$
$296 < 37X$
$\Rightarrow 8 < X$ (i.e. $X > 8$)
[4 marks available in total]:
- ***1 mark for taking moments about O***
- ***1 mark for correct expression for sum of moments about O***
- ***1 mark for correct use of inequality***
- ***1 mark for correct range for X***

3 a)

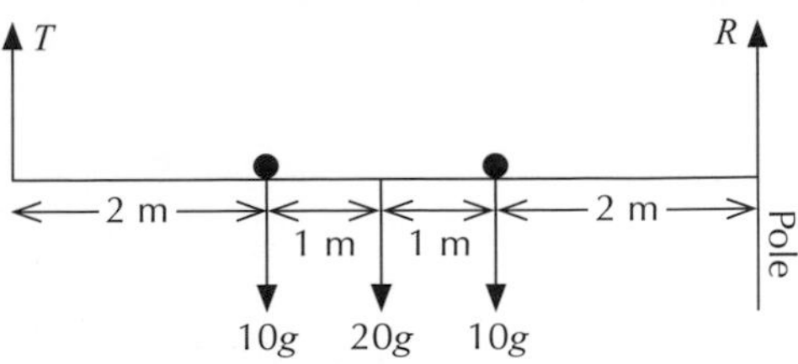

[2 marks available in total]:
- ***1 mark for diagram***
- ***1 mark for correct labelling***

b) Taking moments about the pole:
$6T = (2 \times 10g) + (3 \times 20g) + (4 \times 10g)$
$6T = 20g + 60g + 40g = 120g$
$\Rightarrow T = 20g$ N
[3 marks available in total]:
- ***1 mark for taking moments about the pole***
- ***1 mark for correct workings***
- ***1 mark for correct value of T***

Taking moments about the pole means you don't have to worry about the unknown reaction force.

c) Resolving vertically:
$T + R = 10g + 20g + 10g$
$20g + R = 40g$
$\Rightarrow R = 20g$ N
[2 marks available in total]:
- ***1 mark for resolving vertically***
- ***1 mark for correct value of R***

4 a)

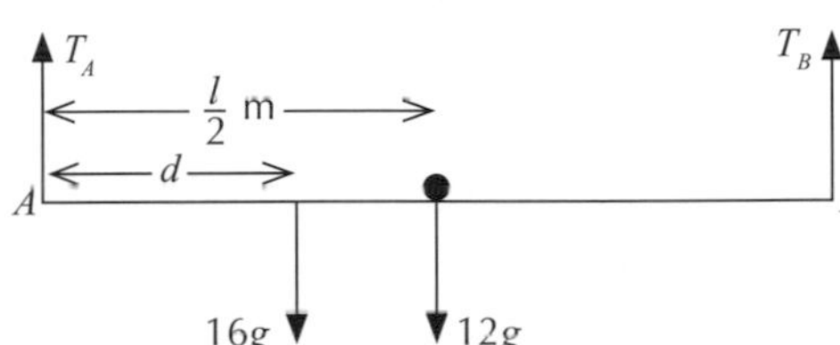

$T_A = 4X$, $T_B = 3X$
Resolving vertically:
$T_A + T_B = 16g + 12g$
$4X + 3X = 28g$
$X = 4g$
So $T_A = 4 \times 4g = 16g$ N and $T_B = 3 \times 4g = 12g$ N
Taking moments about A:
$(16g \times d) + (12g \times \frac{l}{2}) = T_B \times l$
$16gd + 6gl = 12gl$
$16d = 6l$
$d = 0.375l$ m
[4 marks available in total]:
- ***1 mark for resolving vertically***
- ***1 mark for taking moments***
- ***1 mark for correct workings***
- ***1 mark for correct expression for distance***

b)

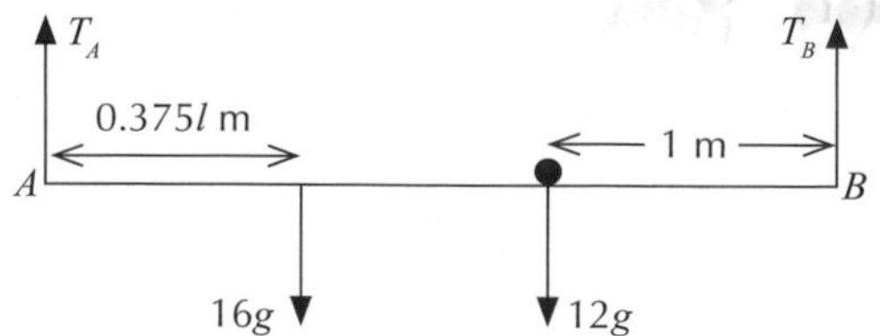

Resolving vertically:
$T_A + T_B = 16g + 12g$
But $T_A = T_B$, so:
$2T = 28g$
$\Rightarrow T = 14g$
Taking moments about A:
$(16g \times 0.375l) + 12g(l - 1) = 14g \times l$
$6gl + 12gl - 12g = 14gl$
$4gl = 12g$
$\Rightarrow l = 3$ m

[4 marks available in total]:

- ***1 mark for resolving vertically to find tension***
- ***1 mark for taking moments***
- ***1 mark for correct workings***
- ***1 mark for correct value of l***

c) E.g. The plank is modelled as a non-uniform rod, the boy is modelled as a particle, no other external forces are acting, the ropes are modelled as light, inextensible strings.
[2 marks available in total — 1 mark for one appropriate assumption stated, 2 marks for two or more appropriate assumptions stated].

5 a)

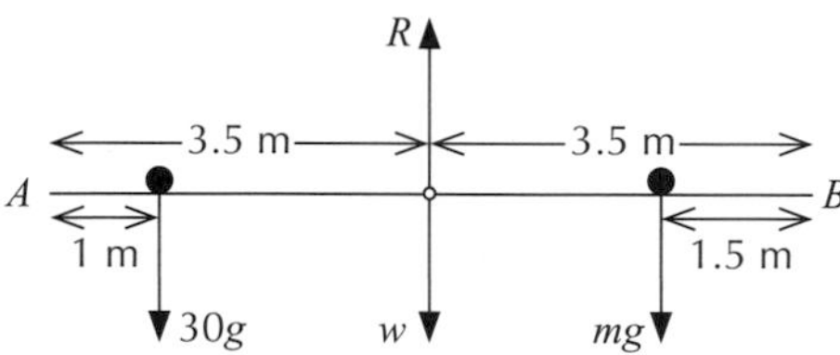

[2 marks available in total]:

- ***1 mark for diagram***
- ***1 mark for correct labelling***

b) Taking moments about midpoint, with clockwise positive:
$(mg \times 2) - (30g \times 2.5) = 2mg - 75g$
For A to move upwards and B to move downwards (i.e. for the beam to rotate clockwise as viewed in the diagram above), the sum of moments must be positive:
$2mg - 75g > 0$
$2mg > 75g$
$\Rightarrow m > 37.5$ kg

[4 marks available in total]:

- ***1 mark for taking moments about midpoint***
- ***1 mark for correct expression for sum of moments***
- ***1 mark for correct use of inequality***
- ***1 mark for correct range for m***

c)

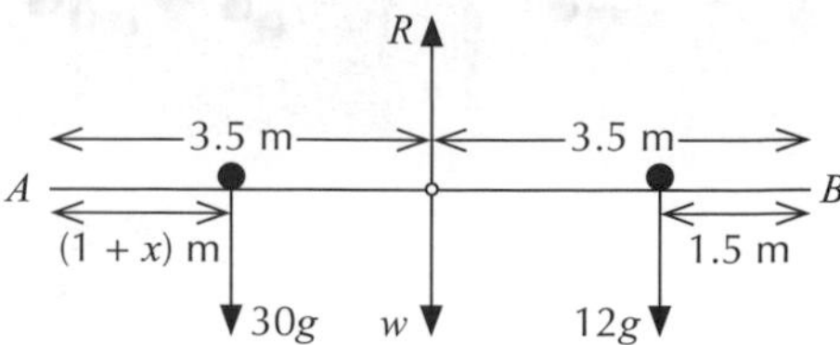

Taking moments about midpoint:
$(12g \times 2) = 30g(3.5 - (1 + x))$
$24g = 75g - 30gx$
$30gx = 51g$
$x = 51g \div 30g = 1.7$ m

[3 marks available in total]:

- ***1 mark for taking moments about midpoint***
- ***1 mark for correct workings***
- ***1 mark for correct value for distance***

6 a)

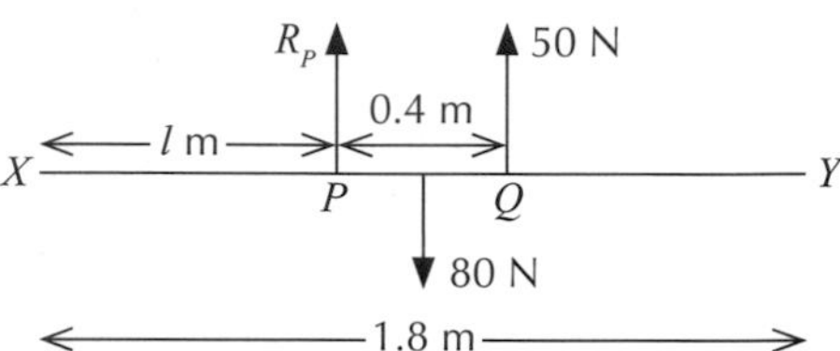

[2 marks available in total]:

- ***1 mark for diagram (ensure that 0.5 < l < 0.9)***
- ***1 mark for labelling***

b) Taking moments about P:
$80(0.9 - l) = 0.4 \times 50$
$72 - 80l = 20$
$80l = 52 \Rightarrow l = 0.65$ m

[3 marks available in total]:

- ***1 mark for taking moments***
- ***1 mark for correct workings***
- ***1 mark for correct value of l***

You are told that 0.5 < l < 0.9 so you know that P and Q are on either side of the midpoint.

c) E.g. The log is a rod, the bird is a particle, the bird's weight acts exactly at the end of the log, the log doesn't bend or break, acceleration due to gravity is constant at 9.8 ms^{-2}, each support acts at a single point.
[3 marks available in total — 1 mark for each appropriate assumption]

d) Distance $QY = 1.8 - (0.4 + 0.65) = 0.75$ m
At the point of tipping about Q, $R_P = 0$
Taking moments about Q:
$0.75mg = 80(0.9 - 0.75)$
$0.75mg = 12 \Rightarrow mg = 16$ N
$m = 1.63$ kg (3 s.f.)

[4 marks available in total]:

- ***1 mark for taking moments about Q***
- ***1 mark for $R_P = 0$***
- ***1 mark for correct workings***
- ***1 mark for correct value of m***

e) Resolving vertically:
$R_P + R_Q = 80 + 16 = 96$ N
$R_P = 0$ (about to tip about Q), so $R_Q = 96$ N

[2 marks available in total]:

- ***1 mark for resolving vertically***
- ***1 mark for correct value of R_Q***

Glossary

Acceleration
The rate of change of an object's **velocity** with respect to time.

Assumption
A simplification of a real-life situation used in a **model**.

Bead
A **particle** which has a hole in it through which a **wire** can pass.

Beam
A long, **thin**, straight body.

Bearing
A direction, given as an angle measured clockwise from north.

Centre of mass
The point where an object's **weight** can be considered to act.

Coalesce
What happens when **particles** join together as a result of a collision and move together with the same **speed** in the same direction.

Coefficient of friction
A number greater than or equal to zero which measures the effect of **friction** between an object and a surface.

Component
The effect of a **vector** in a given direction.

Deceleration
An **acceleration** where the object's **speed** is decreasing.

Displacement
A **vector** measurement of an object's distance from a particular point.

Equilibrium
A state where there is no **resultant force** acting on a body, hence the body is at **rest** (or moving with constant **velocity**).

Force
An influence which can change the motion of a body (i.e. cause an **acceleration**).

Friction
A frictional force is a resistive **force** due to **roughness** between a body and surface. It always acts against motion, or likely motion.

g
Acceleration due to gravity.
g is usually assumed to be 9.8 ms^{-2}.

i
The horizontal **unit vector**.

Impulse (of a force)
The product of the **force** and the time for which it is applied to a body.
It is equal to the resulting change in **momentum** of the body.

Inextensible
Describes a body which can't be stretched. (Usually a **string** or **wire**.)

J

j
A **unit vector** perpendicular to **i**, usually taken to be vertical.

K

Kinematics
The study of the motion of objects.

Lamina
A flat two-dimensional body whose thickness can be ignored.

Light
Describes a body which is modelled as having no mass.

Limiting equilibrium
Describes a body which is at **rest** in **equilibrium**, but is on the point of moving.

Magnitude
The size of a quantity.

Model
A mathematical description of a real-life situation, in which certain **assumptions** are made about the situation.

Moment
The turning effect a **force** has around a pivot point.

Momentum
The product of an object's mass and its **velocity**.

Non-uniform
Describes a body whose mass is unevenly distributed throughout the body.

Normal reaction
The reaction **force** from a surface acting on an object. Acts at 90° to the surface.

P

Particle
A body whose mass is considered to act at a single point, so its dimensions don't matter.

Peg
A fixed support which a body can hang from or rest on.

Plane
A flat surface.

Position vector
The position of a point relative to a fixed origin, O, given in **vector** form.

Pulley
A wheel, usually modelled as fixed and **smooth**, over which a **string** passes.

Resolving
Splitting a **vector** up into **components**.

Rest
Describes a body which is not moving. Often used to describe the initial state of a body.

Resultant (force or vector)
The single **force/vector** which has the same effect as two or more forces/vectors added together.

Rigid
Describes a body which does not bend.

Rod
A long, **thin**, straight, **rigid** body.

Rough
Describes a surface for which a **frictional force** will oppose the motion of a body in contact with the surface.

Scalar
A quantity which has a **magnitude** but not a direction.

Sense
The direction of a rotation (clockwise or anticlockwise).

Smooth
Describes a surface for which there is no **friction** between the surface and a body in contact with it.

Speed
The **magnitude** of an object's **velocity**.

Static
Describes a body which is not moving. Often used to describe a body in **equilibrium**.

String
A **thin** body, usually modelled as being **light** and **inextensible**.

Taut
Describes a **string** or **wire** which is experiencing a **tension force** and is tight and straight.

Tension
The **force** in a **taut wire** or **string**.

Thin
Describes a body which is modelled as having no thickness, only length.

Thrust
The **force** in a compressed **rod**.

Uniform
Describes a body whose mass is evenly spread throughout the body.

Unit vector
A **vector** of **magnitude** one unit.

Vector
A quantity which has both a **magnitude** and a direction.

Velocity
The rate of change of an object's **displacement** with respect to time.

Weight
The **force** due to a body's mass and the effect of gravity: $W = mg$.

Wire
A **thin**, **rigid**, **light** body.

Index

P

R

S

T

U

V

W

MEM1T51